FREE Plan Rebate
See Page 281

FREE Material Take-Off
See Page 284

Featuring small & stylish home plans from Lowe's Legacy Series.

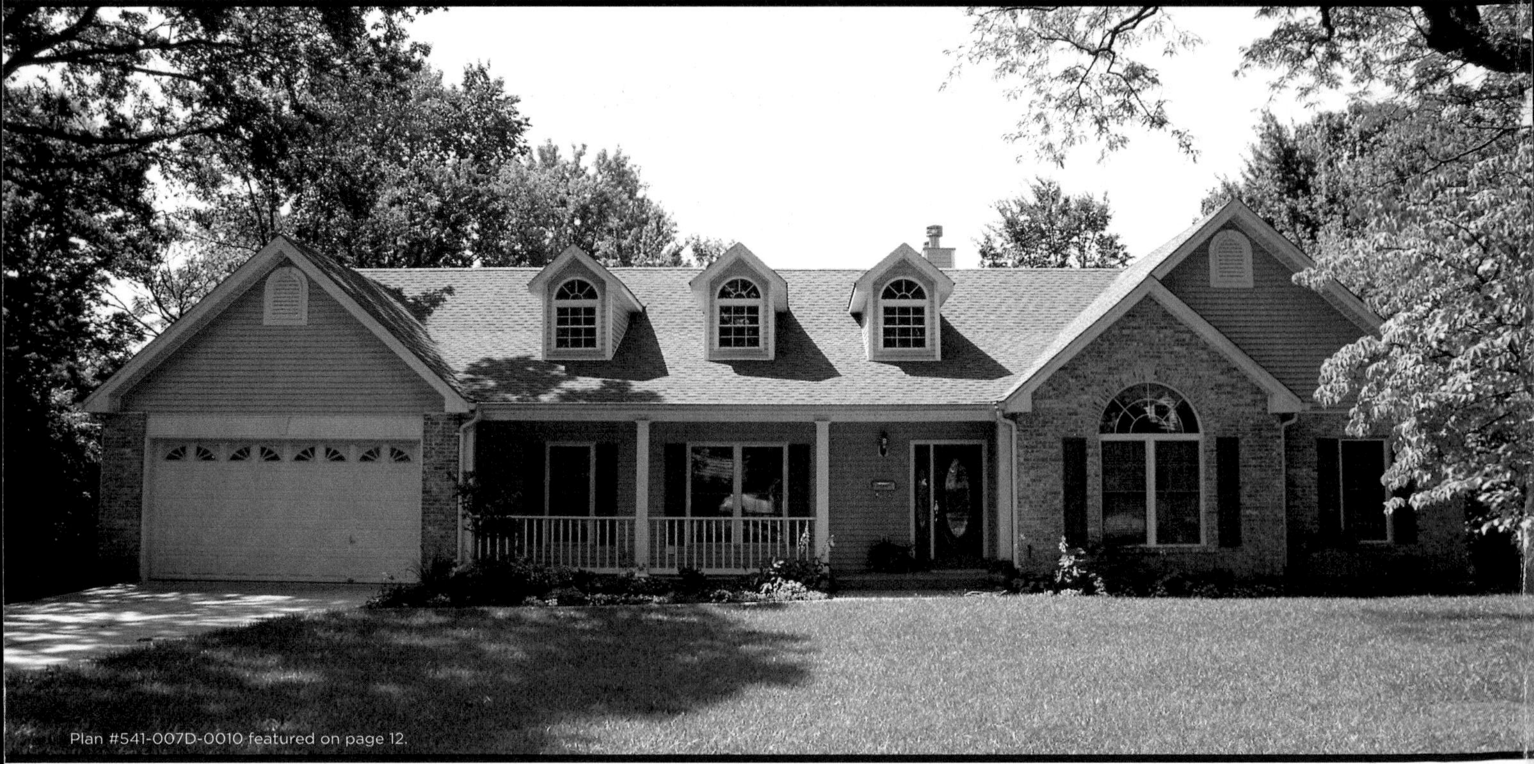

Plan #541-007D-0010 featured on page 12.

HDA INC

COVER HOMES - The homes shown on the front cover are Plan #541-072L-1108, featured on page 25, courtesy of Lifestyles Home Design and Plan #541-077L-0097, featured on page 32, courtesy of House Plan Gallery, Inc.

LOWE'S SMALL & STYLISH HOME PLANS
is published by HDA, Inc., 944 Anglum Road, St. Louis, MO, 63042.
 Artist drawings and photos shown in this publication may vary slightly from the actual working drawings. Some photos are shown in mirror reverse. Please refer to the floor plan for accurate layout.

ISBN-13: 978-1-58678-061-6
ISBN-10: 1-58678-061-1

Current Printing

10 9 8 7 6 5 4 3

HDA, Inc.
944 Anglum Rd.
St. Louis, Missouri 63042
corporate website - www.hdainc.com

Contents

Plan #541-065L-0154 featured on page 61.

FROM SELF-DISCIPLINE COMES STRENGTH.
Our rigid, self-imposed specifications and third-party inspections ensure that the strength and integrity of Top Choice® lumber and hardwoods won't be compromised by defects such as knots, twists or wane.
CERTIFIED QUALITY
TOP CHOICE®
LUMBER PRODUCTS
Consistent Quality. Consistent Results.™
Exclusively at
LOWE'S®
Let's Build Something Together™
For the store nearest you, call 1-800-993-4416. ©2010 by Lowe's.
trademarks of LF, LLC.

Making Changes To Your Plan

We understand that it is difficult to find blueprints that will meet all your needs. That is why HDA, Inc. is pleased to offer plan modification services.

Thinking About Customizing Your Plan?

If you're like many customers, you may want to make changes to your home plan to make it the dream home you've always wanted. That's where our expert design and modification team comes in. You won't find a more efficient and economic way to get your changes done than by using our design services.

Whether it's enlarging a kitchen, adding a porch or converting a crawl space to a basement, we can customize any plan and make it perfect for your family. Simply create your wish list and let us go to work. Soon you'll have the blueprints for your new home and at a fraction of the cost of hiring an architect!

The HDA Modification Advantage

- We can customize any of the thousands of plans on www.houseplansandmore.com.
- FREE cost estimates for your home plan modifications within 24 hours (Monday-Friday, 8am-5pm CST).
- Average turn-around time to complete the modifications is 2-3 weeks.
- One-on-one design consultations.

3 Easy Steps For Fast Service

1. Visit **www.houseplansandmore.com** to download the modification request form, complete the form and email it to customize@hdainc.com.
2. Fax the completed modification form to 651-602-5050.
3. Call 888-355-5728 for your free estimate.

If you are not able to access the internet, please call 1-877-379-3420 (Monday-Friday, 8am-5pm CST).

Customizing Facts

- The average cost for us to customize a house plan is typically less than 1 percent of the building costs — compare that to the national average of 7 percent of building costs.
- The average modification cost for a home is typically \$800 to \$1,500 (this does not include the cost of the reproducible blueprint, which is required to make plan changes).
- The average cost to modify a project plan is typically between \$200-\$500.

Other Helpful Information

- Feel free to include a sketch, or a specific list of changes you'd like to make.
- One of our designers will contact you within 24 hours with your free estimate.
- Upon accepting the estimate, you will need to purchase the reproducible set of plans.
- A contract, which includes a specific list of changes and fees will be sent to you for approval.
- Upon approving the contract, our designers will keep you up to date by emailing or faxing sketches throughout the project.
- Plan can be converted to metric.
- Barrier Free Conversion (accommodating a plan for special needs, transforming your living space for everyone).
- Customizing is also available for project plans, such as sheds, garages, apartment garages and more.

What's The Right Plan For You?

Choosing a home plan is an exciting but difficult task. Many factors play a role in what home plan is best for you and your family. To help you get started, we have pinpointed some of the major factors to consider when searching for your dream home. Take the time to evaluate your family's needs and you will have an easier time sorting through all of the home plans offered in this book.

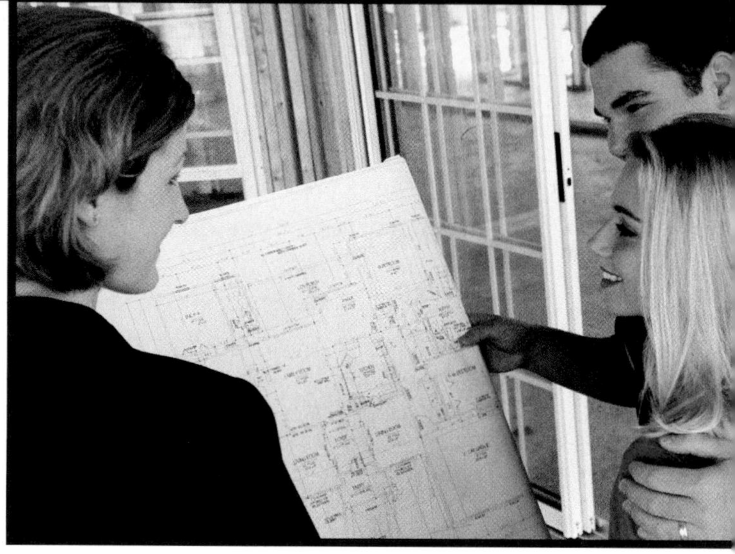

Budget: The first thing to consider is your budget. Many items take part in this budget, from ordering the blueprints to the last doorknob purchased. When you find your dream home plan, visit your commercial sales specialist at your local Lowe's store to get a cost-to-build estimate to ensure that the finished product will be within your cost range.

Family Lifestyle: After your budget is deciphered, you need to assess you and your family's lifestyle needs. Think about the stage of life you are at now, and what stages you will be going through in the future. Ask yourself questions to figure out how much room you need now and if you will need room for expansion. Are you married? Do you have children? How many children do you plan on having? Are you an empty-nester?

Incorporate in your planning any frequent guests you may have, including elderly parents, grandchildren or adult children who may live with you.

Does your family entertain a lot? If so, think about the rooms you will need to do so. Will you need both formal and informal spaces? Do you need a gourmet kitchen? Do you need a game room and/or a wet bar?

Experts in the field suggest that the best way to determine your needs is to begin by listing everything you like or dislike about your current home.

Floor Plan Layouts: When looking through our home plans, imagine yourself walking through the house. Consider the flow from the entry to the living, sleeping and gathering areas. Does the layout ensure privacy for the master bedroom? Does the garage enter near the kitchen for easy unloading? Does the placement of the windows provide enough privacy from any neighboring properties? Do you plan on using furniture you already have? Will this furniture fit in the appropriate rooms? When you find a plan you want to purchase, be sure to picture yourself actually living in it.

Exterior Spaces: There are many different home styles ranging from Traditional to Contemporary. Flip through and find which style most appeals to you and the neighborhood in which you plan to build. Also think of your site and how the entire house will fit on this site. Picture any landscaping you plan on incorporating into the design. Using your imagination is key when choosing a home plan.

Choosing a home plan can be an intimidating experience. Asking yourself these questions before you get started on the search will help you through the process. With our large selection of multiple styles we are certain you will find your dream home in the following pages.

The Lowe's Legacy Series

Leg•a•cy: Something that is handed down or remains for generations

HDA, Inc. is proud to introduce to you the Lowe's Legacy Series. The home plans in this collection carry on the Lowe's tradition of quality and expertise, and will continue to do so for many generations.

Choosing a home plan can be a daunting task. With the Legacy Series, we will set your mind at ease. Selecting a plan from this group will ensure a home designed with the Lowe's standard of excellence, creating a dream home for you and your family.

LOWE'S LEGACY SERIES

This collection of Legacy Series plans includes our most popular small and stylish home plans. Browse through the pages to discover a home with the options and special characteristics you need.

Along with one-of-a-kind craftsmanship, all Legacy Series home plans offer industry-leading material lists. These accurate material lists will save you a considerable amount of time and money, providing you with the quantity, dimensions and descriptions of the major building materials necessary to construct your home. You'll get faster and more accurate bids from your contractor while saving money by paying for only the materials you need.

The Lowe's Legacy Series is the perfect place to start your search for the home of your dreams. You will find the expected beauty you want and the functional efficiency you need, all designed with unmatched quality.

Turn the page and begin the wonderful journey of finding your new home.

Photos clockwise from top: 541-033D-0002, page 10; 541-027D-0003, page 17; 541-013L-0015, page 15; 541-065L-0074, page 20.

First Impressions

Exterior design ideas that add curb appeal to your small and stylish home.

As a homeowner you know that a house is simply the building where you live. It is structurally sound, efficient and does its job. However, your home is so much more. It's where you invite your friends and family to join in making new memories. Your home is infused with your personality, style, and charm. It is so much more than a house.

When building a new house it is important to incorporate those home qualities right from the start. Interior design is often overrun with your personal taste, while the outer appearance fades to the back of your mind. Exterior design is a fantastic opportunity to introduce your personal preferences to the entire neighborhood, reminding neighbors that you are building a home inside and out.

Today's market for exterior design has options that will fit any personality. Color is flooding real estate, capturing the eye, inspiring homeowners and improving curb appeal. When planning your home's exterior colors, trims, railings, doors, and roofs should all be considered; the greater the exterior details, the more colors you can use. Though the palette of colors has expanded immensely, it is necessary to show some restraint when choosing, for example:

- *Colonial style* homes are best finished with soft, reminiscent neutrals that capture the era while defining the details.
- *Southwestern style* stucco homes are full of rich peaches and warm tones.
- *Victorian homes* are often swathed in many colors spotlighting their intricate details.
- *Traditional designs* can be decorated with stone, either natural or synthetic, to capture the home's historic charm.
- *Brick exterior* also allows countless options by combining different brick colors and colored cement for the mortar joints to create an amazing impact.

Plan #541-065L-0170, see page 27.

There are no real restrictions on what styles can utilize what colors, however, do keep in mind that there are other rules about home exteriors. This is especially true in smaller towns or neighborhoods with homeowner associations. Check to make sure the color you love is an option where you build. Though color is a top priority in building a home with curb appeal, there are other components to consider:

Plan #541-027D-0003, see page 17.

- *Regular cleaning* of your home's exterior will prevent the task from becoming overwhelming and extend the life of your siding material. Cleaning and sealing will keep driveways from looking worn and will enhance your home's beauty.
- *Functional objects,* such as mailboxes and door handles, are often overlooked in terms of curb appeal. Whether plain or ornate, be certain that all are sturdy, clean and undamaged.
- *Lawn edges* should be trimmed in order to define walkways and create clean lines.
- *Plantings* in front of the home should be trimmed and minimized so focus is drawn to the home. Pay close attention to blossom colors to keep from clashing with your home. Choose neutral tones for your exterior if you prefer to draw focus to the landscaping rather than the house.

Remember to pay close attention to your surroundings when discussing colors and landscaping. You want to ensure that your home is beautiful and unique while appropriate to the area in which you live. It is often a good idea to ask for opinions of neighbors and frequent visitors, as they can better evaluate color and layout options without bias. In the end, go with what you feel is best. Exciting color and regular maintenance will turn your new house into a beautiful, welcoming home.

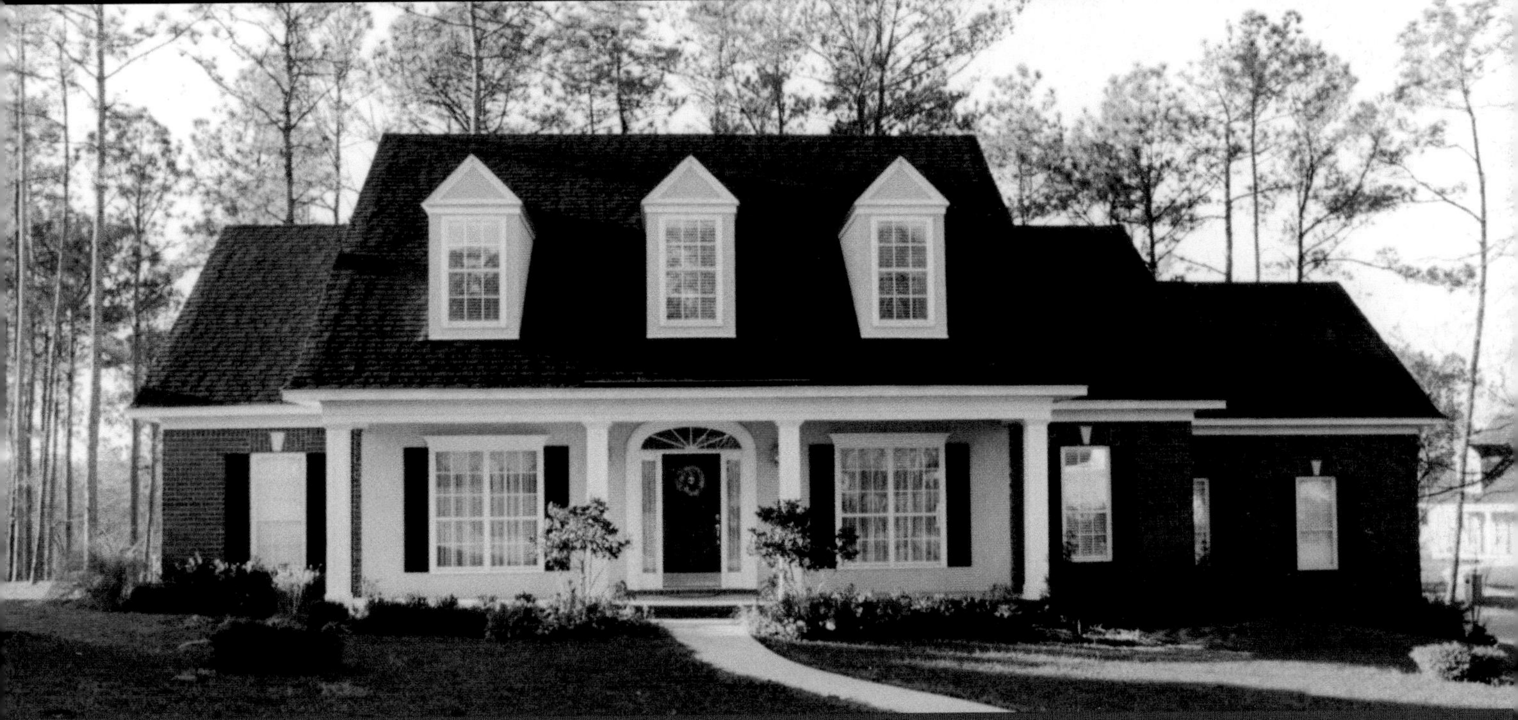

Double French Doors Grace Living Room

- 2,333 total square feet of living area
- 9' ceilings on the first floor
- Master bedroom features a large walk-in closet and an inviting double-door entry into a spacious bath
- Convenient laundry room is located near the kitchen
- Unfinished room on the second floor has an additional 169 square feet of living area
- 4 bedrooms, 3 baths, 2-car side entry garage
- Slab foundation, drawings also include crawl space and partial crawl space/basement foundations

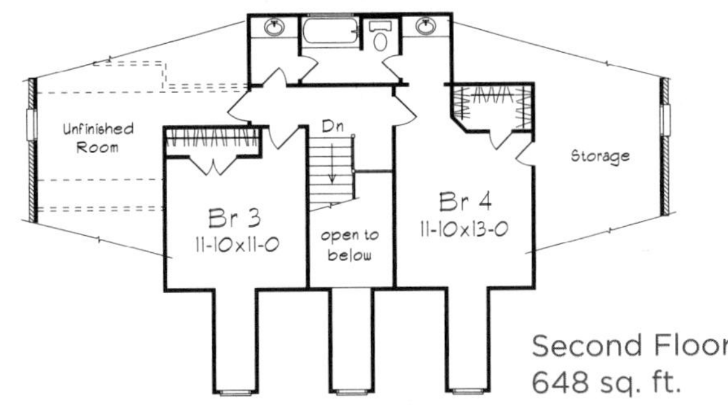

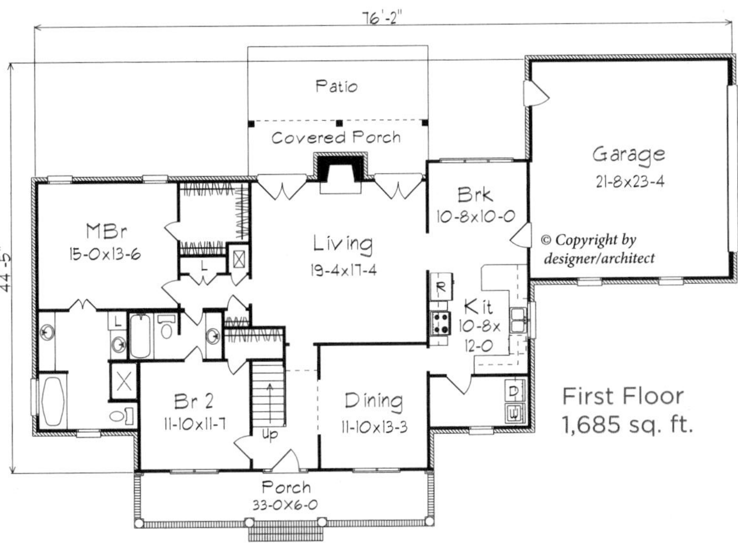

Plan #541-033D-0002 • Price Code D

Striking, Covered Arched Entry

- 1,859 total square feet of living area
- Fireplace highlights the vaulted great room
- Master bedroom includes a large closet and private bath
- The kitchen adjoins the breakfast room providing easy access to the outdoors
- 3 bedrooms, 2 1/2 baths, 2-car garage
- Basement foundation

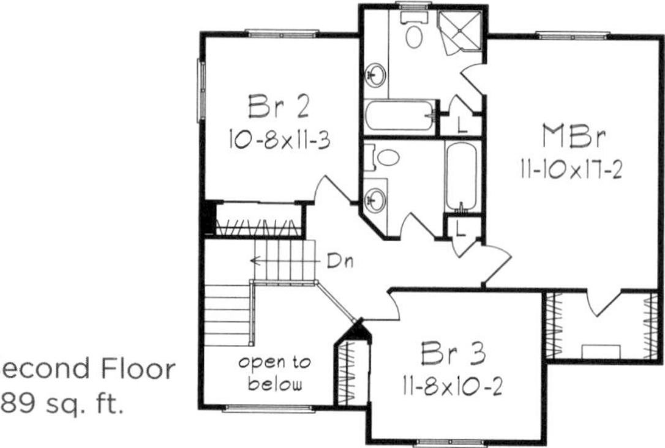

Second Floor
789 sq. ft.

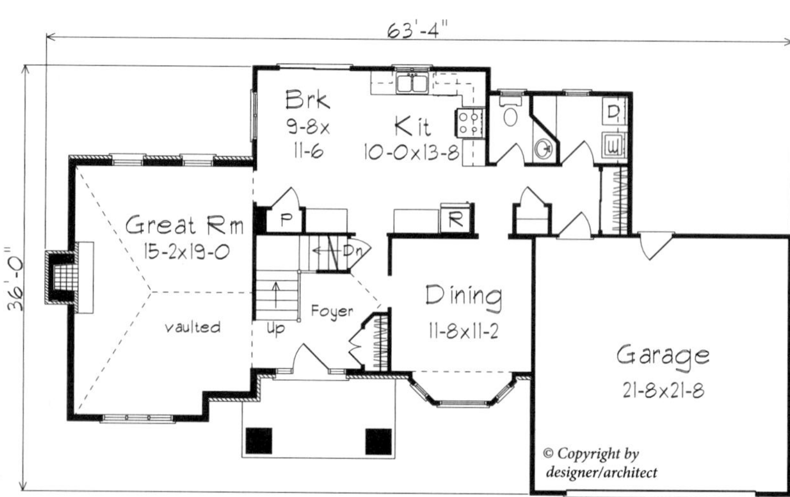

First Floor
1,070 sq. ft.

• To Order See Page 288 or Call Toll-Free 1-877-379-3420

Plan #541-007D-0060 • Price Code B

Distinguished Styling For A Small Lot

- 1,268 total square feet of living area
- Multiple gables, large porch and arched windows create a classy exterior
- Innovative design provides openness in the great room, kitchen and breakfast room
- Secondary bedrooms have private hall with bath
- 2" x 6" exterior walls available, please order plan #541-007E-0060
- Plan also available with energy efficient R-Control® SIPs (Structural Insulated Panels), please call 1-877-379-3420 for more information
- 3 bedrooms, 2 baths, 2-car garage
- Basement foundation, drawings also include crawl space and slab foundations

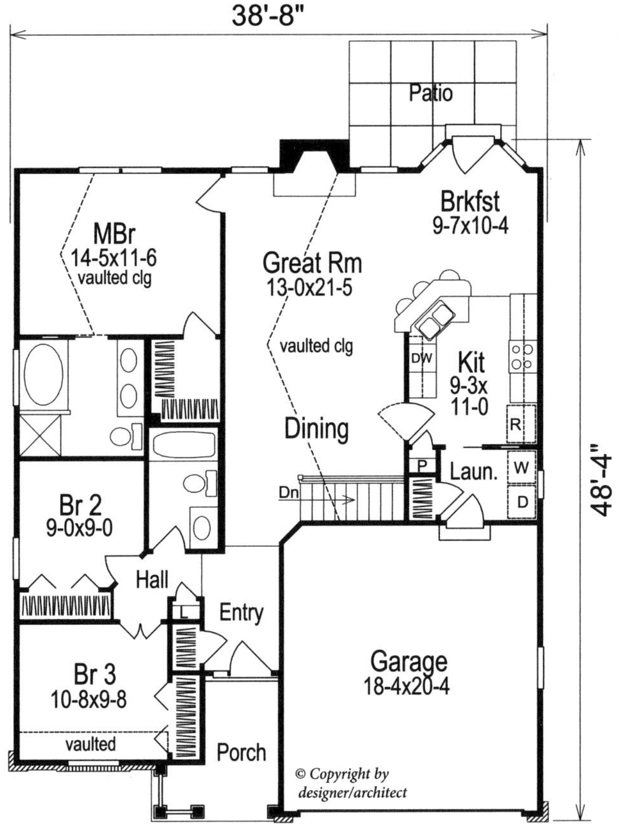

Plan #541-007D-0010 • Price Code C

Atrium's Dramatic Ambiance, Compliments Of Windows

- 1,845 total square feet of living area
- Roof dormers add great curb appeal
- Vaulted dining and great rooms are immersed in light from the atrium window wall
- Functionally designed kitchen
- 2" x 6" exterior walls available, please order plan #541-007E-0010
- Plan also available with energy efficient R-Control® SIPs (Structural Insulated Panels), please call 1-877-379-3420 for more information
- The lower level has an additional 889 square feet of optional living area
- 3 bedrooms, 2 baths, 3-car garage
- Walk-out basement foundation, drawings also include crawl space and slab foundations

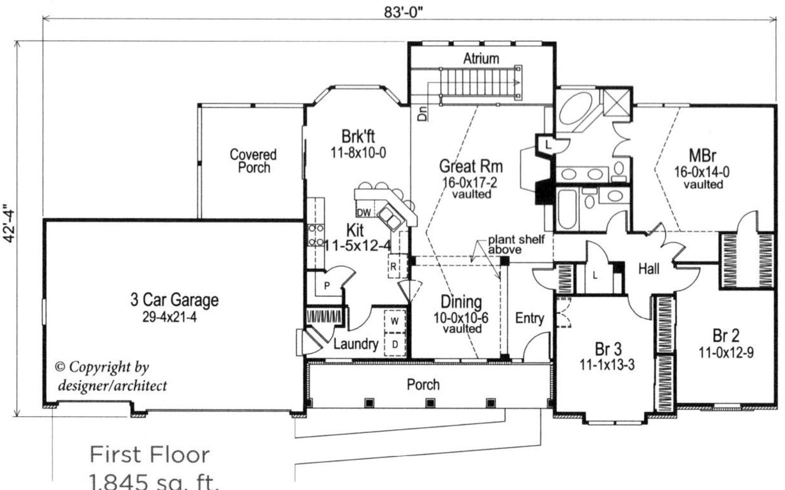

First Floor
1,845 sq. ft.

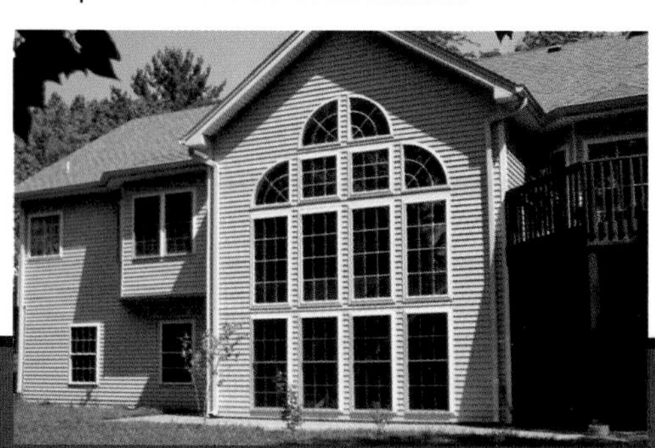

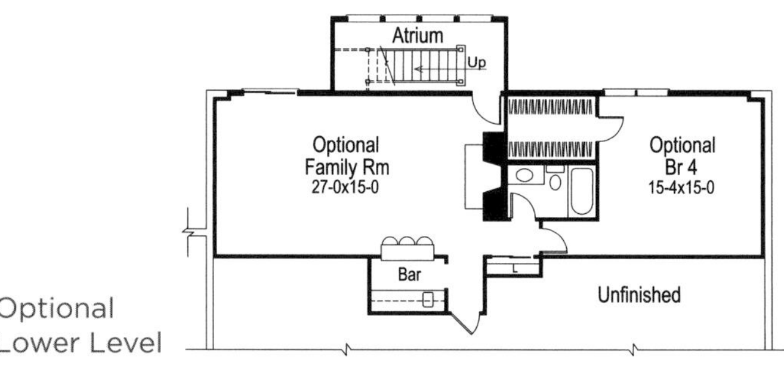

Optional
Lower Level

• To Order See Page 288 or Call Toll-Free 1-877-379-3420

Plan #541-072L-1110 • Price Code A

Eye-Pleasing Exterior Gables

- 1,771 total square feet of living area
- Wonderful three-car garage enters into a mud room with the laundry room conveniently located nearby
- Amazing great room features large windows creating a bold statement while enjoying the lovely fireplace
- A stunning sunroom sits in the corner of this house offering a wonderful place with a view for enjoying family and friends
- 2 bedrooms, 2 baths, 3-car side entry garage
- Walk-out basement foundation

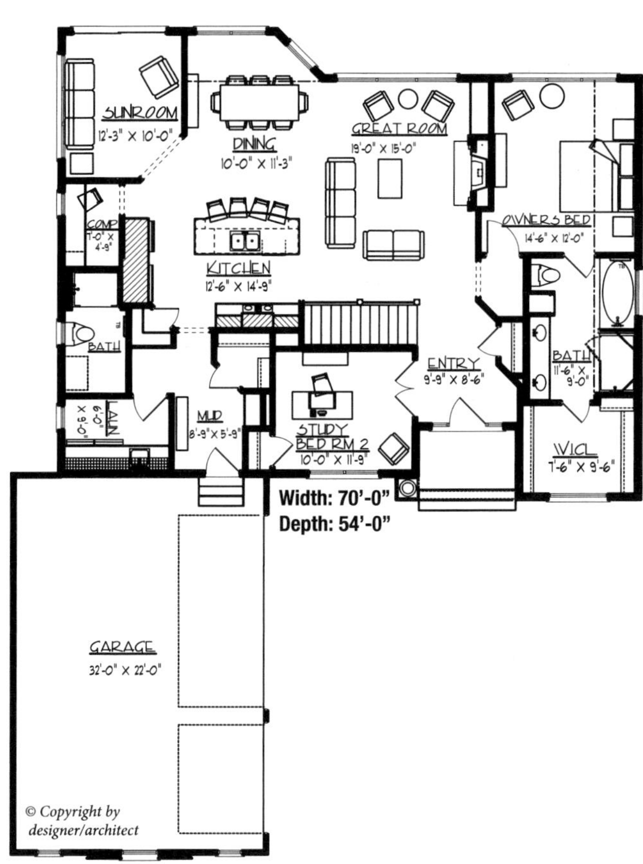

Plan #541-051L-0238 • Price Code D

Two-Story Enjoys Private Bedrooms

- 1,873 total square feet of living area
- Energy efficient home with 2″ x 6″ exterior walls
- This stylish home fits perfectly on a narrow lot
- The vaulted, two-story living room greets guests and offers a dramatic first impression
- The kitchen, bayed dining room and family room combine for an easy flow of household activities
- 3 bedrooms, 2 1/2 baths, 2-car garage
- Basement foundation

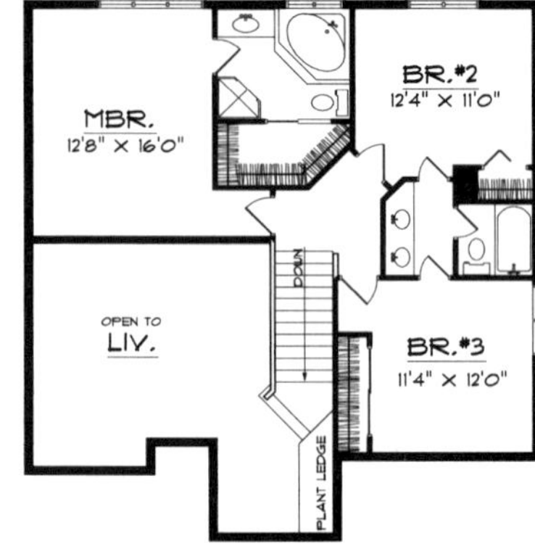

Second Floor
819 sq. ft.

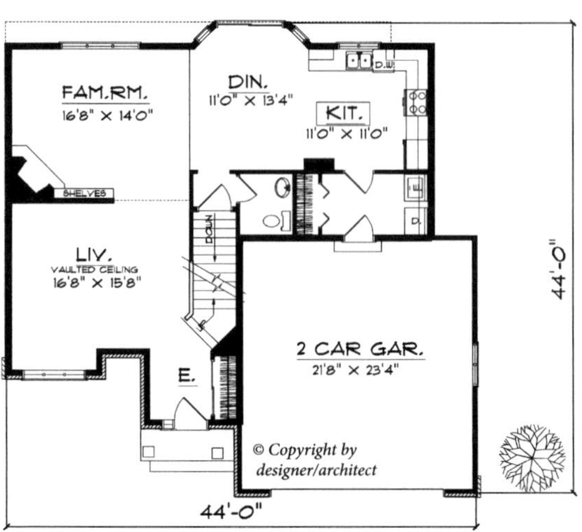

First Floor
1,054 sq. ft.

To Order See Page 288 or Call Toll-Free 1-877-379-3420

Plan #541-013L-0015 • Price Code C

Uncommonly Styled Ranch

- 1,787 total square feet of living area
- Skylights brighten the screen porch that connects to the family room and deck outdoors
- Master bedroom features a comfortable sitting area, large private bath and direct access to the screen porch
- Kitchen has a serving bar which extends dining into the family room
- Bonus room above the garage has an additional 263 square feet of living area
- 3 bedrooms, 2 baths, 2-car side entry garage
- Basement foundation, drawings also include crawl space and slab foundations

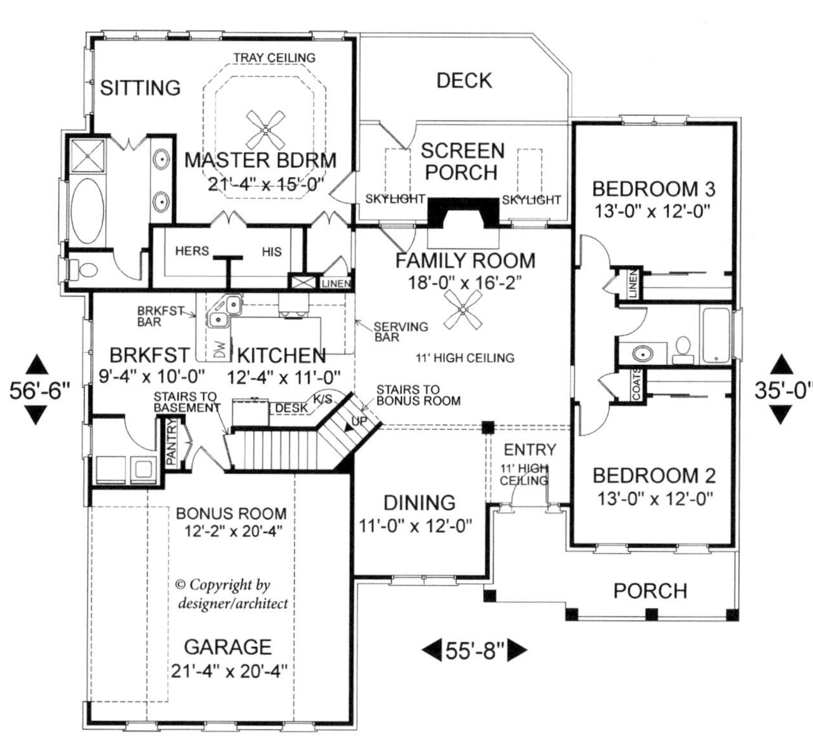

Plan #541-021D-0010 • Price Code B

Central Fireplace Dominates Living Area

- 1,444 total square feet of living area
- 11' ceilings in the living and dining rooms combine with a central fireplace to create a large open living area
- Both secondary bedrooms have large walk-in closets
- Extra space in the garage is suitable for a workshop or play area
- Front and rear covered porches add a cozy touch
- U-shaped kitchen includes a laundry closet and serving bar
- 3 bedrooms, 2 baths, 2-car side entry garage
- Slab foundation, drawings also include crawl space foundation

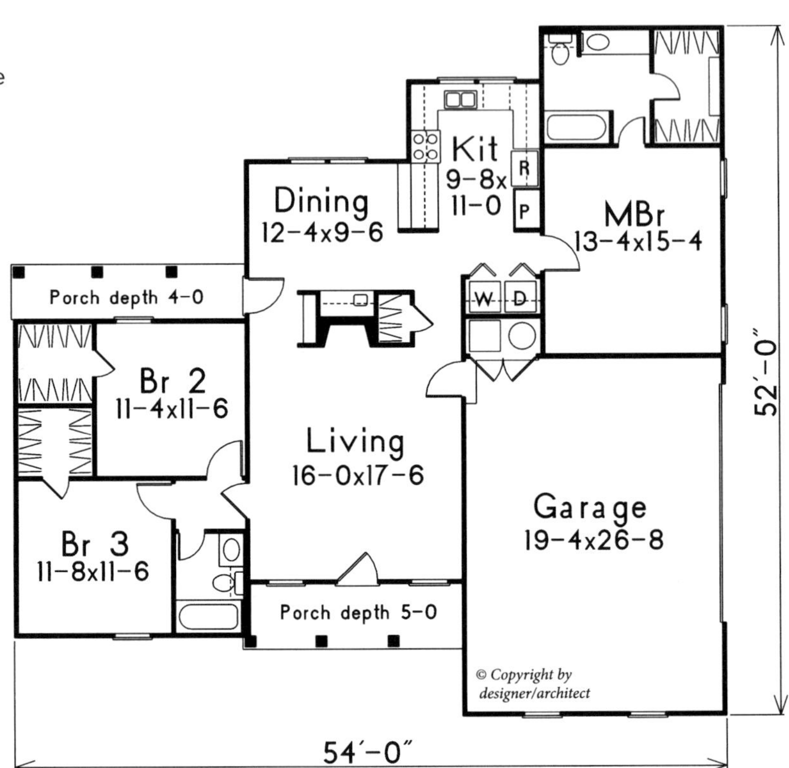

• To Order See Page 288 or Call Toll-Free 1-877-379-3420

Classic Three Bedroom Home

- 2,061 total square feet of living area
- Convenient entrance from the garage into the home through the laundry room
- The master bedroom features a walk-in closet and double-door entrance into the private bath with an oversized tub
- Formal dining room enjoys a tray ceiling
- Kitchen features an island cooktop and adjacent breakfast room
- 3 bedrooms, 2 baths, 2-car garage
- Basement foundation

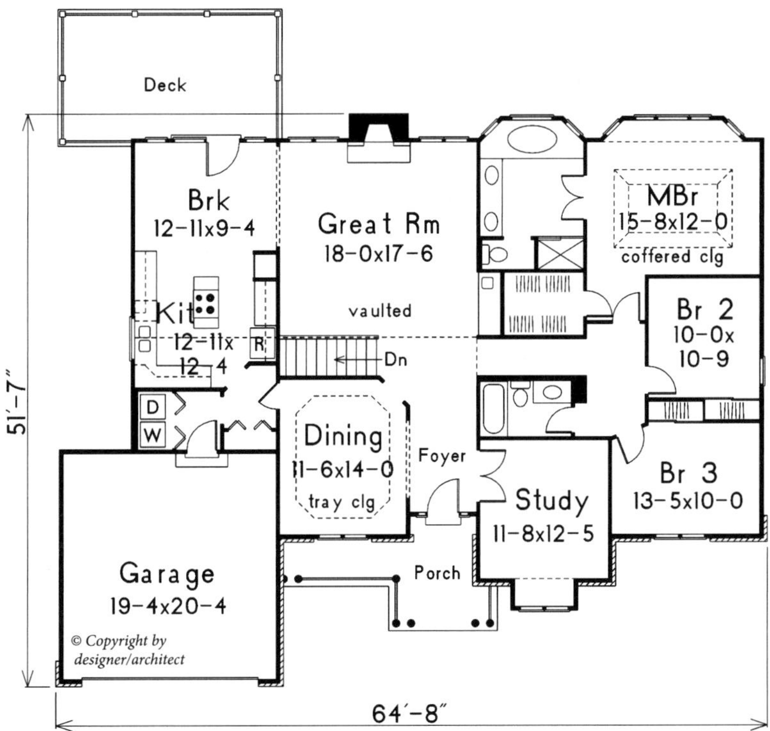

Plan #541-072L-0002 • Price Code A

Charming Combination Of Woodwork And Stone

- 1,767 total square feet of living area
- Vaulted dining room has a view onto the patio
- Master suite is vaulted with a private bath and walk-in closet
- An arched entry leads to the vaulted living room featuring tall windows and a fireplace
- 3 bedrooms, 2 1/2 baths, 2-car garage
- Basement foundation

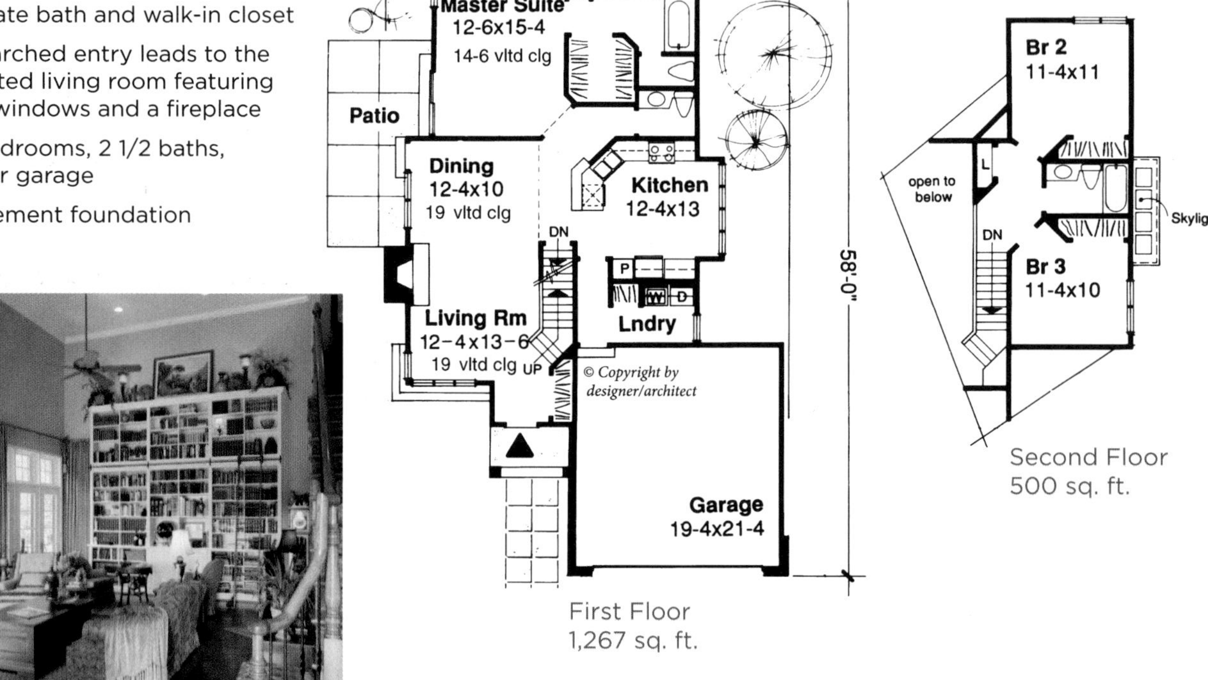

First Floor
1,267 sq. ft.

Second Floor
500 sq. ft.

• To Order See Page 288 or Call Toll-Free 1-877-379-3420

Plan #541-058D-0016 • Price Code B

Lovely, Spacious Floor Plan

- 1,558 total square feet of living area
- The spacious utility room is located conveniently between the garage and kitchen/dining area
- Bedrooms are separated from the living area by a hallway
- Enormous living area with fireplace and vaulted ceiling opens to the kitchen and dining area
- Master bedroom is enhanced with a large bay window, walk-in closet and private bath
- 2″ x 6″ exterior walls available, please order plan #541-058D-0078
- 3 bedrooms, 2 baths, 2-car garage
- Basement foundation

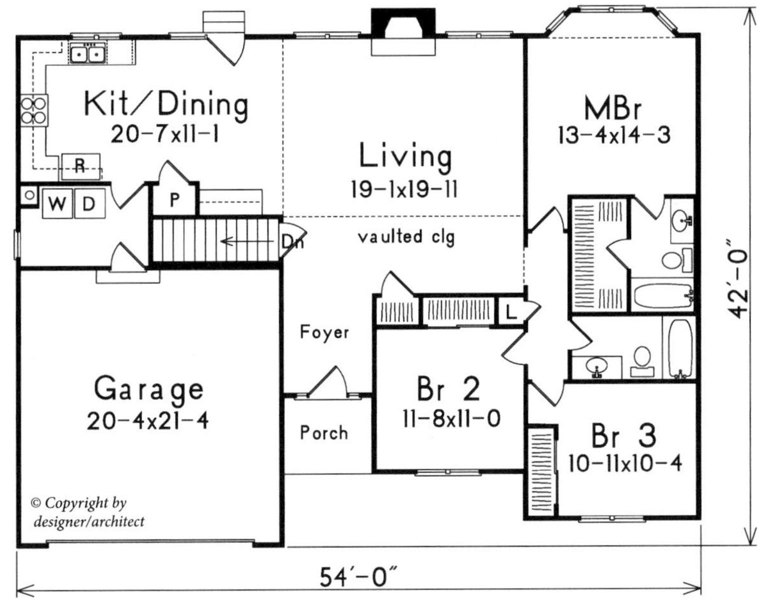

Plan #541-065L-0074 • Price Code B

Wonderful Family Home

- 1,698 total square feet of living area
- An open great room and dining area is topped by a stepped ceiling treatment that reaches a 9' height
- The functional kitchen enjoys a walk-in pantry and a delightful angled snack bar
- Warmth and charm radiate from the corner fireplace through the combined living areas, and a covered porch offers outdoor enjoyment
- 3 bedrooms, 2 baths, 2-car garage
- Basement foundation

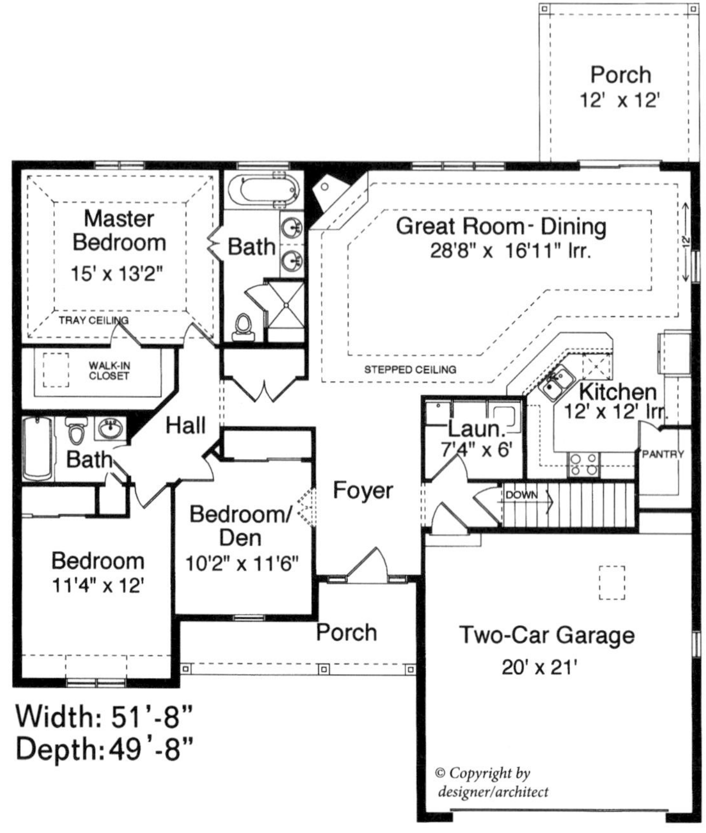

• To Order See Page 288 or Call Toll-Free 1-877-379-3420

Plan #541-007D-0054 • Price Code B

Stylish Living For A Narrow Lot

- 1,575 total square feet of living area
- Inviting porch leads to spacious living and dining rooms
- Kitchen with corner windows features an island snack bar, attractive breakfast room bay, convenient laundry area and built-in pantry
- A luxury bath and walk-in closet adorn the master bedroom suite
- 3 bedrooms, 2 1/2 baths, 2-car garage
- Basement foundation, drawings also include crawl space and slab foundations

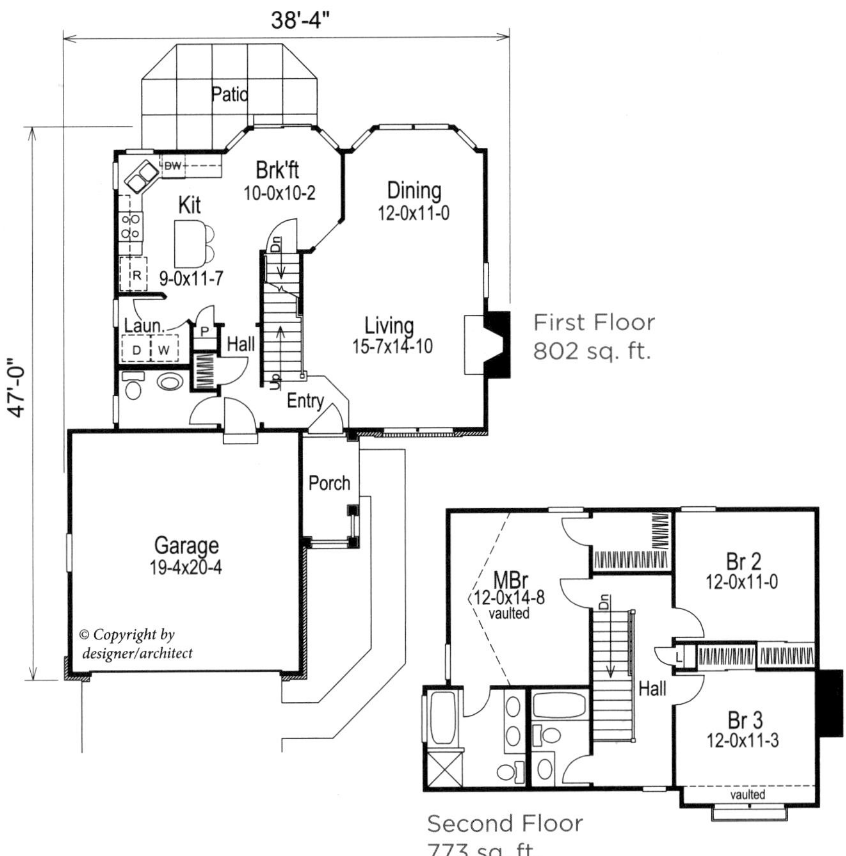

First Floor
802 sq. ft.

Second Floor
773 sq. ft.

Plan #541-051L-0060 • Price Code B

Dramatic Roof Lines Create A Ranch With Style

- 1,591 total square feet of living area
- Energy efficient home with 2" x 6" exterior walls
- Fireplace in great room is accented by windows on both sides
- Practical kitchen is splendidly designed for organization
- Large screen porch is ideal for three-season entertaining
- 3 bedrooms, 2 baths, 3-car garage
- Basement foundation

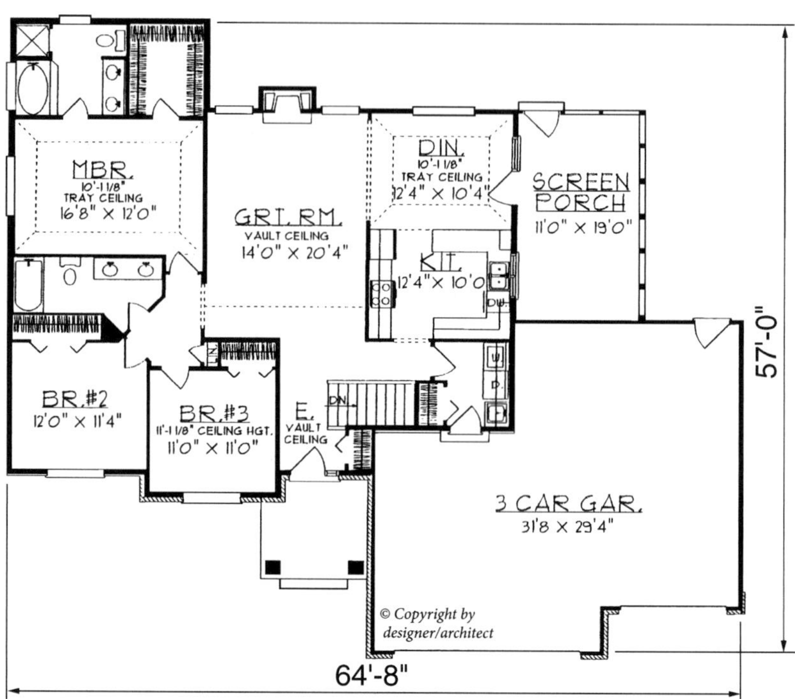

Plan #541-022D-0019 • Price Code A

LOWE'S LEGACY SERIES

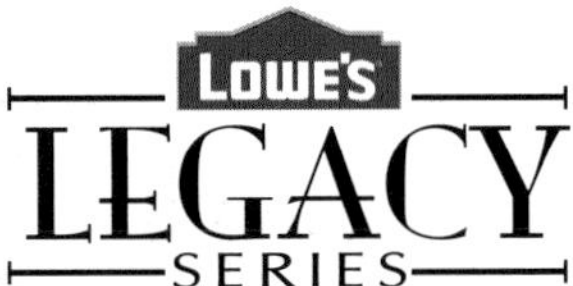

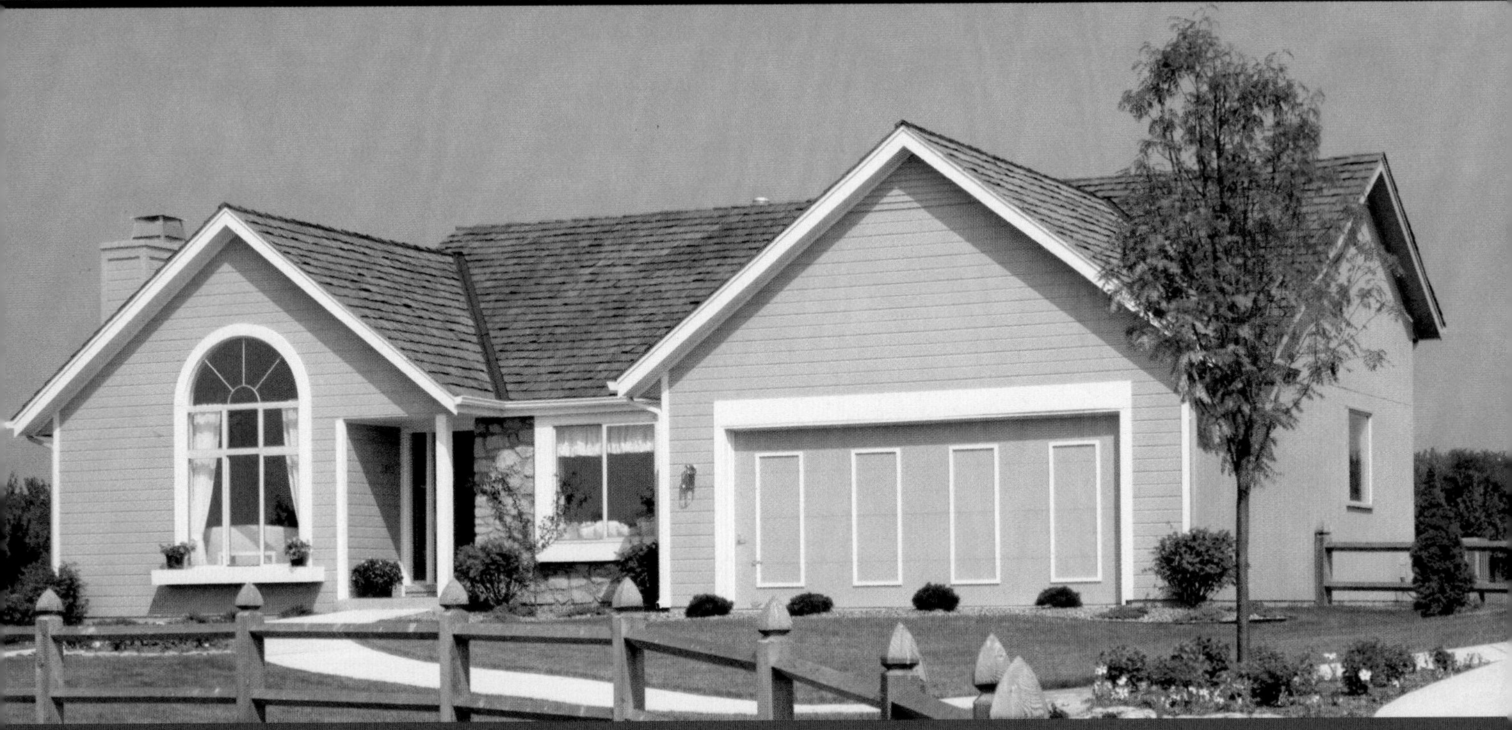

Large Corner Deck Lends Way To Outdoor Living Area

- 1,283 total square feet of living area
- Vaulted breakfast room has sliding doors that open onto the deck
- Kitchen features a convenient corner sink and pass-through to the dining room
- Open living atmosphere in dining area and great room
- Vaulted great room features a fireplace
- 3 bedrooms, 2 baths, 2-car garage
- Basement foundation

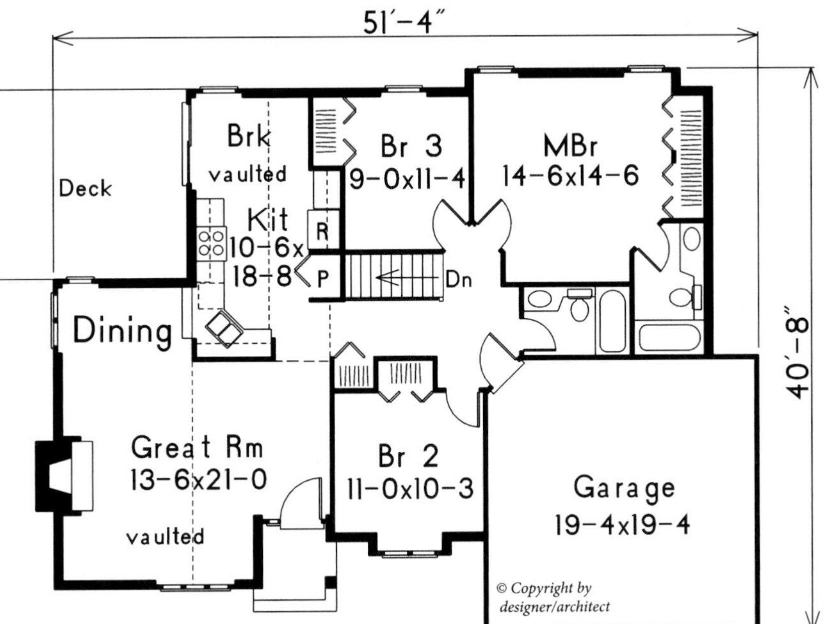

Plan #541-065L-0001 • Price Code B

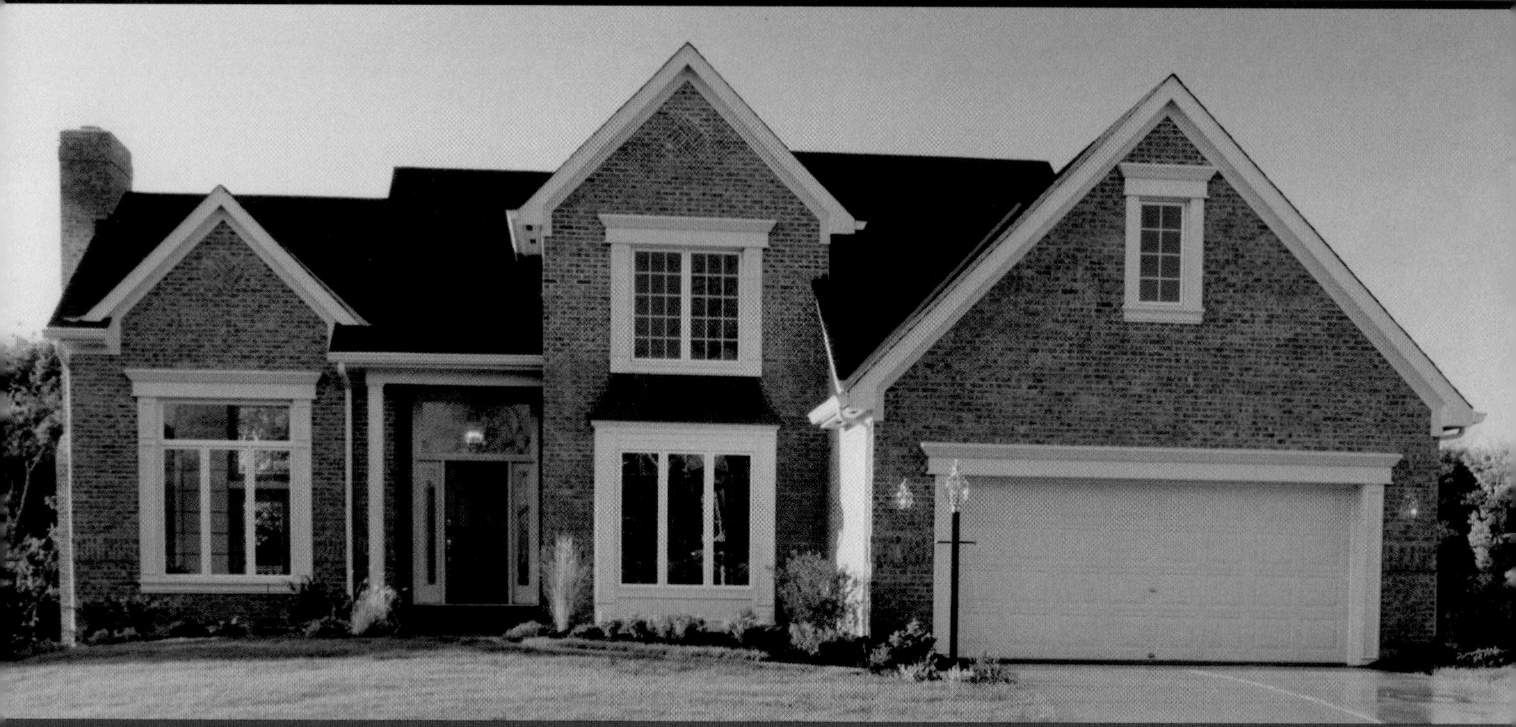

Beautiful Home For The Active Family

- 1,768 total square feet of living area
- The sunken great room features a comforting fireplace and access onto the rear porch
- Second floor master bedroom enjoys a tray ceiling, large walk-in closet and a deluxe bath
- 12' ceilings give the foyer and great room a spacious feel
- 3 bedrooms, 2 1/2 baths, 2-car garage
- Basement foundation

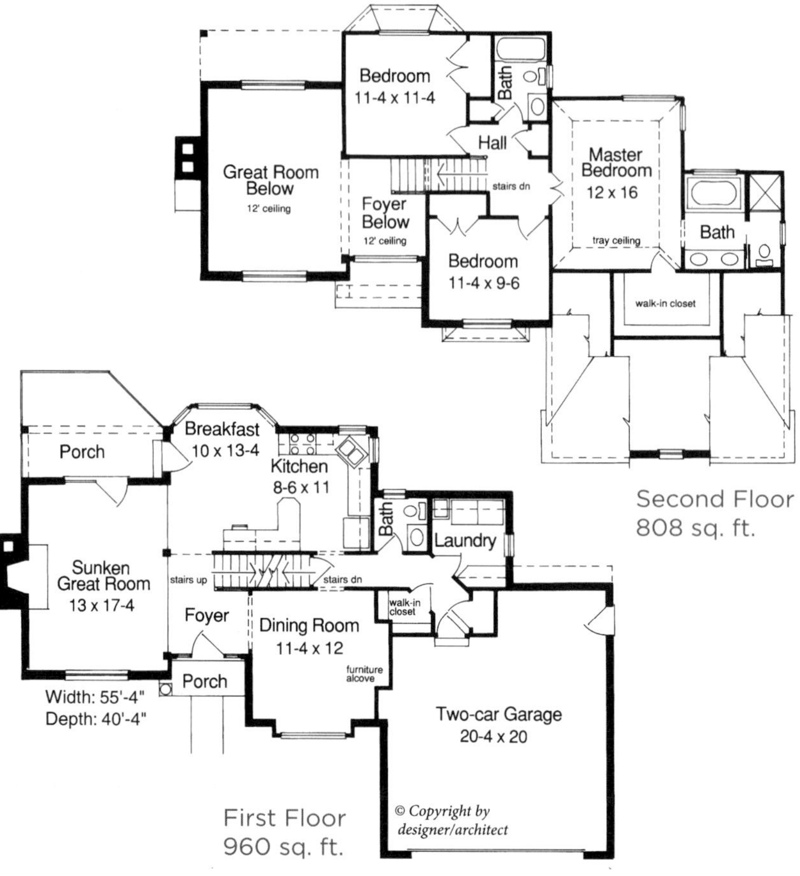

• To Order See Page 288 or Call Toll-Free 1-877-379-3420

Plan #541-072L-1108 • Price Code B

LOWE'S LEGACY SERIES

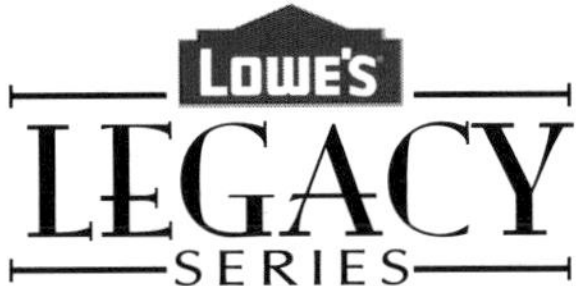

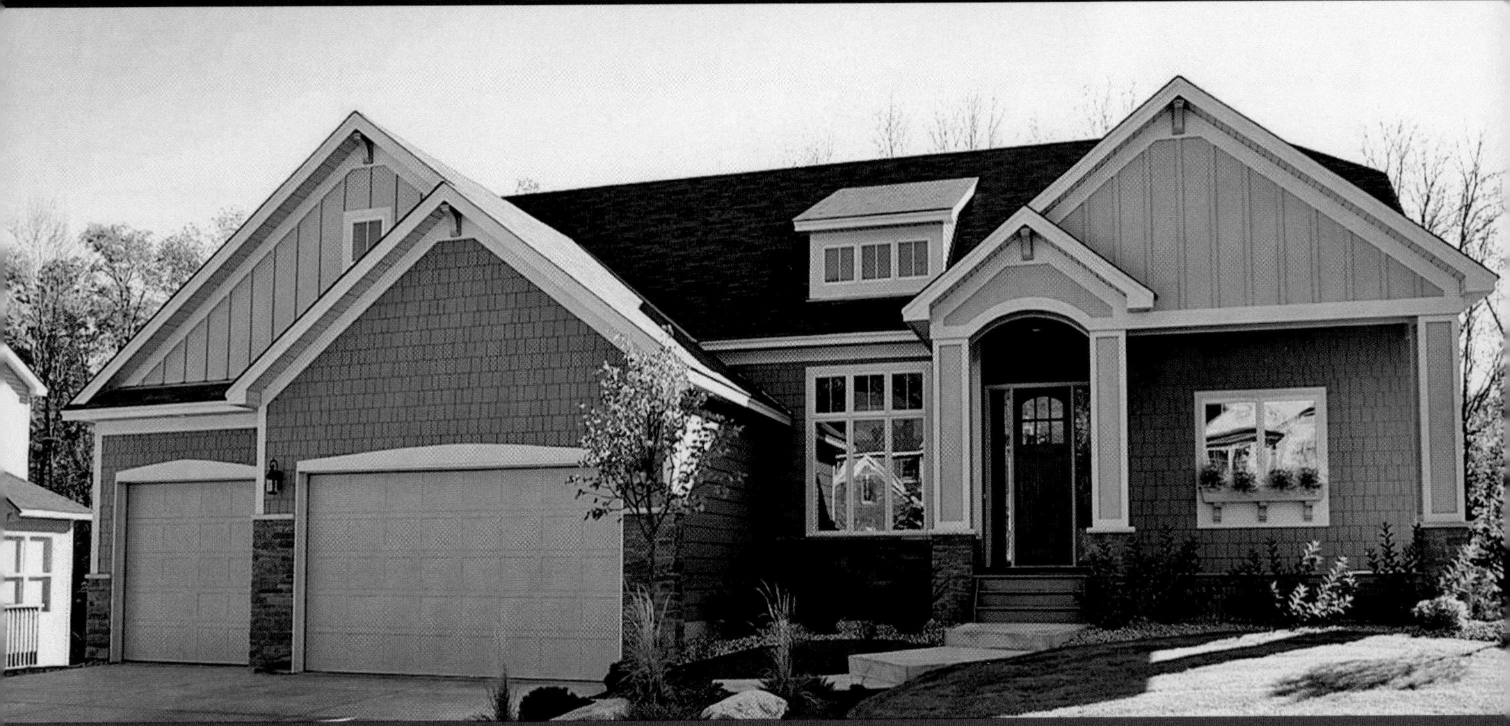

Inviting Front Porch

- 2,445 total square feet of living area
- Enjoy the spacious great room featuring a beautiful fireplace that creates a dramatic ambiance adding character and flair to this home
- Efficient kitchen is quite charming and contains a breakfast island and generous pantry
- The attractive sunroom provides a lovely space for relaxing and reading a good book
- 2 bedrooms, 2 baths, 3-car garage
- Walk-out basement foundation

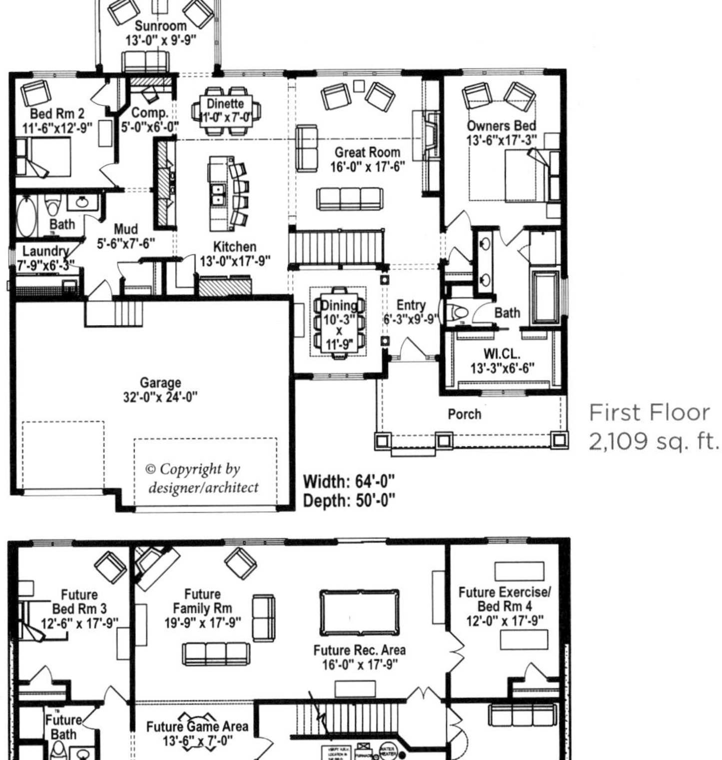

First Floor
2,109 sq. ft.

Lower Level
336 sq. ft.

Plan #541-087L-0262 • Price Code H

Split Bedrooms Promote Privacy

- 1,812 total square feet of living area
- A corner fireplace in the vaulted family room sets the stage for a cozy atmosphere
- The spacious kitchen includes a work island with seating for quick meals
- The master bedroom boasts a coffered ceiling and deluxe bath with whirlpool tub and walk-in closet
- Optional second floor has an additional 323 square feet of living area
- 3 bedrooms, 2 baths, 2-car side entry garage
- Slab foundation

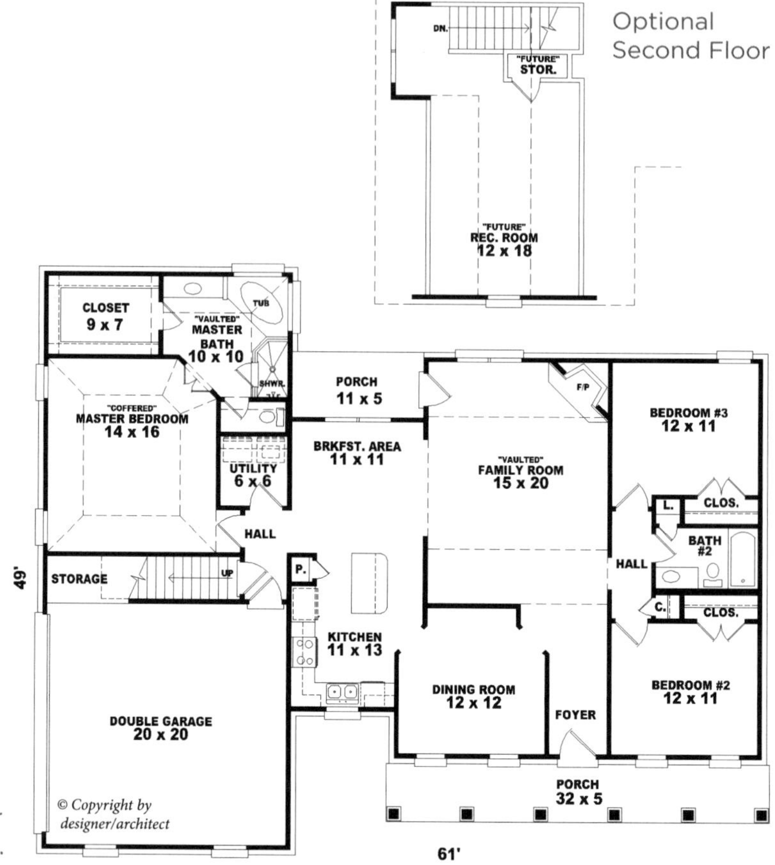

First Floor
1,812 sq. ft.

• To Order See Page 288 or Call Toll-Free 1-877-379-3420

Plan #541-065L-0170 • Price Code B

Decorative Entry Welcomes Guests

- 1,537 total square feet of living area
- A corner fireplace in the great room is visible from the foyer offering a dramatic first impression
- The kitchen island connects to the dining area that features a sloped ceiling and access to the rear porch
- The private master bedroom enjoys its own bath, walk-in closet and access to the rear porch
- 3 bedrooms, 2 baths, 2-car garage
- Basement foundation

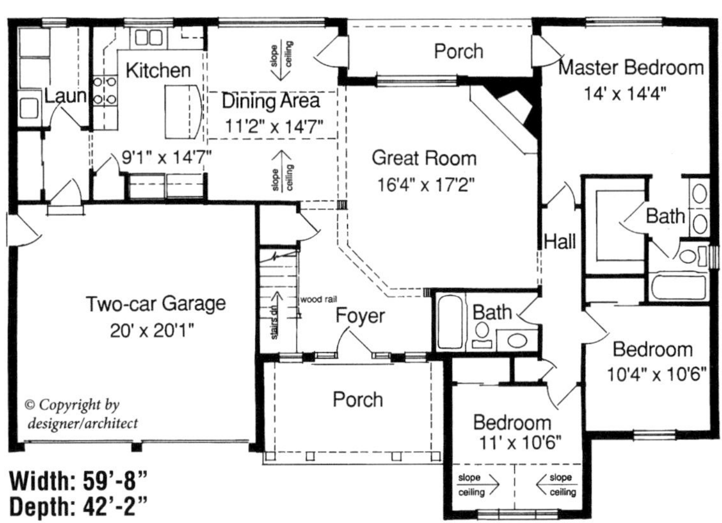

Width: 59'-8"
Depth: 42'-2"

Plan #541-021D-0018 • Price Code E

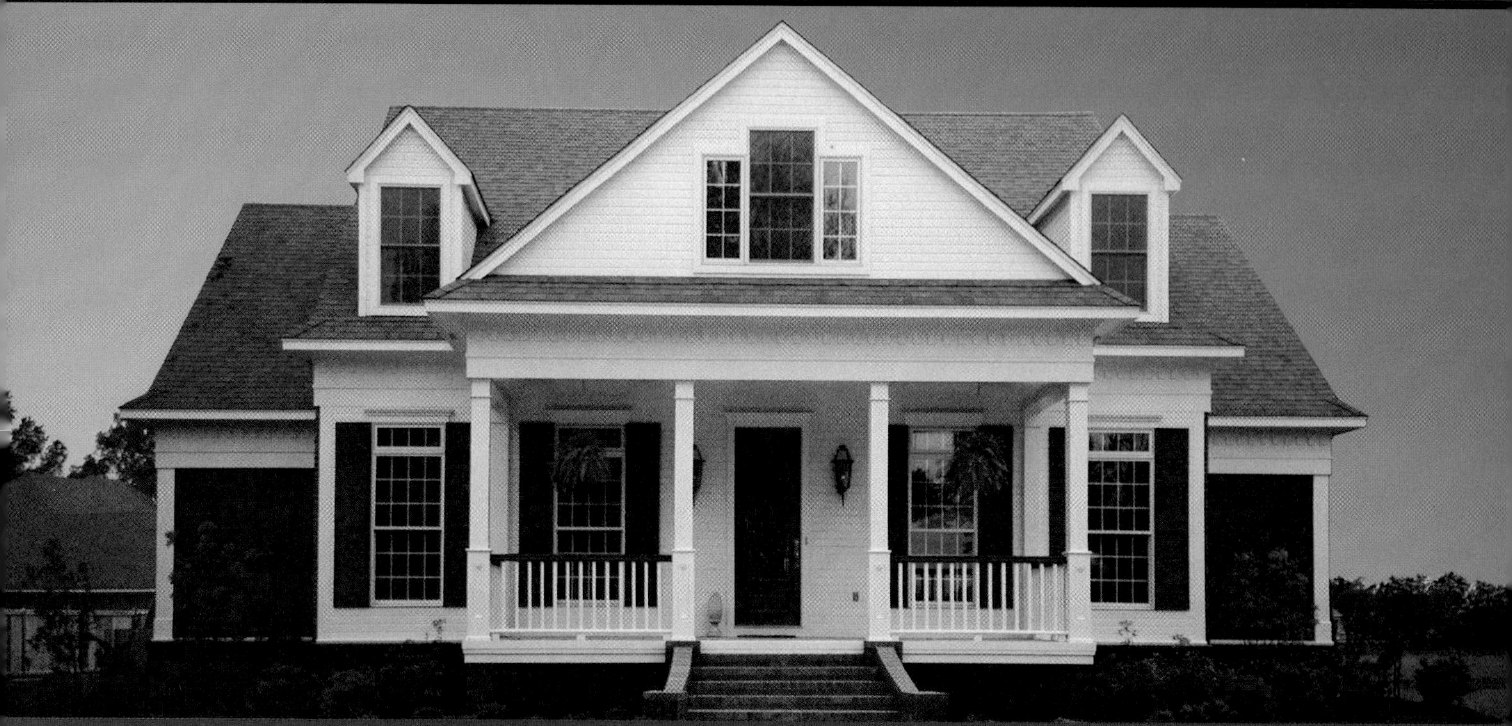

Graceful And Functional Front Porch

- 2,255 total square feet of living area
- Energy efficient home with 2" x 6" exterior walls
- Master bedroom with adjoining bath has an enormous walk-in closet
- Deluxe kitchen features a planning desk and a convenient eating area
- Second floor balcony overlooks the family room below
- Formal dining area has easy access to the kitchen
- 3 bedrooms, 2 baths, 2-car side entry garage
- Crawl space foundation, drawings also include slab and basement foundations

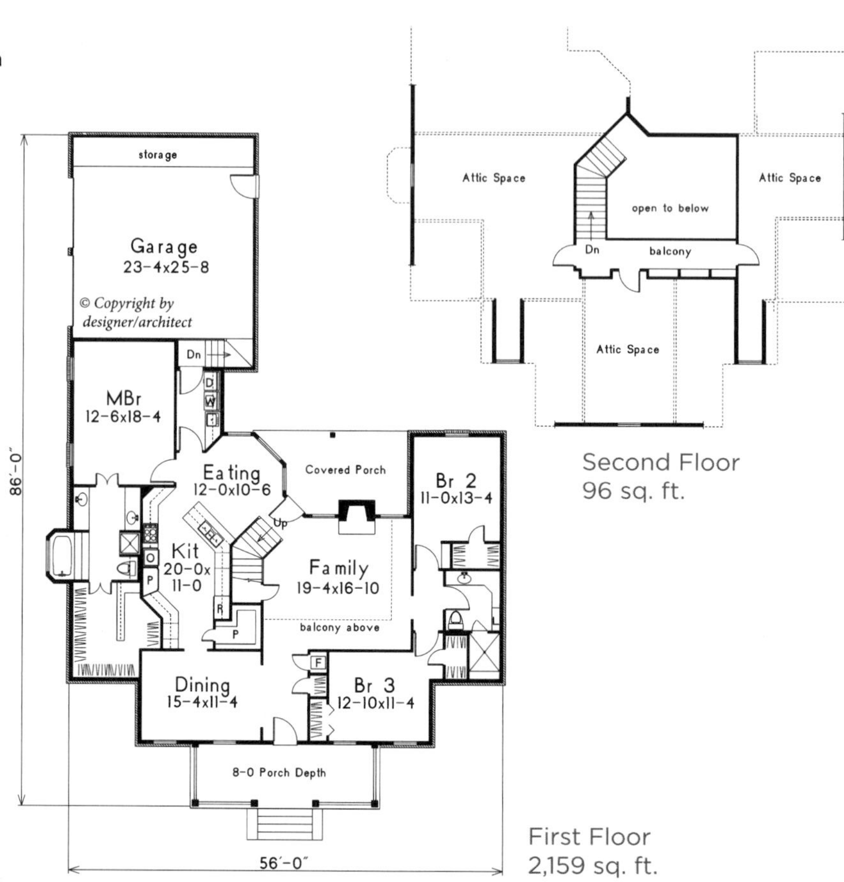

Second Floor
96 sq. ft.

First Floor
2,159 sq. ft.

Plan #541-022D-0004 • Price Code A

Exterior Accents Add Charm To This Compact Cottage

- 1,359 total square feet of living area
- Covered porch, stone chimney and abundant windows lend an outdoor appeal
- The spacious and bright kitchen has a pass-through to the formal dining room
- Large walk-in closets can be found in all bedrooms
- Extensive deck expands dining and entertaining areas
- 3 bedrooms, 2 1/2 baths, 2-car garage
- Basement foundation

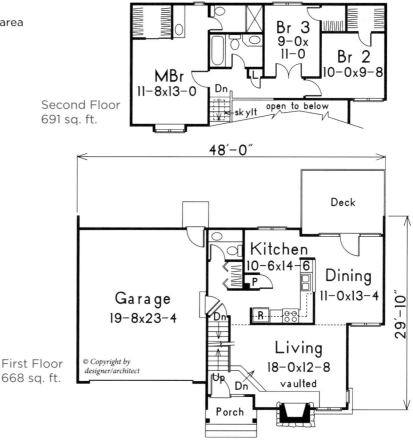

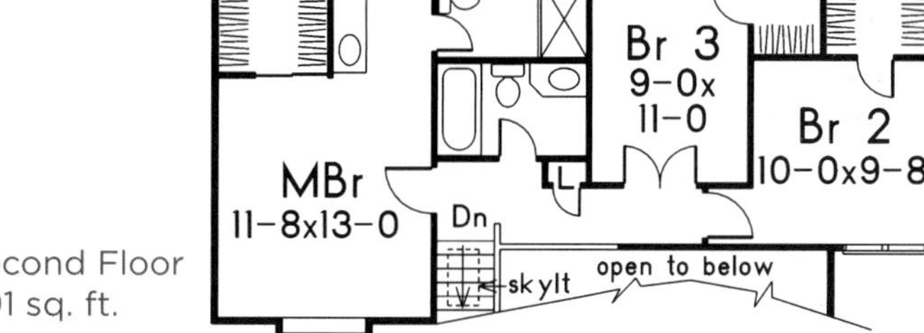

Second Floor
691 sq. ft.

48'-0"
Deck
Kitchen
10-6x14-6
P
Dining
11-0x13-4
Garage
19-8x23-4
R
Dn
Living
18-0x12-8
vaulted
Up
Dn
Porch
29'-10"
© Copyright by designer/architect

First Floor
668 sq. ft.

Plan #541-007D-0038 • Price Code B

Dining With A View

- 1,524 total square feet of living area
- Delightful balcony overlooks the two-story entry illuminated by an oval window
- Roomy first floor master bedroom offers quiet privacy
- All bedrooms feature one or more walk-in closets
- 3 bedrooms, 2 1/2 baths, 2-car garage
- Basement foundation, drawings also include crawl space and slab foundations

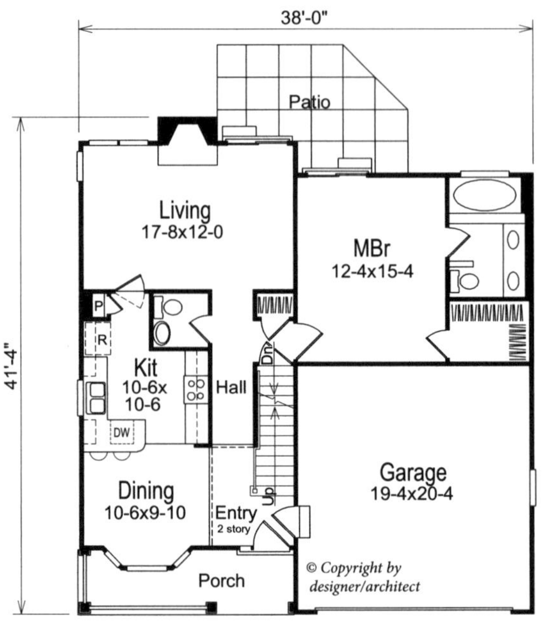

First Floor
951 sq. ft.

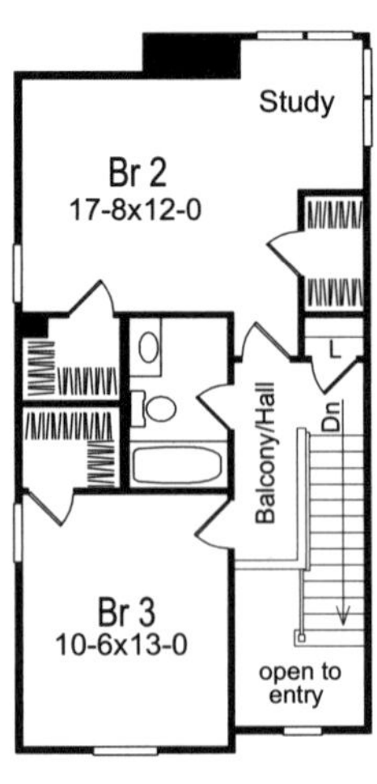

Second Floor
573 sq. ft.

• To Order See Page 288 or Call Toll-Free 1-877-379-3420

Plan #541-065L-0169 • Price Code B

Inviting Front Porch

- 1,557 total square feet of living area
- The large great room features a fireplace flanked with high windows that create a cheerful atmosphere
- The efficient kitchen boasts a breakfast bar open to the dining room and a handy pantry
- The master bedroom enjoys the privacy of the second floor and includes a private bath and walk-in closet
- A bonus room above the garage has an additional 236 square feet of living area
- 3 bedrooms, 2 1/2 baths, 2-car garage
- Basement foundation

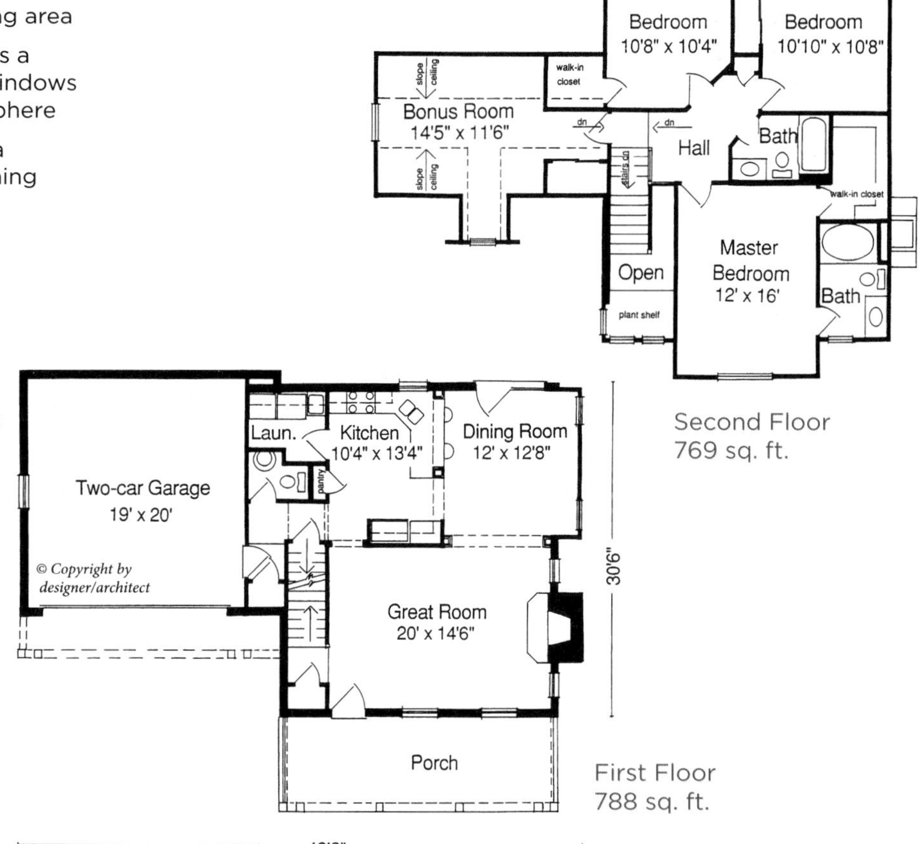

Second Floor
769 sq. ft.

First Floor
788 sq. ft.

Plan #541-077L-0097 • Price Code D

Beautiful Brick And Siding Combination

- 1,800 total square feet of living area
- Double doors open into the foyer crowned with a 10′ ceiling
- The vaulted great room opens into the combined kitchen and bayed breakfast room with decorative columns
- The unfinished bonus room has an additional 302 square feet of living area
- 3 bedrooms, 2 baths, 2-car side entry garage
- Slab foundation, drawings also include crawl space and basement foundations

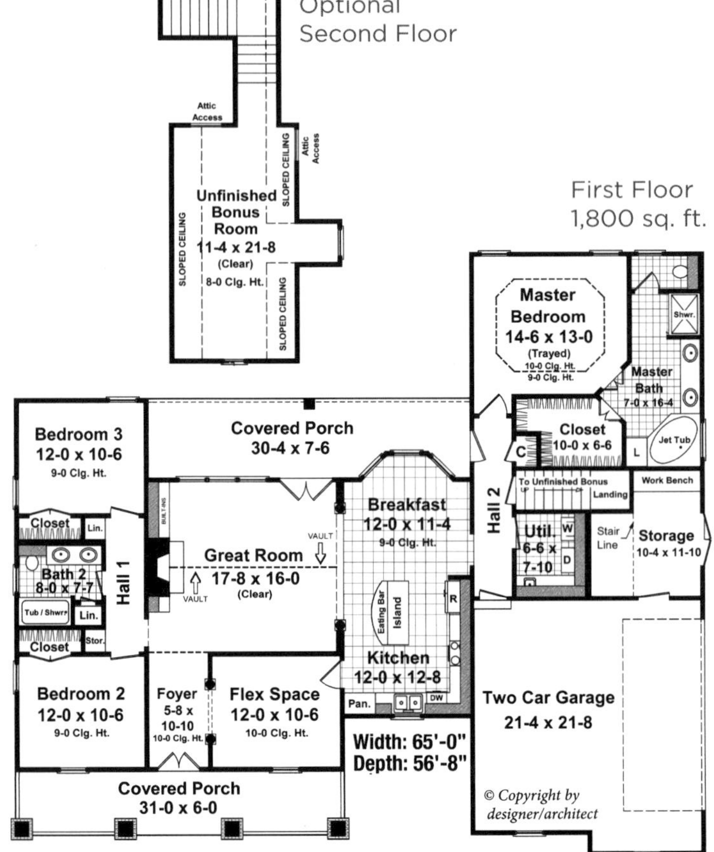

• To Order See Page 288 or Call Toll-Free 1-877-379-3420

Plan #541-051L-0439 • Price Code E

LOWE'S LEGACY SERIES

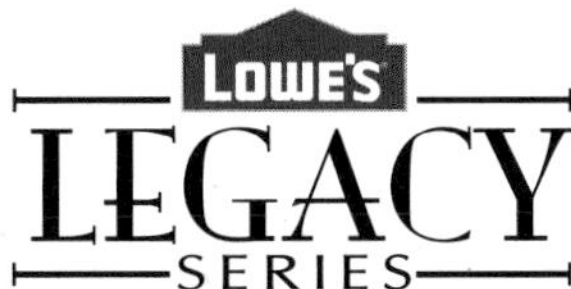

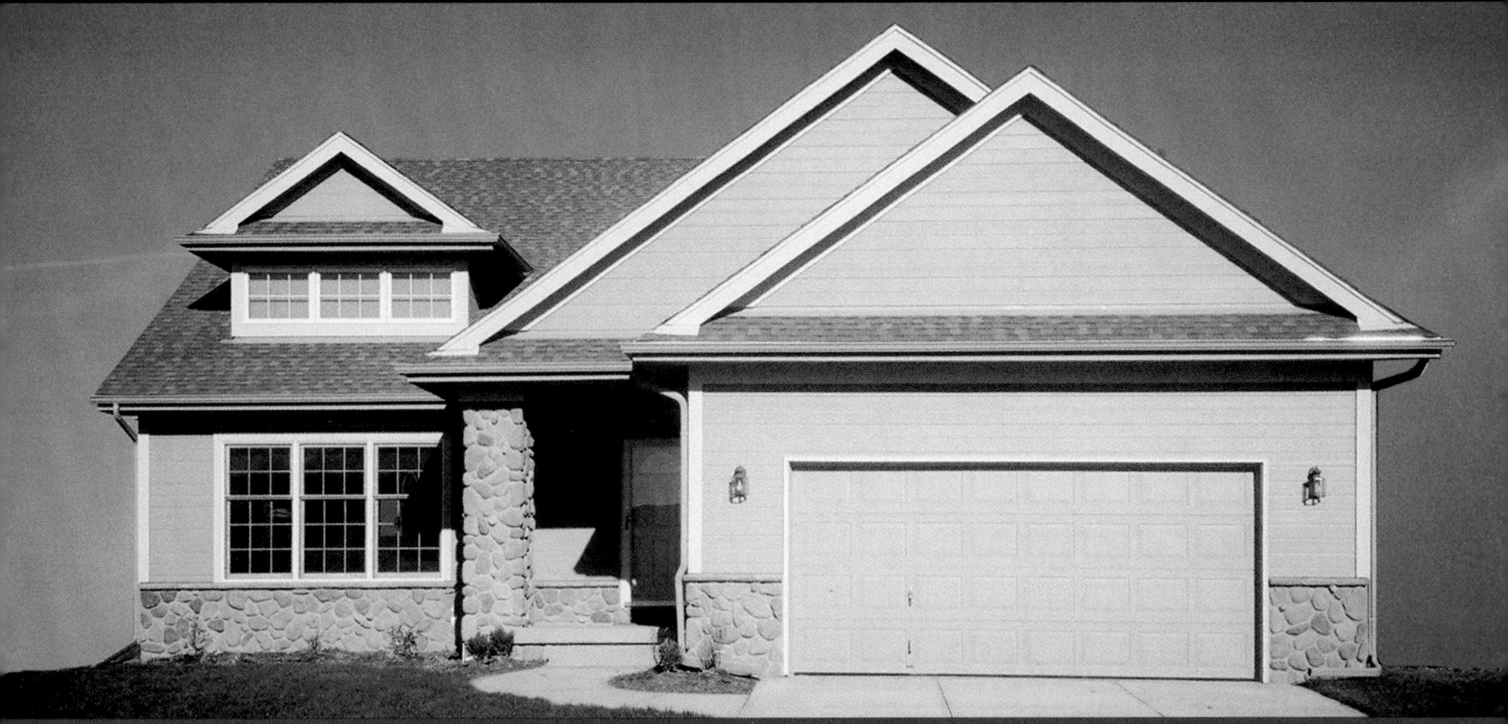

Stylish Stone Accents Add Style To This Traditional Ranch

- 1,735 total square feet of living area
- Both a shower and an oversized garden tub add great efficiency to the private master bath
- Seating for three can be found in the kitchen/dining area island
- Arched soffits are found throughout the entire first floor of this home adding a touch of elegance around every corner
- 3 bedrooms, 2 baths, 2-car garage
- Basement foundation

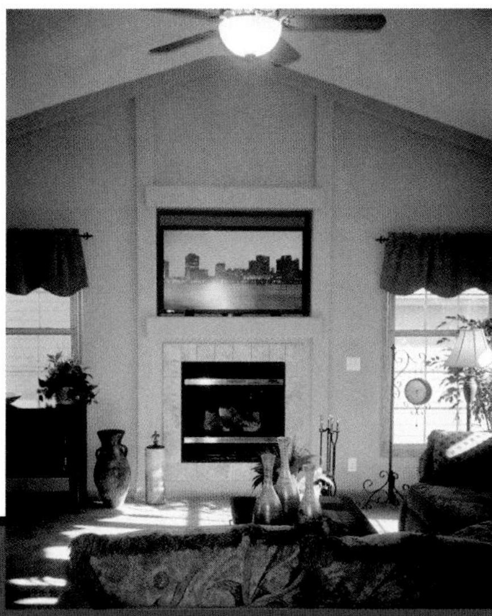

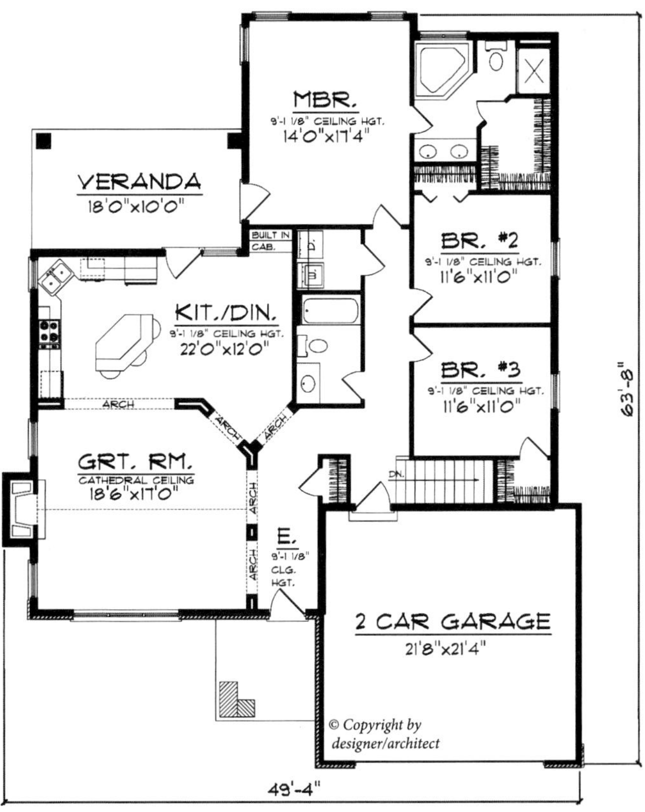

Plan #541-065L-0013 • Price Code C

Splendid Master Bedroom

- 2,041 total square feet of living area
- Great room accesses directly to the covered rear deck with ceiling fan above
- Private master bedroom has a beautiful octagon-shaped sitting area that opens and brightens the space
- Two secondary bedrooms share a full bath
- 3 bedrooms, 2 baths, 2-car side entry garage
- Walk-out basement foundation

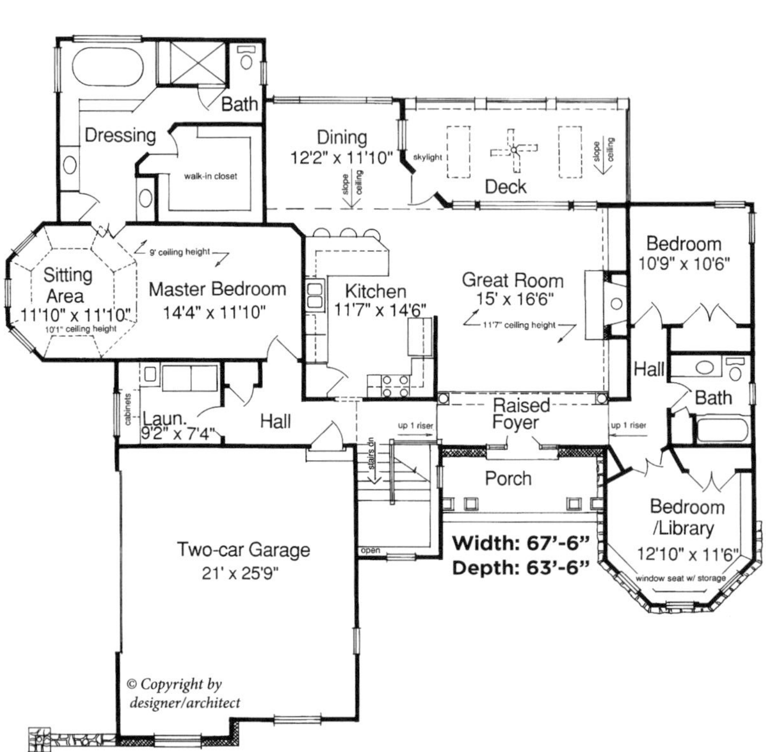

• To Order See Page 288 or Call Toll-Free 1-877-379-3420

Plan #541-022D-0026 • Price Code D

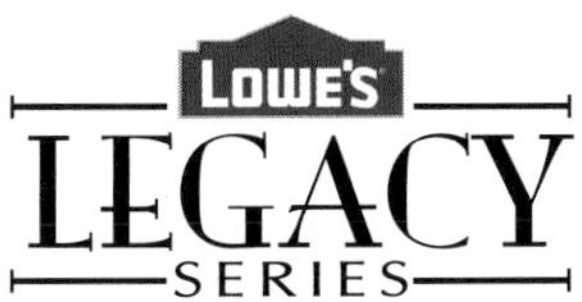

Provides Family Living At Its Best

- 1,993 total square feet of living area
- Spacious country kitchen boasts a fireplace and plenty of natural light from windows
- Formal dining room features a large bay window and steps down to the sunken living room
- Master bedroom features corner windows, plant shelves and a deluxe private bath
- Entry opens into the vaulted living room with windows flanking the fireplace
- 3 bedrooms, 2 baths, 2-car garage
- Basement foundation

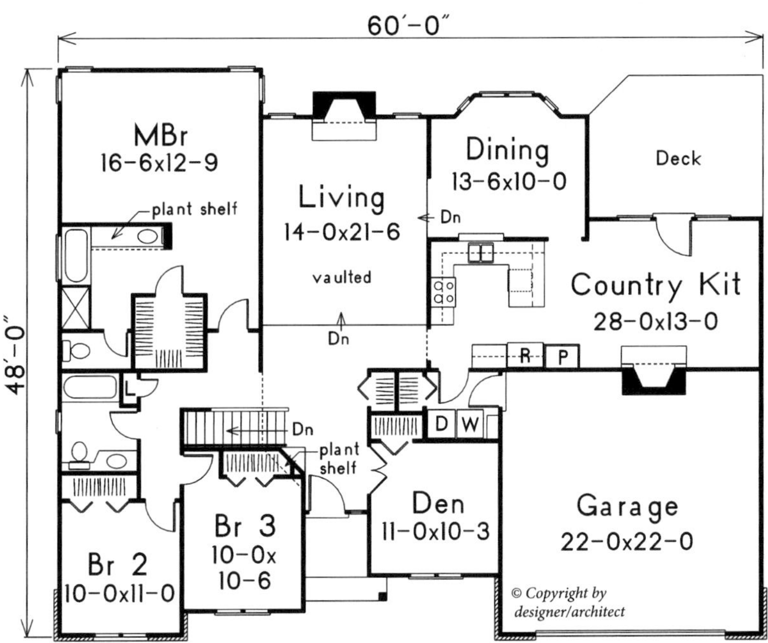

Lowe's LEGACY SERIES

Plan #541-072L-0264 • Price Code D

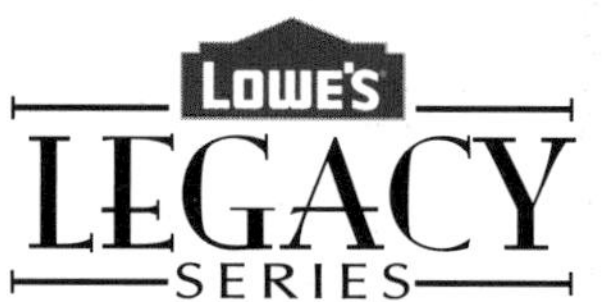

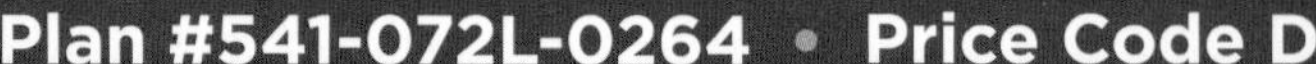

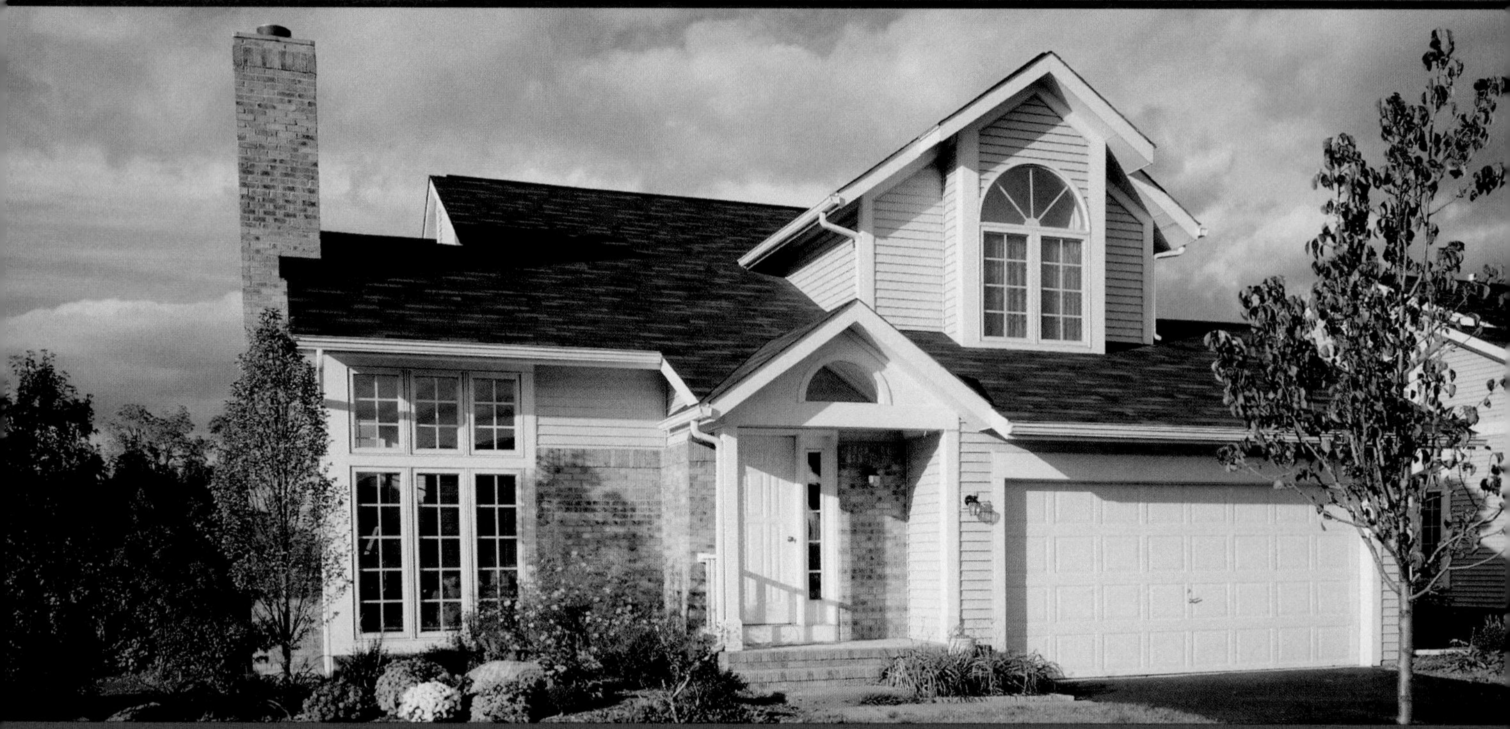

Stunning Curb Appeal

- 1,556 total square feet of living area
- A compact home with all the amenities
- The country kitchen combines practicality with access to other areas for eating and entertaining
- A three-sided fireplace joins the dining and living areas
- A plant shelf and vaulted ceiling highlight the master bedroom
- 3 bedrooms, 2 1/2 baths, 2-car garage
- Basement foundation

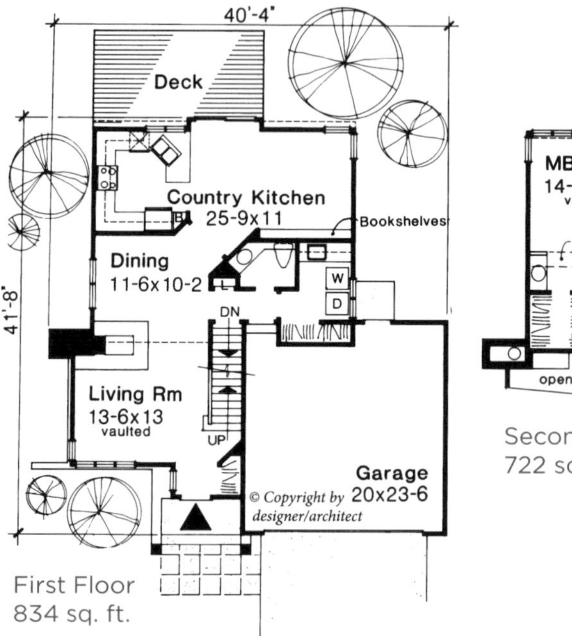

First Floor
834 sq. ft.

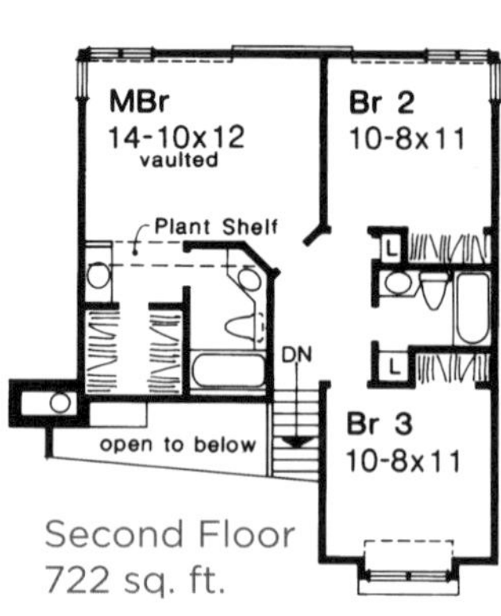

Second Floor
722 sq. ft.

• To Order See Page 288 or Call Toll-Free 1-877-379-3420

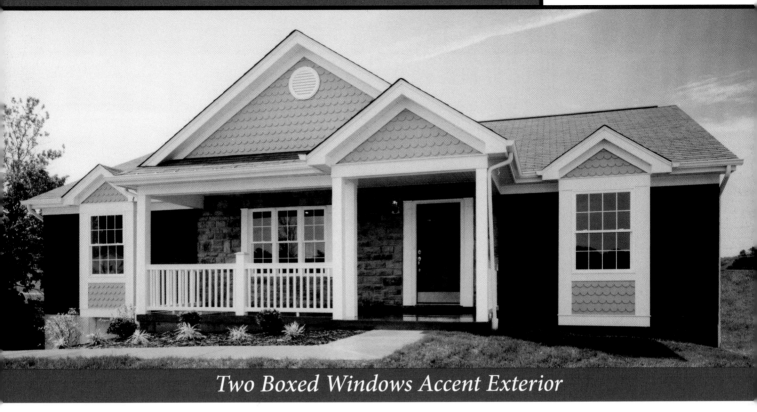

Two Boxed Windows Accent Exterior

- 2,057 total square feet of living area
- A large great room has a sloped ceiling for added drama
- A unique shaped whirlpool tub is certainly the focal point of the private master bath
- The dining area has direct access onto the large rear deck
- 4 bedrooms, 3 baths, 2-car rear entry garage
- Walk-out basement foundation

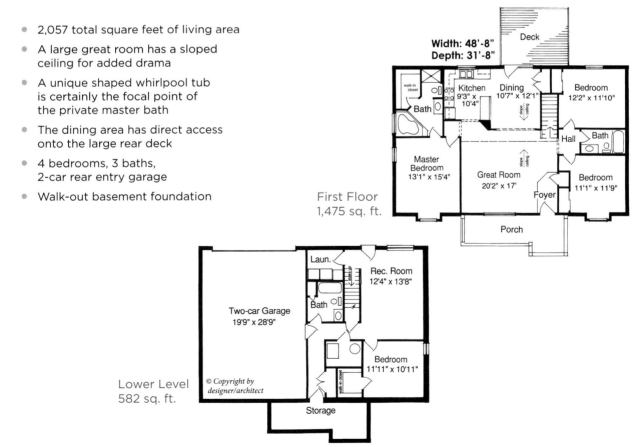

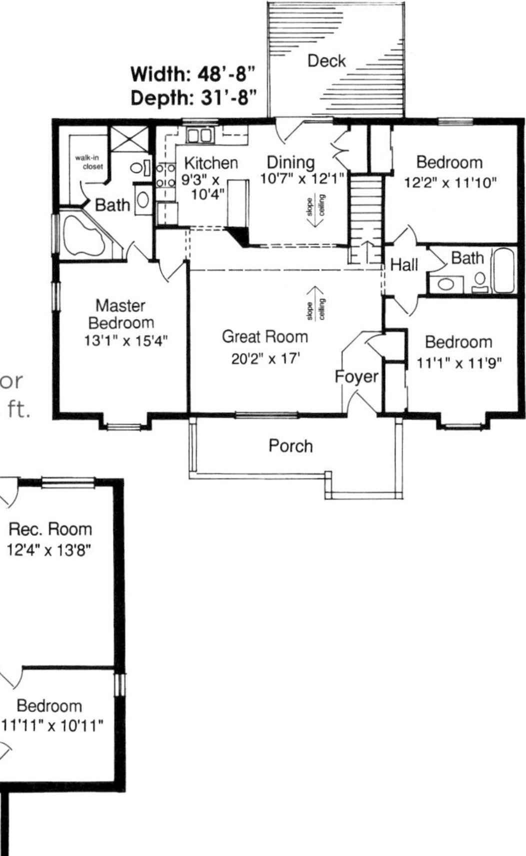

First Floor
1,475 sq. ft.

Lower Level
582 sq. ft.

Plan #541-072L-0027 • Price Code D

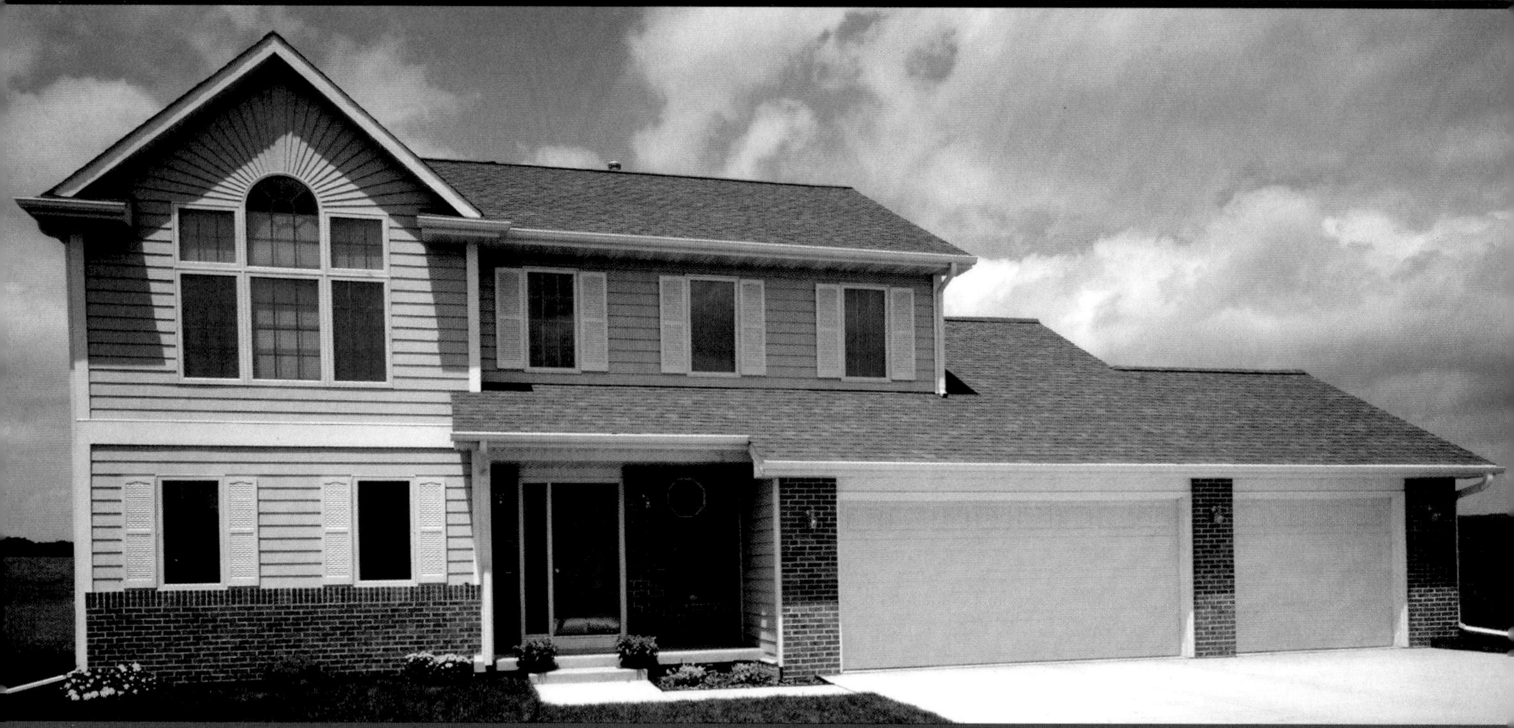

Exciting Two-Story

- 1,820 total square feet of living area
- A bay window and cozy fireplace create enticing surroundings in the casual family room
- Decorative columns are pleasing to the eye and separate the dining and living rooms while maintaining an open feeling
- An 11'-6" vaulted ceiling creates an airy interior in the master suite
- 4 bedrooms, 2 1/2 baths, 3-car garage
- Basement foundation

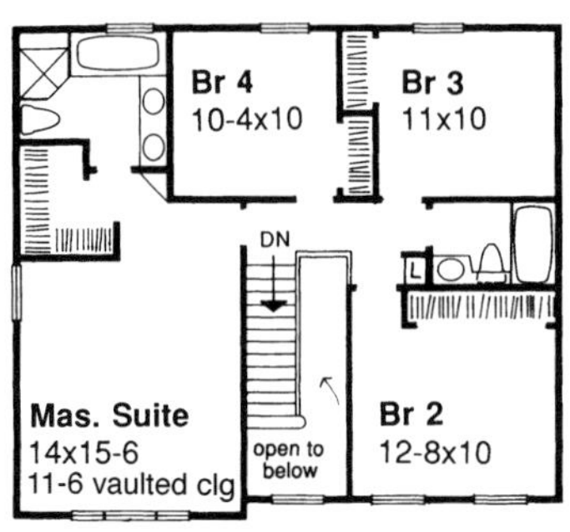

Second Floor
833 sq. ft.

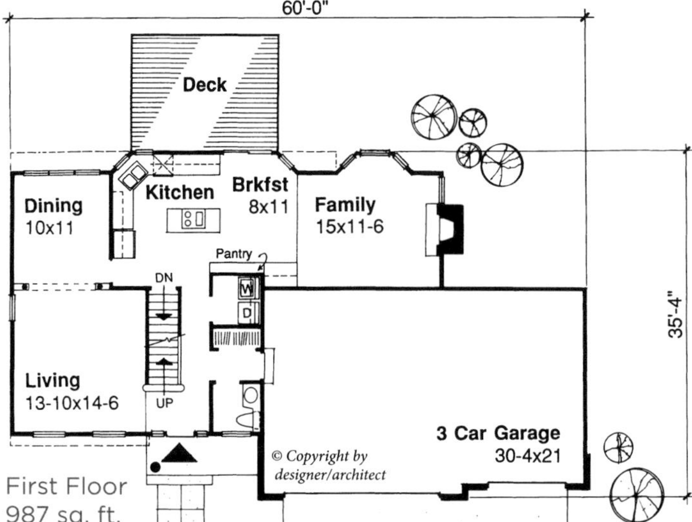

First Floor
987 sq. ft.

Spacious Front Porch

- 1,759 total square feet of living area
- The large kitchen with pantry, island and serving bar easily serves the bayed breakfast area and formal dining room
- Angles dramatically create the shape for the screened porch, providing a delightful seasonal room
- The master bedroom suite coupled with the luxurious dressing room pampers the homeowners
- 3 bedrooms, 2 baths, 2-car side entry garage
- Basement foundation

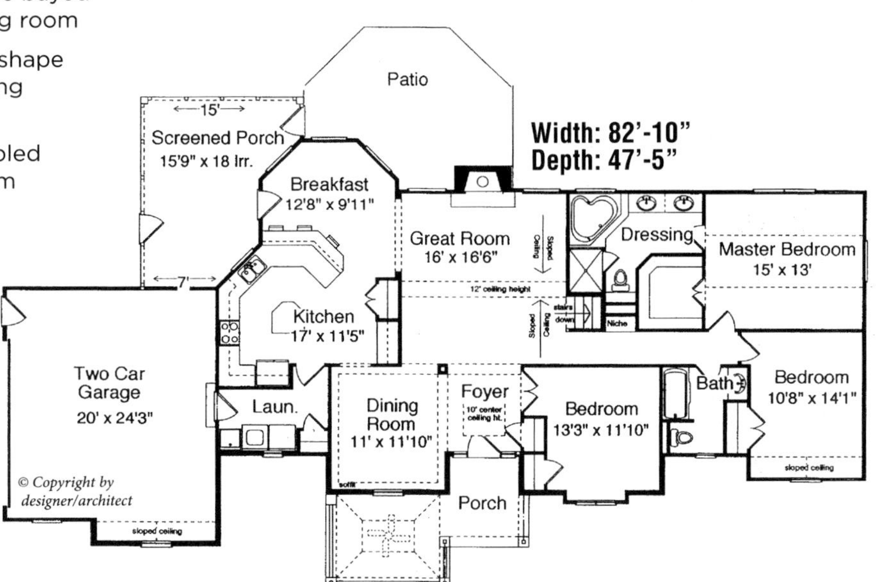

Plan #541-065L-0103 • Price Code C

Delightful One Level Home

- 1,860 total square feet of living area
- Extended counter in the kitchen offers dining space
- A bayed breakfast area is open to the great room and kitchen creating a spacious atmosphere
- A beautiful corner fireplace in the great room is angled perfectly so it can also be enjoyed by the formal dining room
- 3 bedrooms, 2 baths, 2-car garage
- Basement foundation, drawings also include walk-out basement foundations

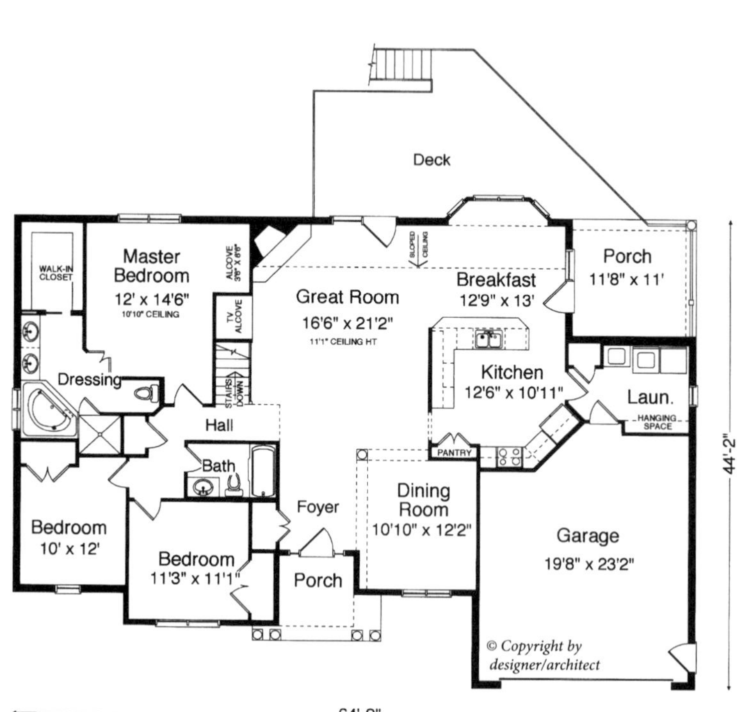

• To Order See Page 288 or Call Toll-Free 1-877-379-3420

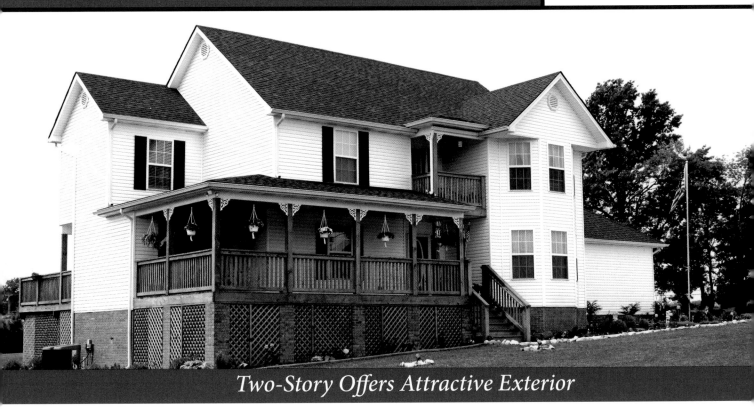

Two-Story Offers Attractive Exterior

- 2,262 total square feet of living area
- Charming exterior features include large front porch, two patios, front balcony and double bay windows
- Den provides an impressive entry to a sunken family room
- Conveniently located first floor laundry
- Large master bedroom has a walk-in closet, dressing area and bath
- 2″ x 6″ exterior walls available, please order plan #541-001D-0117
- 3 bedrooms, 2 1/2 baths, 2-car rear entry garage
- Crawl space foundation, drawings also include basement and slab foundations

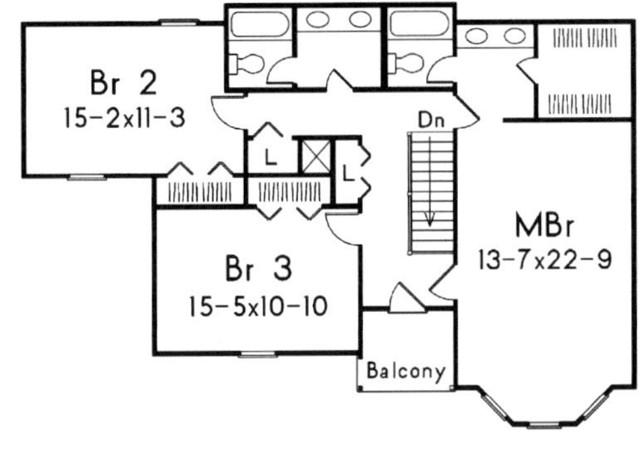

Second Floor
1,135 sq. ft.

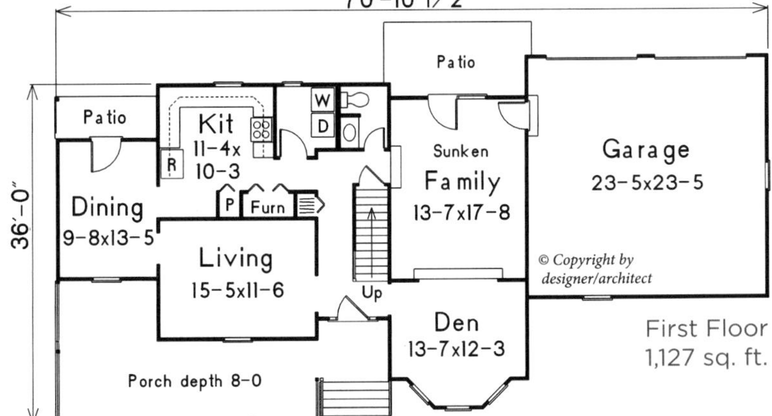

First Floor
1,127 sq. ft.

Plan #541-072L-0007 • Price Code C

Authentic Cape Cod Cottage

- 2,143 total square feet of living area
- Energy efficient home with 2" x 6" exterior walls
- The kitchen handles every task because of its efficiency
- A cozy casual family room has a fireplace for warmth and a convenient log bin accessible from the garage as well
- Dining and living rooms combine, perfect for entertaining
- 4 bedrooms, 3 baths, 2-car garage
- Basement foundation

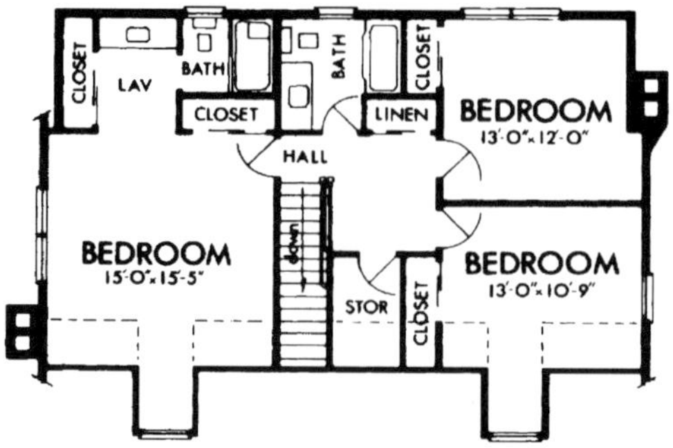

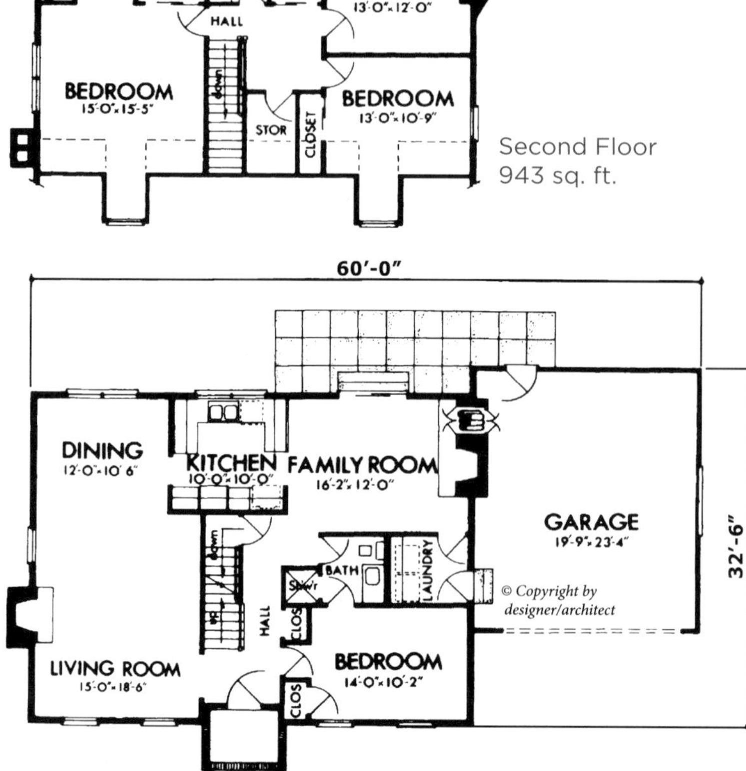

Second Floor
943 sq. ft.

First Floor
1,200 sq. ft.

• To Order See Page 288 or Call Toll-Free 1-877-379-3420

Impressive Country Design

- 2,193 total square feet of living area
- The airy great room is ideal for entertaining or gathering the family around the fireplace, while the open kitchen has a center island for easy meal preparation
- A formal dining room offers elegance when entertaining, while the nook is perfect for casual family dinners
- On the second floor, the master bedroom features a full bath and walk-in closet, while three additional bedrooms share a full bath
- 4 bedrooms, 2 1/2 baths, 3-car garage
- Basement foundation

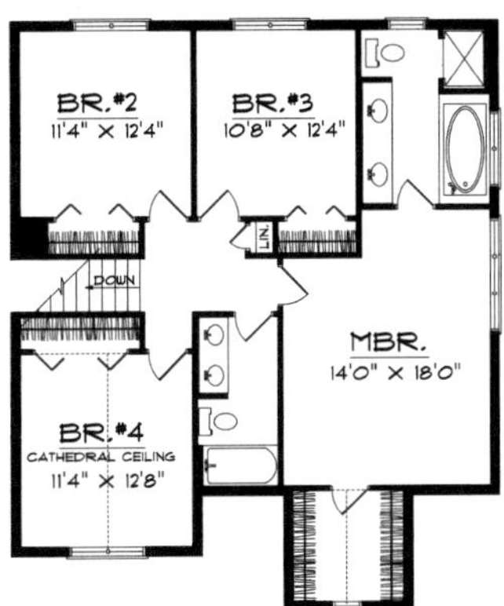

Second Floor
1,080 sq. ft.

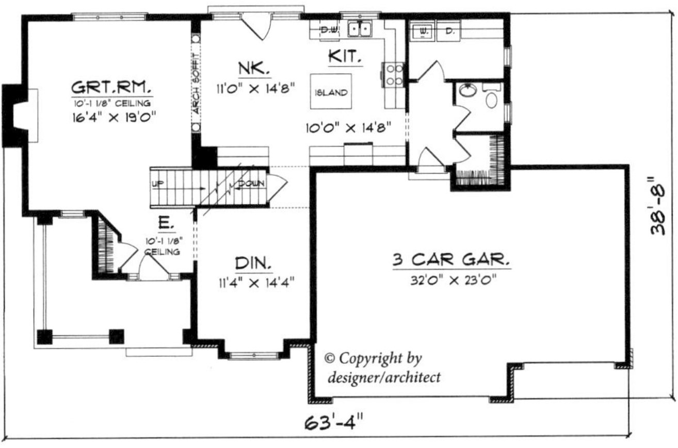

First Floor
1,113 sq. ft.

Plan #541-072L-1111 • Price Code A

Well-Designed Front Gables

- 1,728 total square feet of living area
- The second bedroom can easily be converted into an office with ample shelf space
- You will love the master bath equipped with a large walk-in closet, a relaxing shower and a spa-style tub to pamper yourself from time to time
- The charming kitchen includes a breakfast island perfect for family gatherings in the mornings
- 2 bedrooms, 1 1/2 baths, 3-car side entry garage
- Walk-out basement foundation

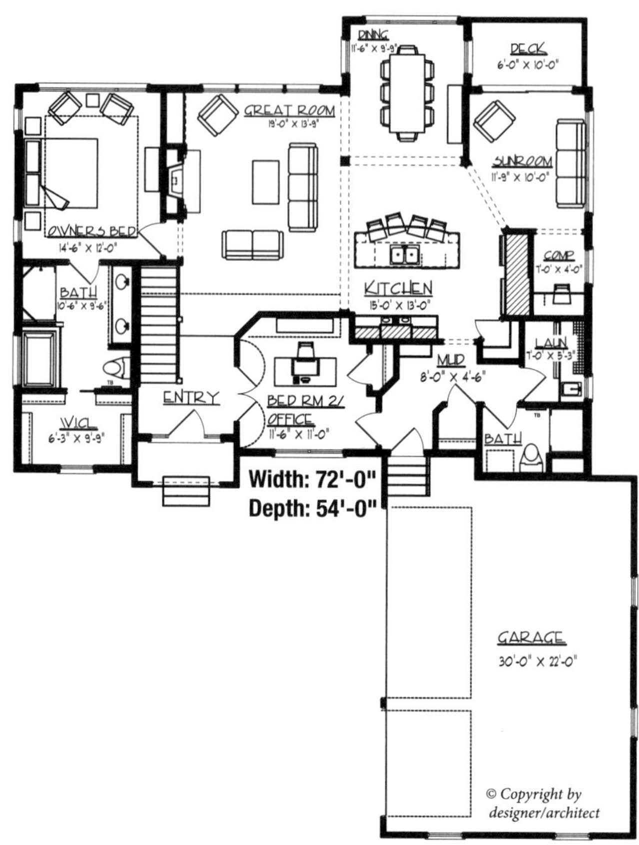

• To Order See Page 288 or Call Toll-Free 1-877-379-3420

Plan #541-065L-0006 • Price Code C

Computer Area Is A Handy Feature

- 2,082 total square feet of living area
- This home is designed with an insulated foundation system featuring pre-mounted insulation on concrete walls providing a drier, warmer and smarter structure
- Master bedroom boasts a deluxe bath and a large walk-in closet
- Natural light floods the breakfast room through numerous windows
- Great room features a 12' ceiling, cozy fireplace and stylish French doors
- Bonus room on the second floor has an additional 267 square feet of living area
- 3 bedrooms, 2 1/2 baths, 2-car garage
- Basement foundation

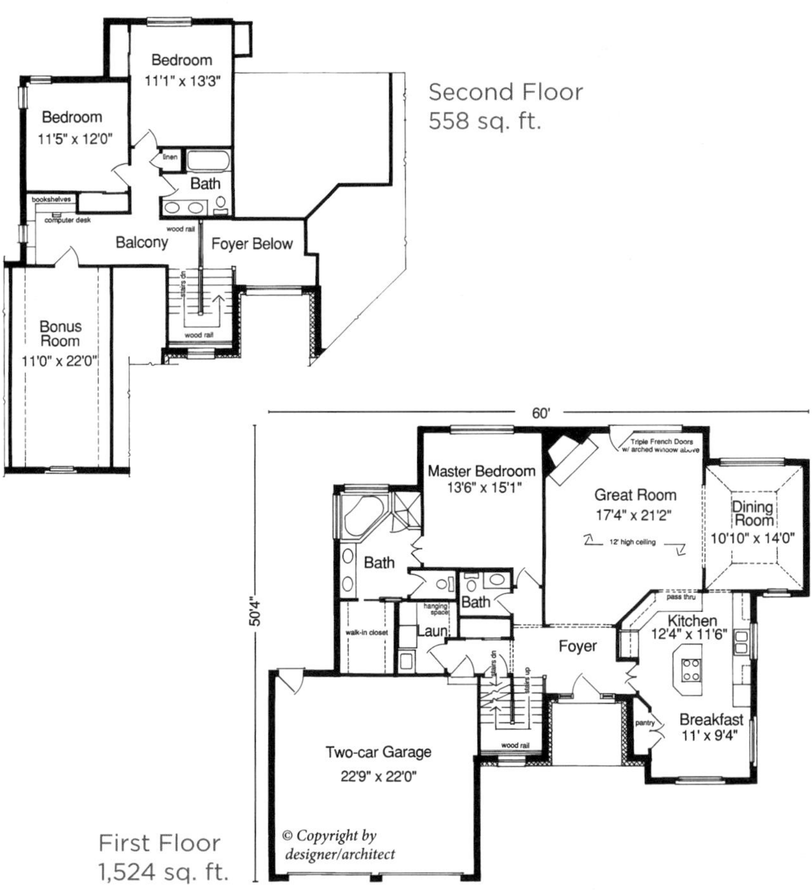

Plan #541-065L-0066 • Price Code B

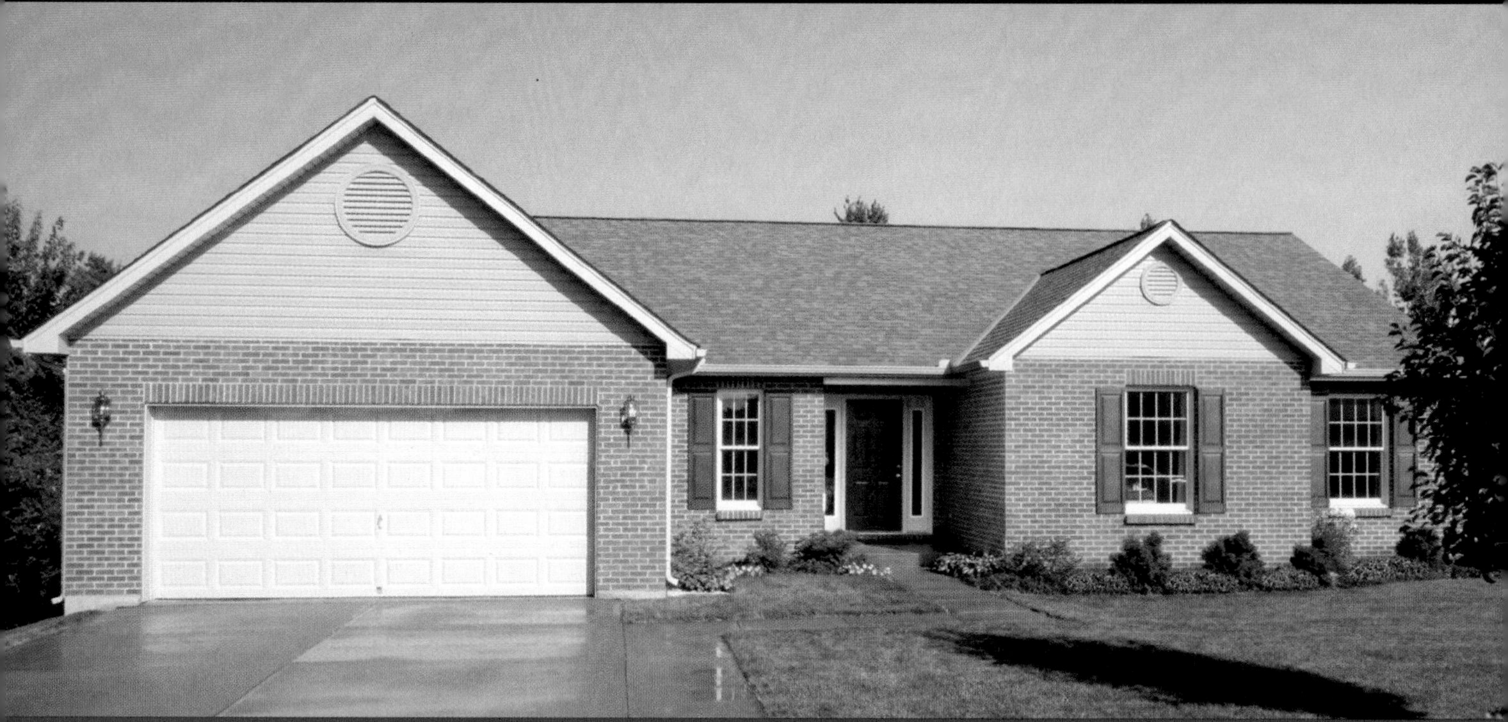

Charming Simplicity

- 1,598 total square feet of living area
- A spacious great room with fireplace and sloped ceiling opens generously to the dining area
- Sliding glass doors lead to a covered porch, expanding enjoyment of this home to the outdoors
- The spacious kitchen offers an abundance of cabinets and counterspace as well as a peninsula with seating
- A master bedroom and two secondary bedrooms make this a great family sized home
- 3 bedrooms, 2 baths, 2-car garage
- Basement foundation

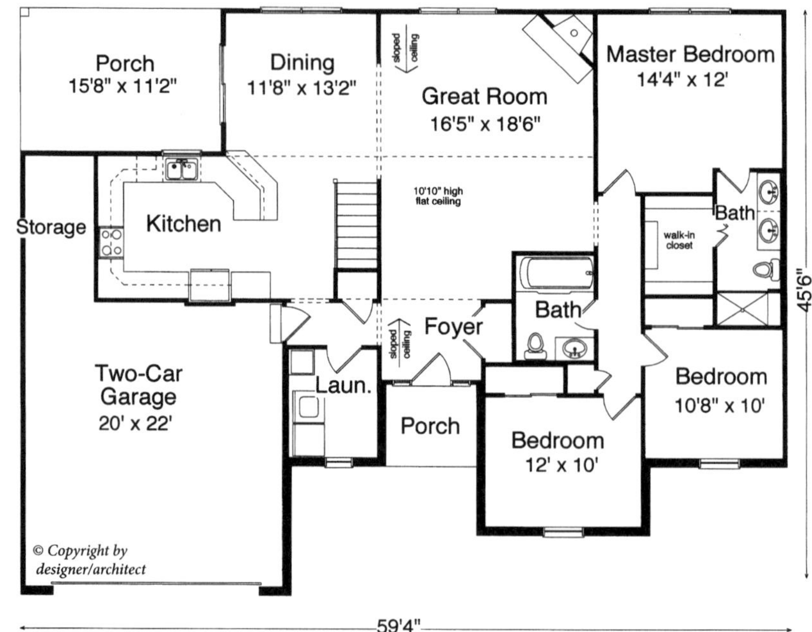

Plan #541-065L-0198 • Price Code C

Visually Open Floor Plan

- 2,063 total square feet of living area
- Detailed ceiling treatments add elegance to the open dining and great rooms
- The kitchen connects to the bayed breakfast room with a wrap-around snack counter
- The master bedroom is designed to pamper homeowners with a large bath and walk-in closet
- 3 bedrooms, 2 baths, 2-car side entry garage
- Basement foundation

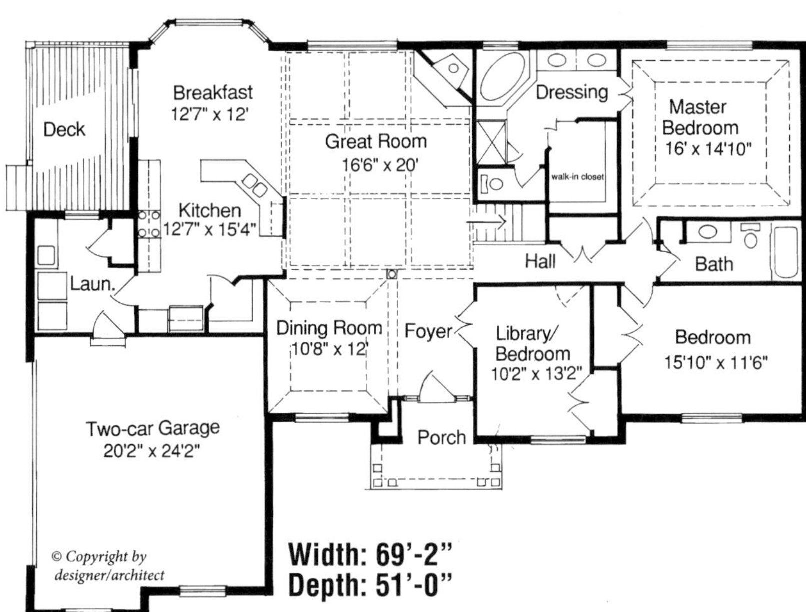

LOWE'S LEGACY SERIES

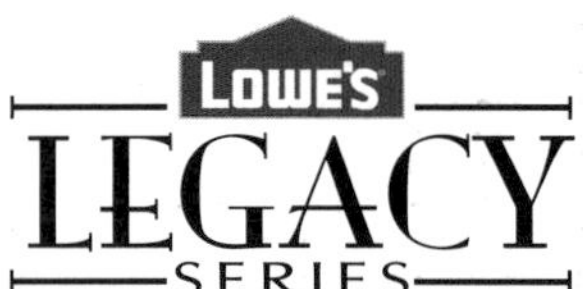

Plan #541-065L-0164 • Price Code C

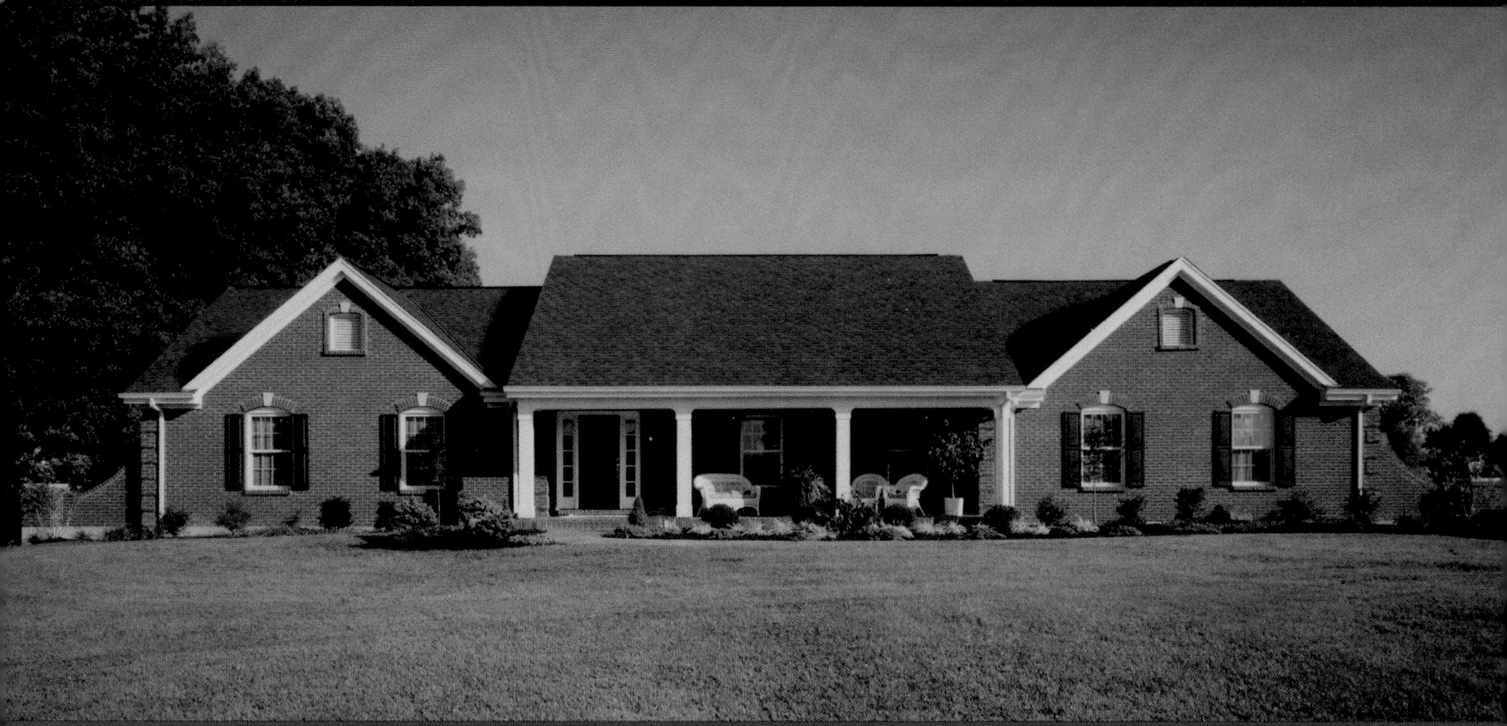

Country Style Ranch Home

- 1,860 total square feet of living area
- The spacious foyer opens to the combination living and dining rooms creating an attractive formal area for greeting guests
- The breakfast area is surrounded by windows, offering a spectacular view of the backyard
- The great room ceiling slopes to 12' high and offers a comfortable gathering space for family and friends
- 3 bedrooms, 2 baths, 2-car side entry garage
- Basement foundation

Width: 85'-4"
Depth: 36'-8"

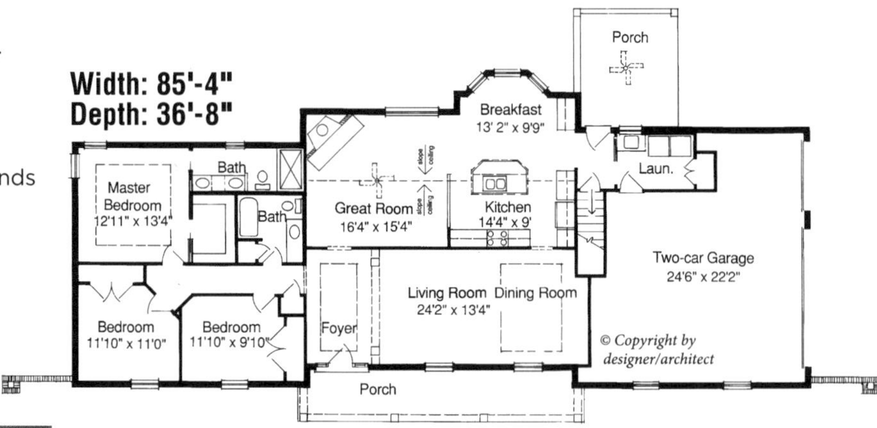

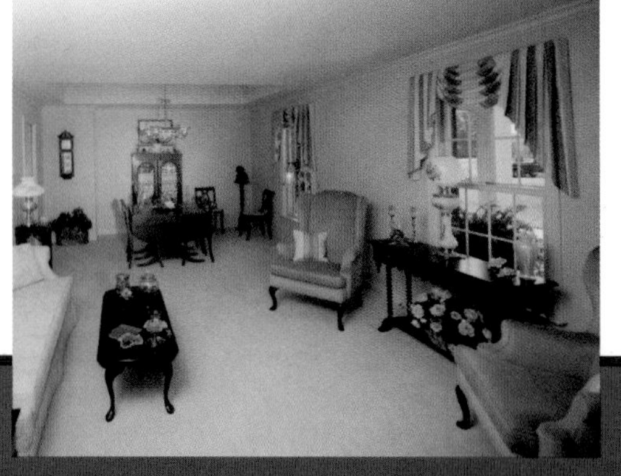

• To Order See Page 288 or Call Toll-Free 1-877-379-3420

Plan #541-001D-0003 • Price Code E

Impressive Victorian Blends Charm And Efficiency

- 2,286 total square feet of living area
- Fine architectural detail makes this home a showplace with its large windows, intricate brickwork and fine woodwork and trim
- Stunning two-story entry with attractive wood railing and balustrades in the foyer
- Convenient wrap-around kitchen enjoys a window view, planning center and pantry
- Oversized master bedroom includes a walk-in closet and master bath
- 4 bedrooms, 2 1/2 baths, 2-car garage
- Basement foundation, drawings also include crawl space and slab foundations

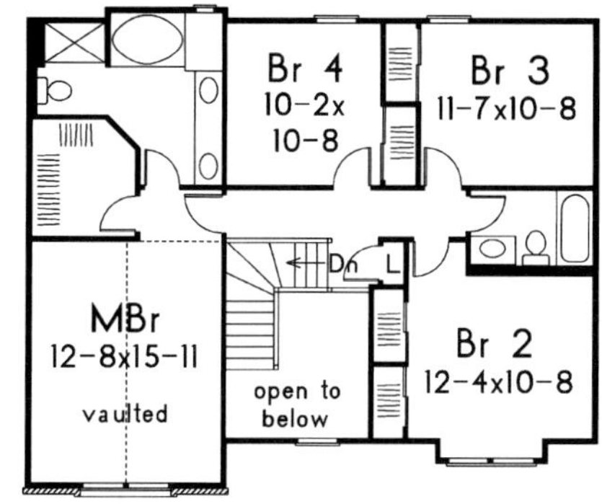

Second Floor
1,003 sq. ft.

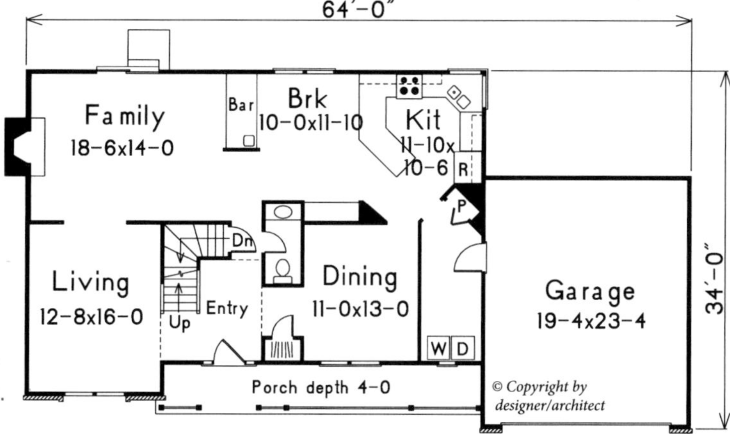

First Floor
1,283 sq. ft.

Plan #541-027D-0011 • Price Code B

Efficient Design

- 2,164 total square feet of living area
- Formal and informal spaces create an exceptional family home whether entertaining or relaxing
- The master bedroom enjoys a walk-in closet, private bath and the option of a bay window
- The second floor loft area is an ideal reading nook
- 4 bedrooms, 2 1/2 baths, 2-car garage
- Basement foundation, drawings also include walk-out basement foundation

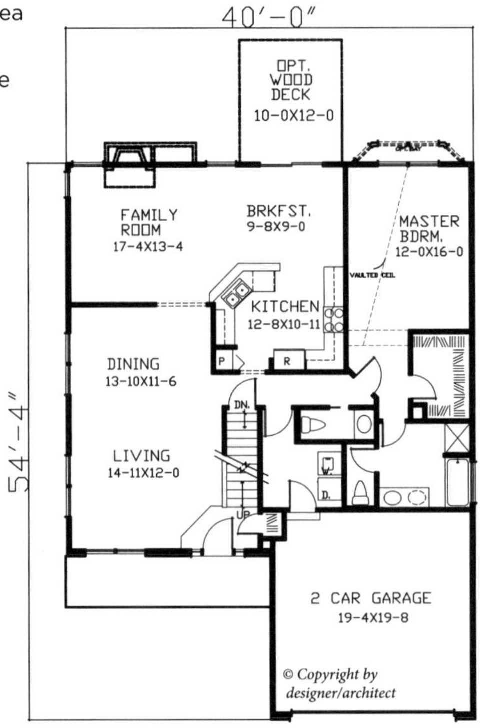

First Floor
1,441 sq. ft.

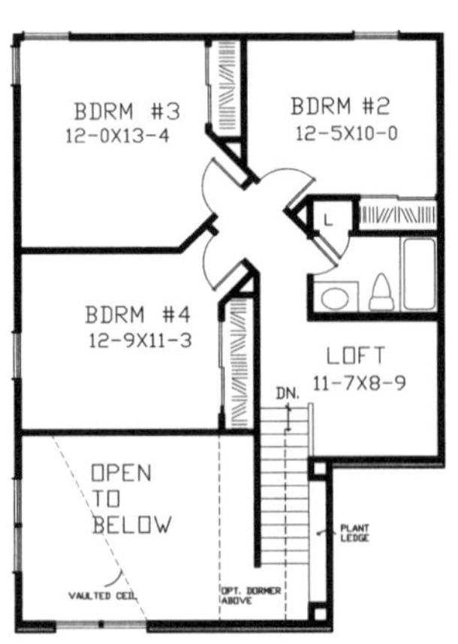

Second Floor
723 sq. ft.

• To Order See Page 288 or Call Toll-Free 1-877-379-3420

Transom Windows Create Impressive Front Entry

- 1,800 total square feet of living area
- Energy efficient home with 2" x 6" exterior walls
- Covered front and rear porches add outdoor living area
- 12' ceilings in the kitchen, breakfast area, dining and living rooms
- Private master bedroom features an expansive bath
- Side entry garage has two storage areas
- Pillared styling with brick and stucco exterior finish
- 3 bedrooms, 2 baths, 2-car side entry garage
- Crawl space foundation, drawings also include slab foundation

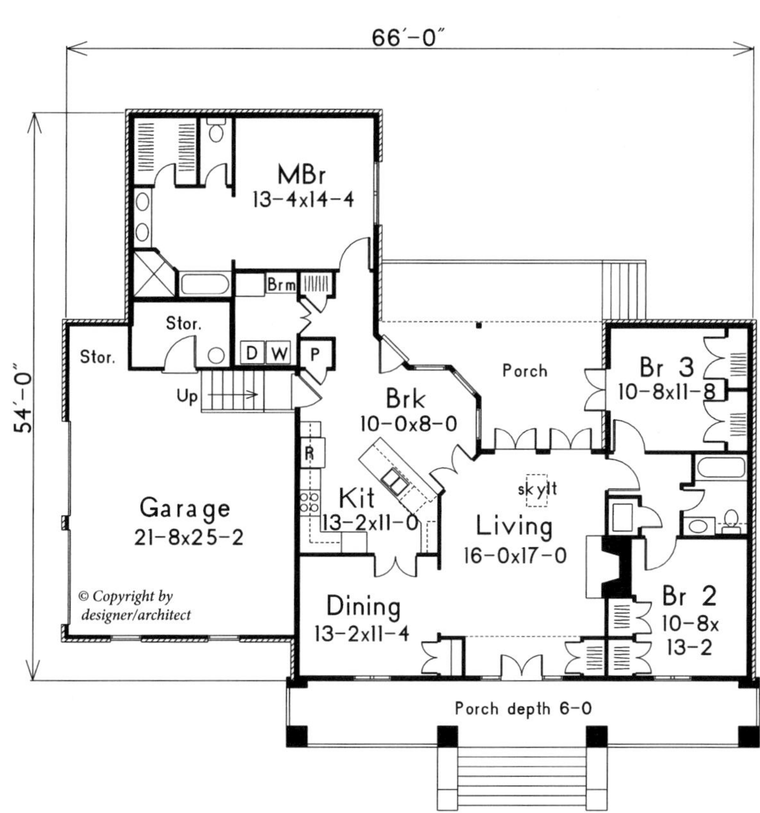

Plan #541-072L-0036 • Price Code D

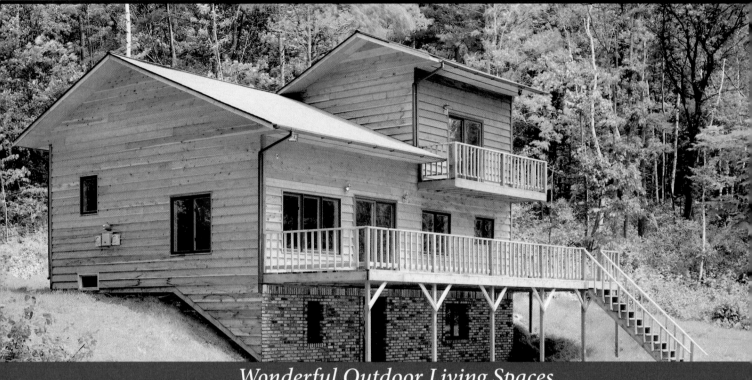

Wonderful Outdoor Living Spaces

- 1,188 total square feet of living area
- The large living room with fireplace enjoys a ceiling height of 15' and access to the large deck
- The second floor bedroom is a nice escape with its own bath and private deck
- A large eating counter in the kitchen creates casual dining space
- 3 bedrooms, 2 baths, 1-car drive under side entry garage
- Walk-out basement foundation

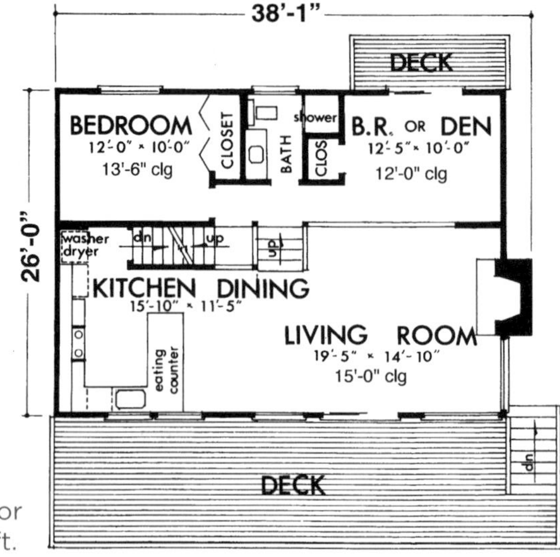

First Floor
936 sq. ft.

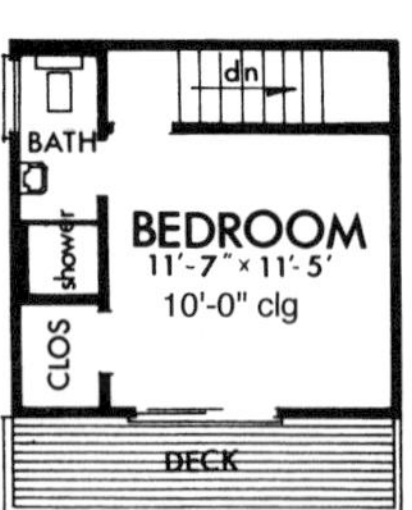

Second Floor
252 sq. ft.

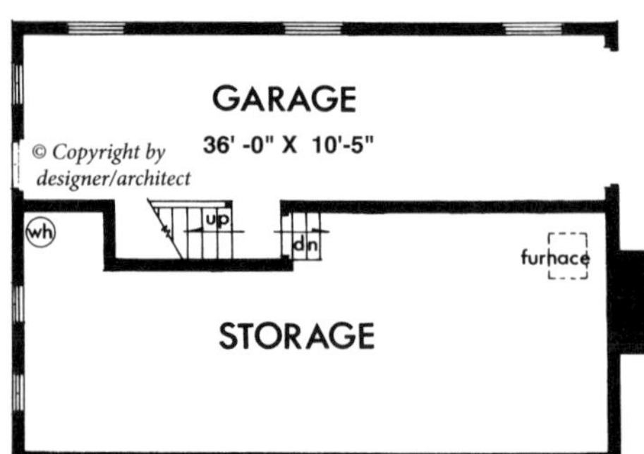

Lower Level

• To Order See Page 288 or Call Toll-Free 1-877-379-3420

Plan #541-065L-0166 • Price Code B

Efficient Two-Story Home

- 1,698 total square feet of living area
- The massive great room runs the entire depth of the home offering a view of the front porch and easy access to the backyard
- The adjacent breakfast area offers a relaxed atmosphere and enjoys close proximity to the U-shaped kitchen
- All bedrooms are located on the second floor, including the master bedroom that features a deluxe bath and walk-in closet
- The optional bonus room over the garage has an additional 269 square feet of living area
- 3 bedrooms, 2 1/2 baths, 2-car side entry garage
- Basement foundation, drawings also include crawl space foundation

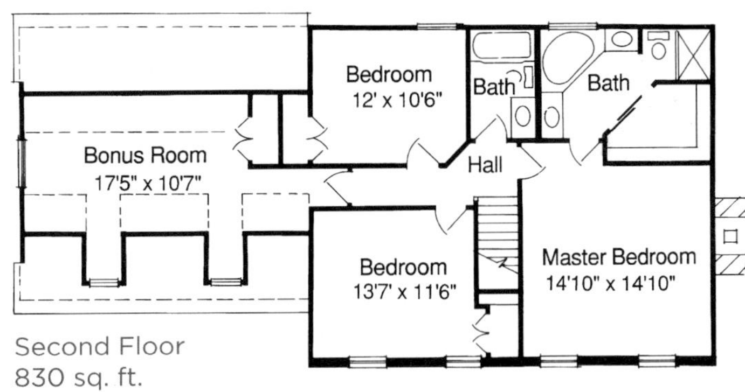

Second Floor
830 sq. ft.

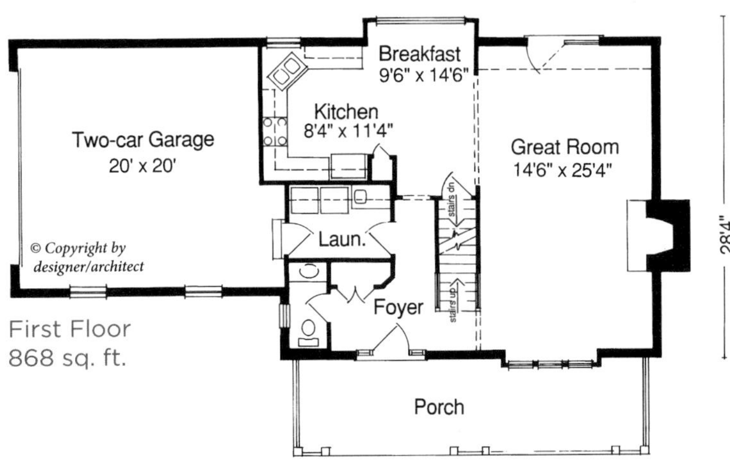

First Floor
868 sq. ft.

Plan #541-065L-0002 • Price Code C

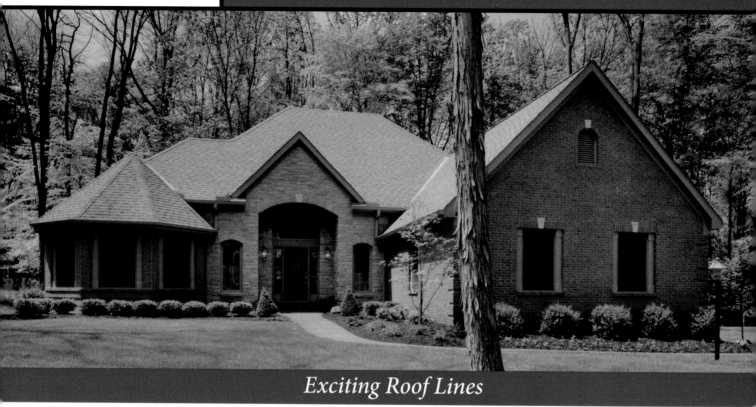

Exciting Roof Lines

- 2,101 total square feet of living area
- The sunken great room has a balcony above
- Octagon-shaped master bedroom is spacious and private
- Luxurious amenities are located throughout this modest sized home
- 3 bedrooms, 2 1/2 baths, 2-car garage
- Basement foundation

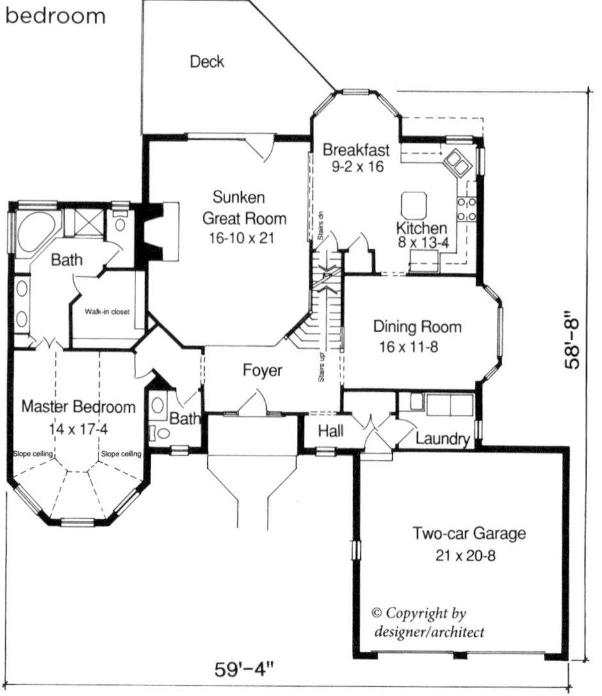

First Floor
1,626 sq. ft.

Second Floor
475 sq. ft.

Plan #541-121D-0020 • Price Code B

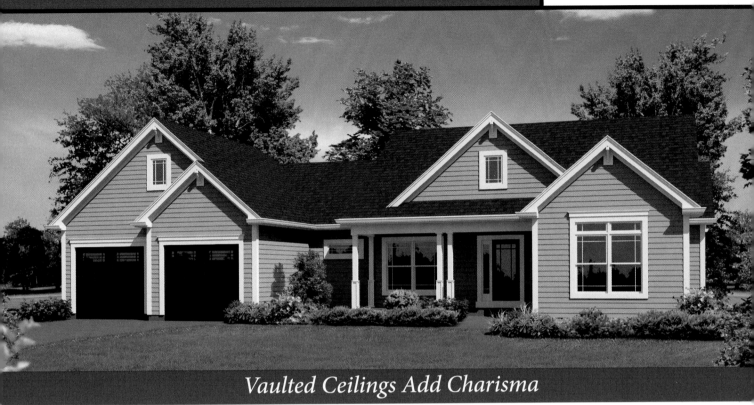

Vaulted Ceilings Add Charisma

- 2,037 total square feet of living area
- The vaulted kitchen/breakfast area enjoys a walk-in pantry and a sunny bay window with access to the rear patio
- There is extra storage space in the garage that has access to the outdoors
- Two spacious walk-in closets and a private bath are some of the amenities of the master bedroom
- 3 bedrooms, 2 1/2 baths, 2-car garage
- Basement foundation

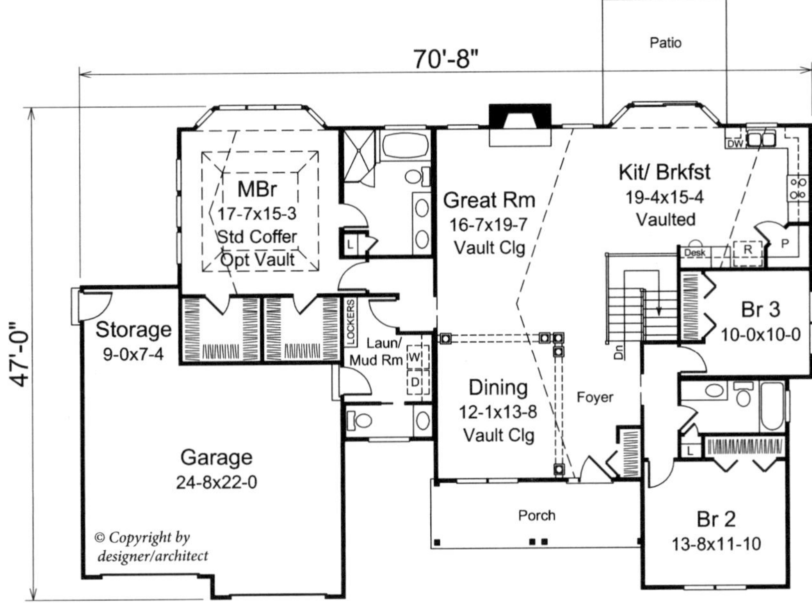

LOWE'S LEGACY SERIES

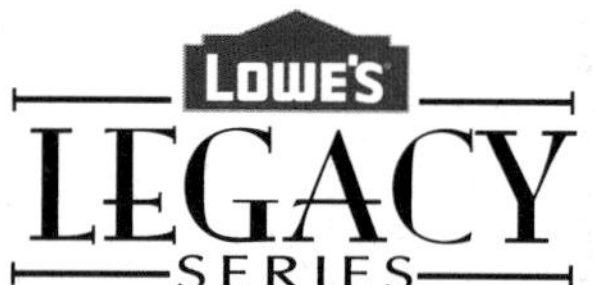

Plan #541-022D-0008 • Price Code B

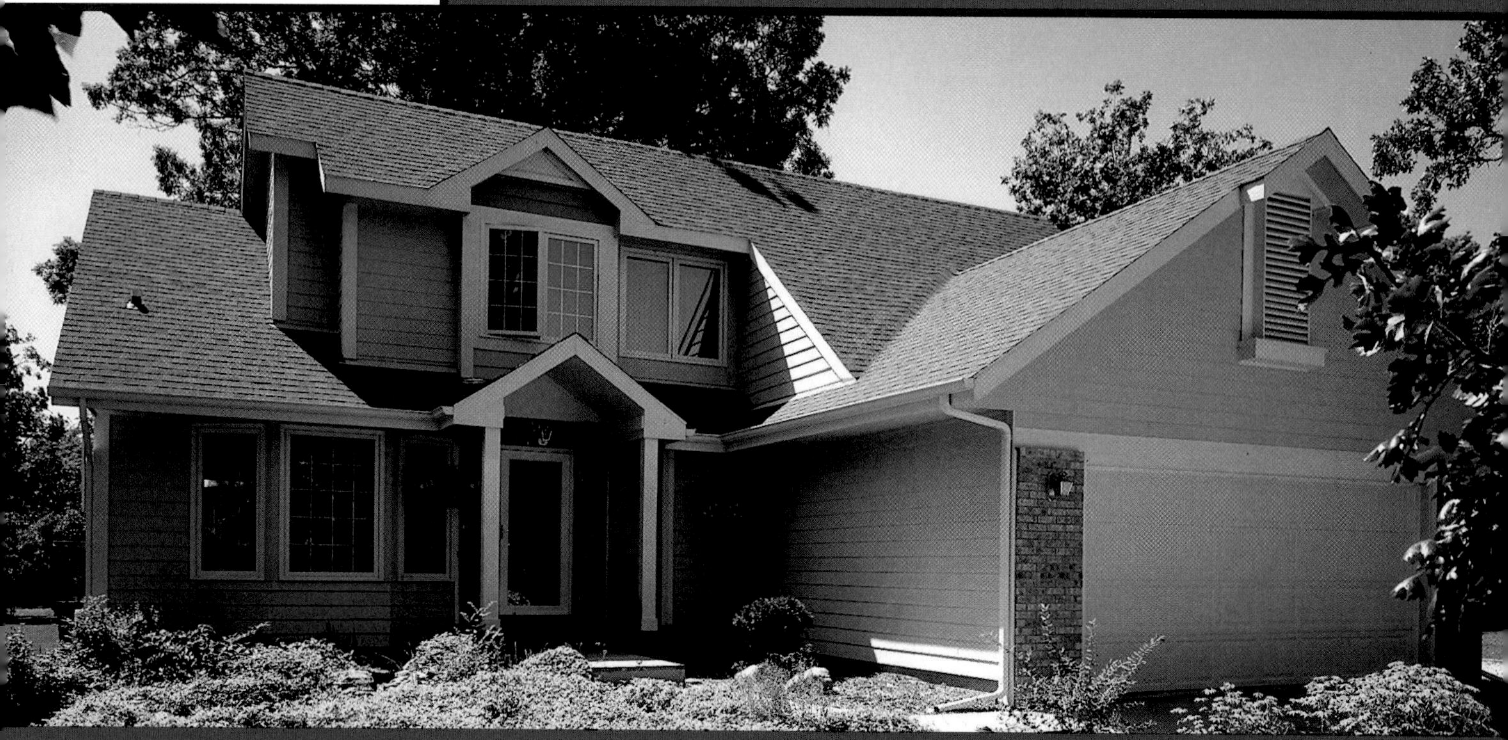

Stylish Master Bedroom Off By Itself

- 1,565 total square feet of living area
- Highly-detailed exterior adds value
- Large vaulted great room with several windows opens onto the corner deck
- Loft/bedroom #3 opens to the rooms below and adds to the spacious feeling
- Bay-windowed kitchen has a cozy morning room
- Master bath features a platform tub, separate shower and a large walk-in closet
- 3 bedrooms, 2 1/2 baths, 2-car garage
- Basement foundation

Second Floor
460 sq. ft.

First Floor
1,105 sq. ft.

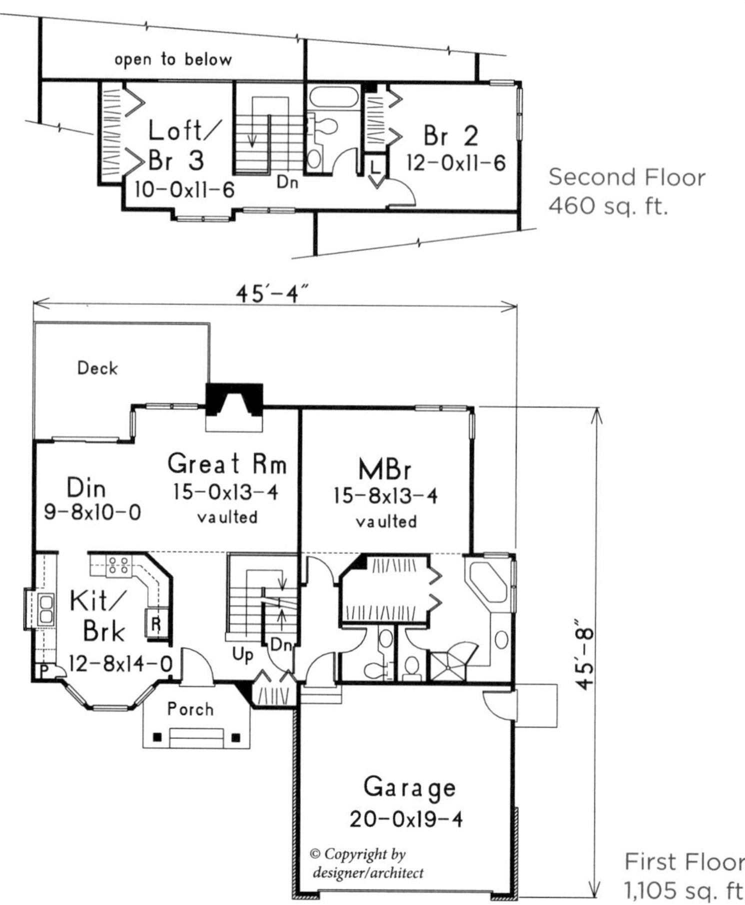

• To Order See Page 288 or Call Toll-Free 1-877-379-3420

Plan #541-065L-0233 • Price Code B

Desirable Ranch Home For Family Living

- 1,758 total square feet of living area
- A terrific deck can be found off the screened porch, perfect for a barbecue grill
- A cozy corner fireplace warms all the surroundings in the combination great room/dining area
- The kitchen is compact in design and features a spacious center island full of workspace and dining space for three people
- The optional lower level has an additional 997 square feet of living area and includes two bedrooms, a full bath and recreation room
- 2 bedrooms, 2 baths, 2-car side entry garage
- Basement foundation

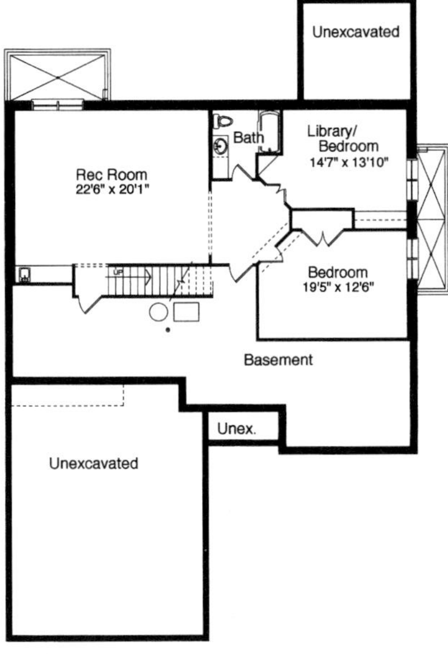

Optional
Lower Level

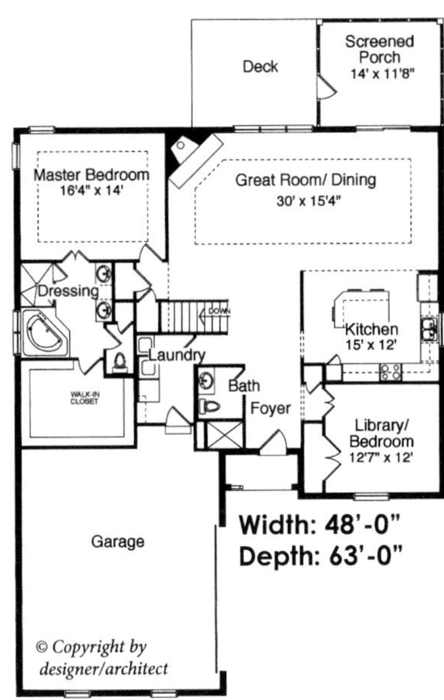

First Floor
1,758 sq. ft.

Plan #541-072L-0022 • Price Code D

Exciting Two-Story Home

- 1,891 total square feet of living area
- Step down into the combined dining and great rooms topped with a vaulted ceiling
- A bay window highlights the family room
- Three bedrooms enjoy the privacy of the second floor
- 3 bedrooms, 2 1/2 baths, 2-car garage
- Basement foundation

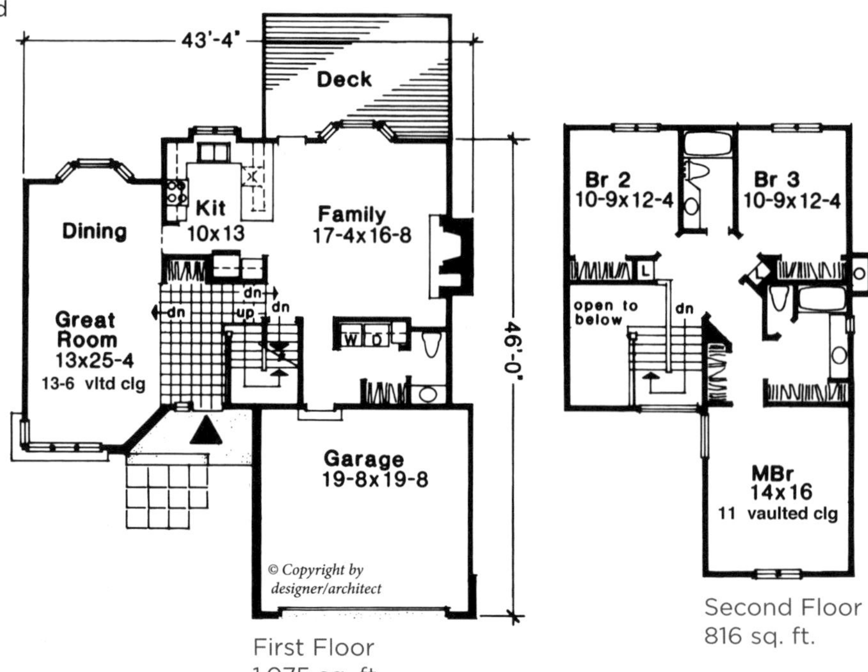

First Floor
1,075 sq. ft.

Second Floor
816 sq. ft.

• To Order See Page 288 or Call Toll-Free 1-877-379-3420

Plan #541-053D-0003 • Price Code A

LOWE'S LEGACY SERIES

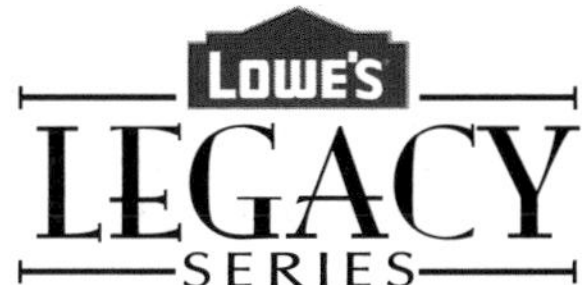

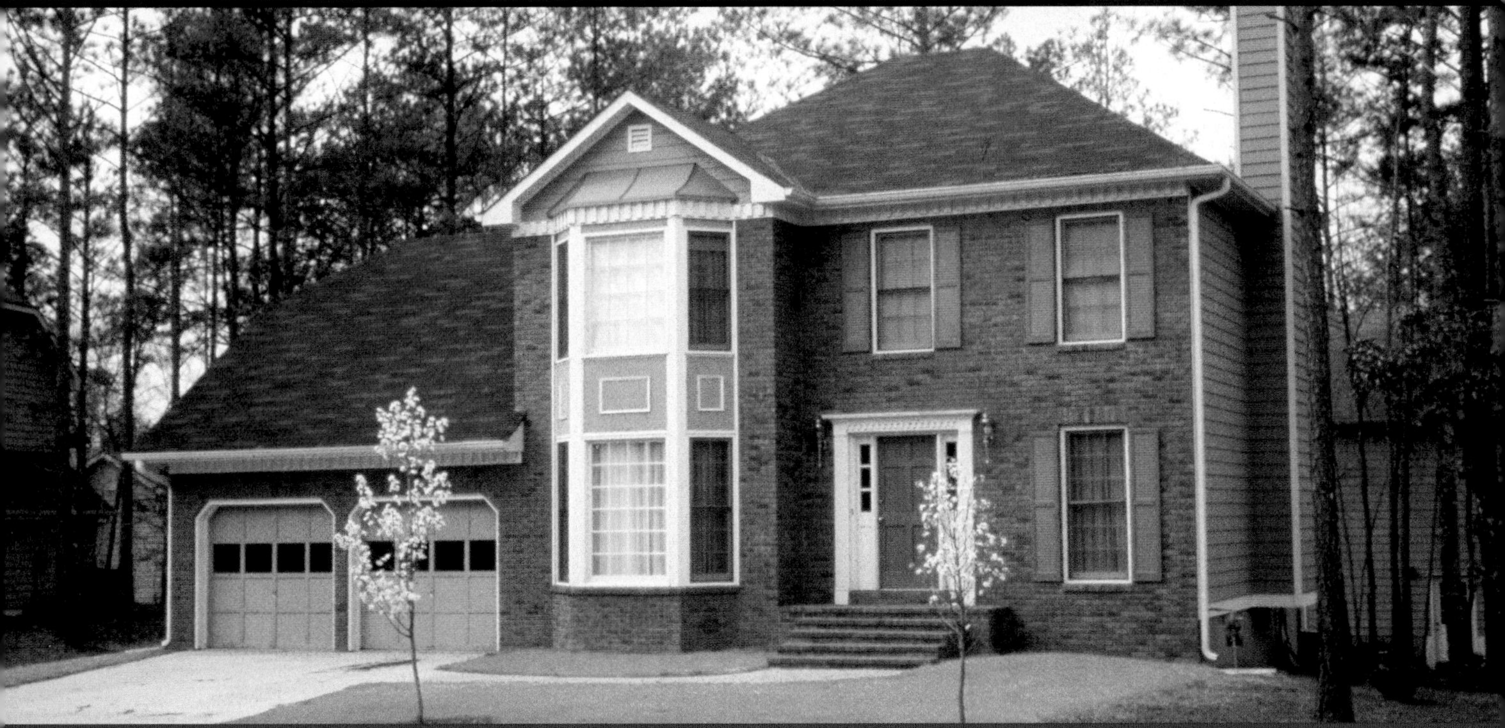

Double Bay Enhances Front Entry

- 1,992 total square feet of living area
- Distinct living, dining and breakfast areas
- Master bedroom boasts a full-end bay window and a cathedral ceiling
- Storage and laundry area are located adjacent to the garage
- Bonus room over the garage for future office or playroom is included in the square footage
- 3 bedrooms, 2 1/2 baths, 2-car garage
- Crawl space foundation, drawings also include basement foundation

Second Floor
1,124 sq. ft.

First Floor
868 sq. ft.

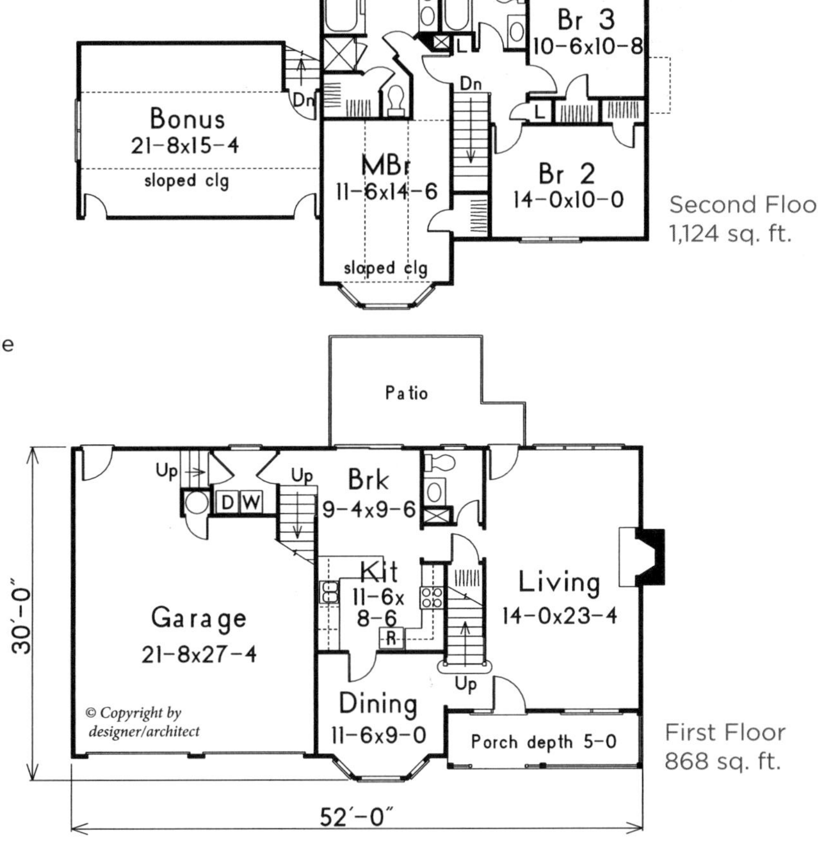

Plan #541-001D-0013 • Price Code D

Traditional Exterior With Handsome Accents

- 1,882 total square feet of living area
- Wide, handsome entrance opens to the vaulted great room with fireplace
- Living and dining areas are conveniently joined but still allow privacy
- Private covered porch extends breakfast area
- Practical passageway runs through the laundry room from the garage to the kitchen
- Vaulted ceiling in the master bedroom
- 3 bedrooms, 2 baths, 2-car garage
- Basement foundation

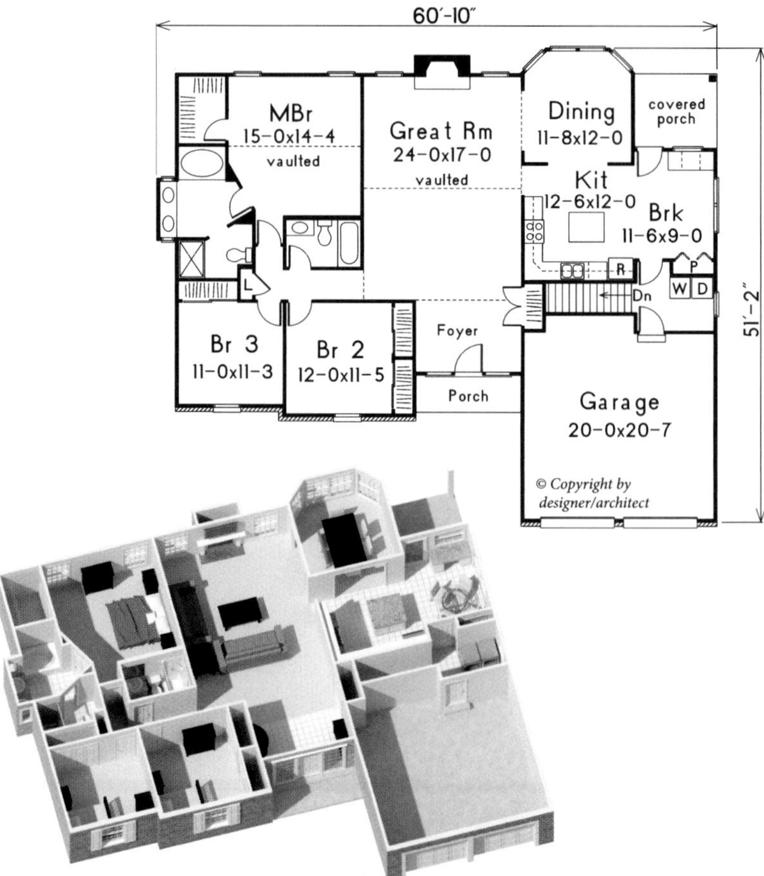

Desirable, Brick Home With Great Curb Appeal

- 1,897 total square feet of living area
- A high ceiling tops the terrific great room with a fireplace centered on one wall
- A large breakfast room is just steps away from the kitchen for convenience
- All the bedrooms are located on the second floor for convenience with family living
- 3 bedrooms, 2 1/2 baths, 2-car garage
- Basement foundation

Second Floor
861 sq. ft.

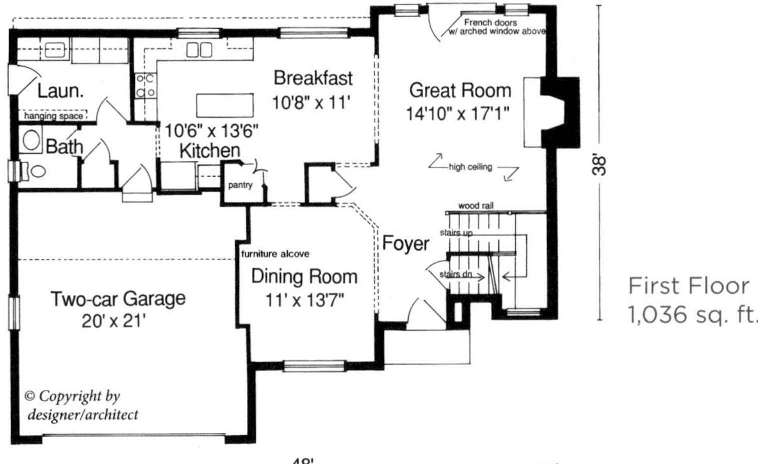

First Floor
1,036 sq. ft.

LOWE'S LEGACY SERIES

Plan #541-055L-0289 • Price Code C

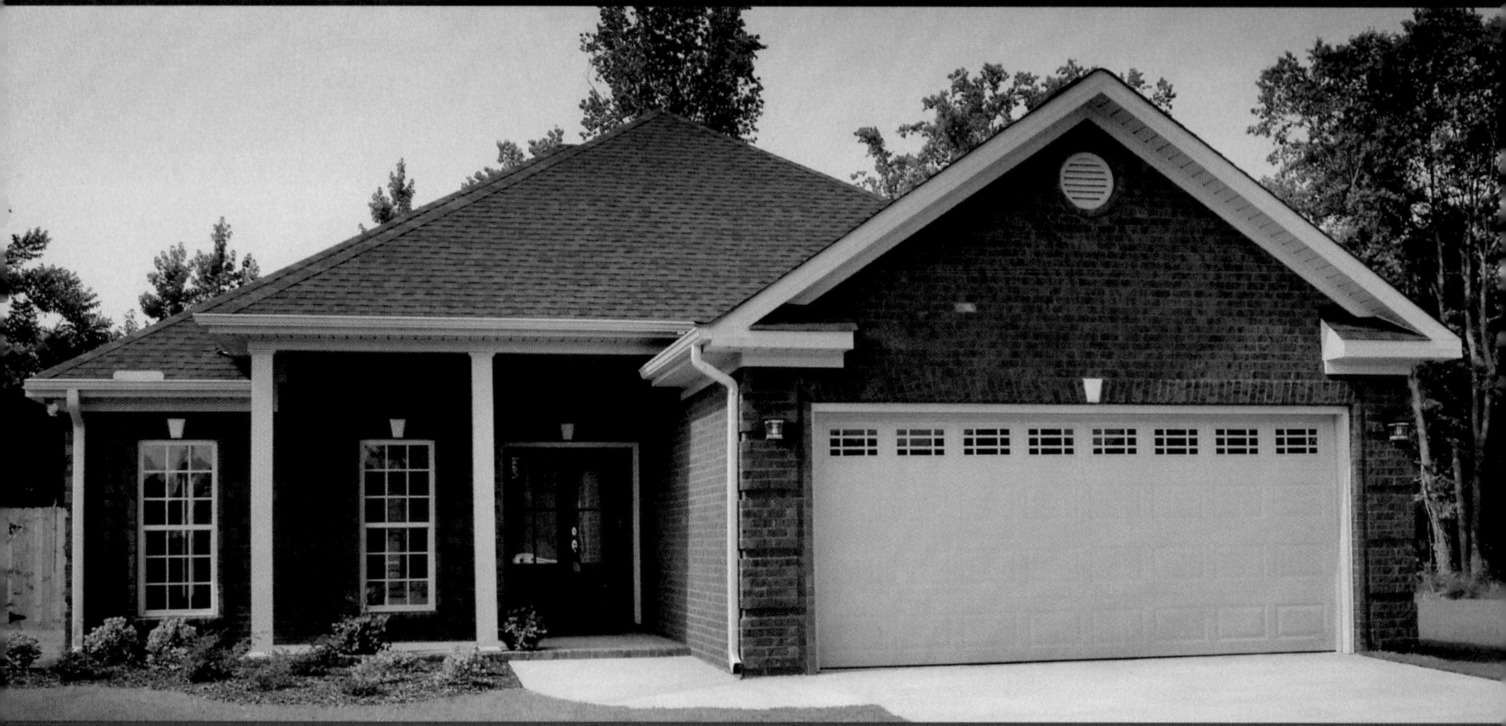

Lavishing Southern Design

- 1,504 total square feet of living area
- A private master suite has its own luxury bath featuring an oversized tub and shower
- A full bath is positioned between the two secondary bedrooms for convenience
- Enjoy the outdoors on the covered porch directly off the breakfast room
- 3 bedrooms, 2 baths, 2-car garage
- Crawl space or slab foundation, please specify when ordering

© Copyright by designer/architect

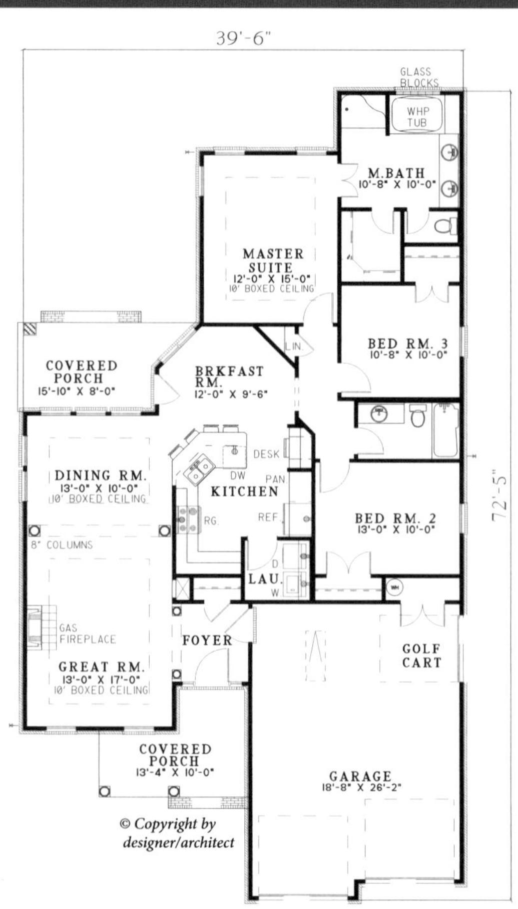

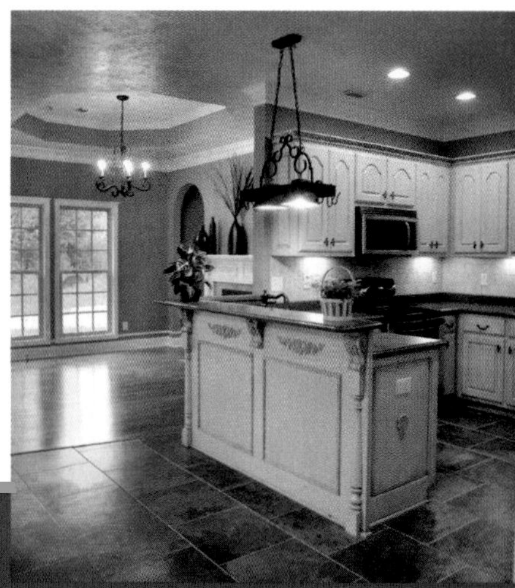

• To Order See Page 288 or Call Toll-Free 1-877-379-3420

Balcony Provides Dramatic View Below To Great Room

- 2,157 total square feet of living area
- Varied ceiling treatments, spacious rooms and lots of windows combine to set this home apart from the ordinary
- A spacious kitchen has a peninsula counter and walk-in pantry
- The master bedroom has every luxury imagined
- 4 bedrooms, 2 1/2 baths, 2-car side entry garage
- Walk-out basement foundation

Second Floor
646 sq. ft.

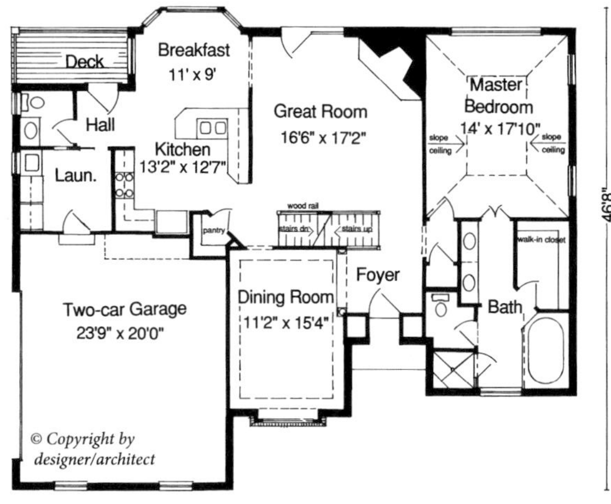

First Floor
1,511 sq. ft.

Plan #541-121D-0023 • Price Code A

Handsome Ranch Home With Shingle Siding

- 1,762 total square feet of living area
- The vaulted great room boasts a warming corner fireplace and flows into the vaulted dining area
- An island with eating bar in the kitchen is a perfect gathering spot for casual meals
- A private bath, large walk-in closet and vaulted ceiling are some of the amenities of the master bedroom
- 3 bedrooms, 2 baths, 2-car garage
- Basement foundation

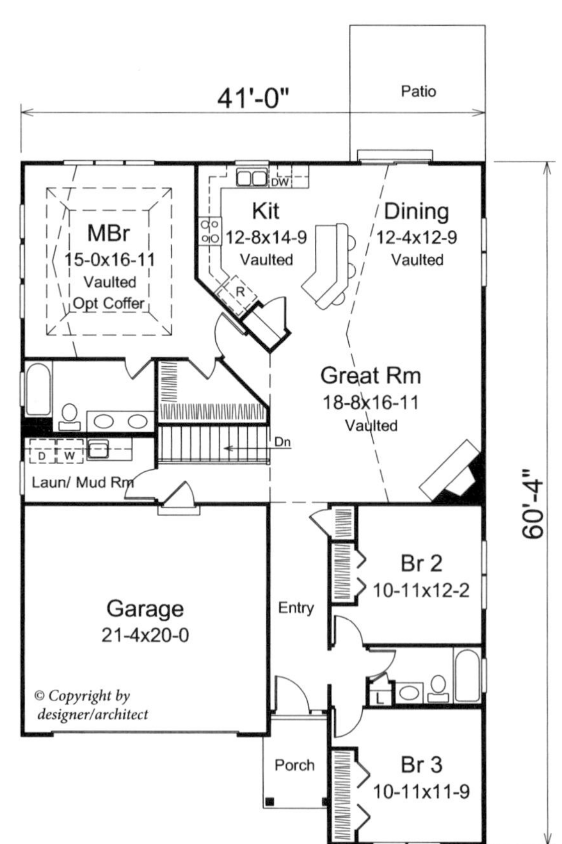

• To Order See Page 288 or Call Toll-Free 1-877-379-3420

Plan #541-065L-0005 • Price Code B

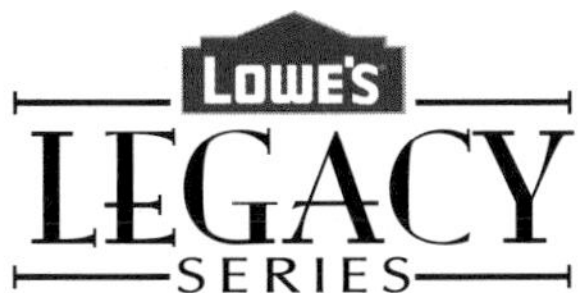

Sloped Ceilings Throughout

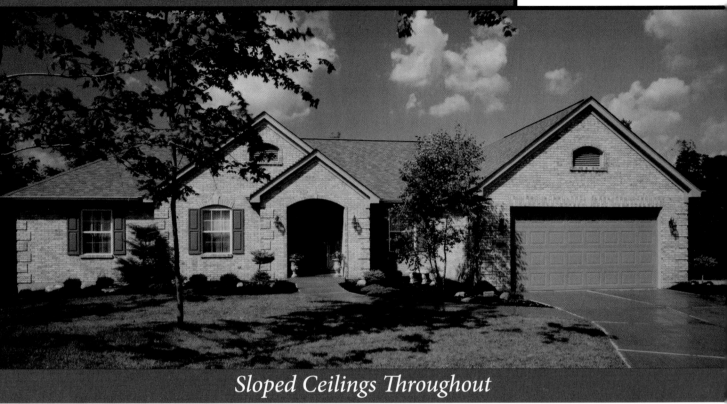

- 1,782 total square feet of living area
- Outstanding breakfast area has direct access to a screened-in porch
- Generous counterspace and cabinets combine to create an ideal kitchen
- The master bedroom is enhanced with a beautiful bath featuring a whirlpool tub and double-bowl vanity
- 3 bedrooms, 2 baths, 2-car garage
- Basement foundation

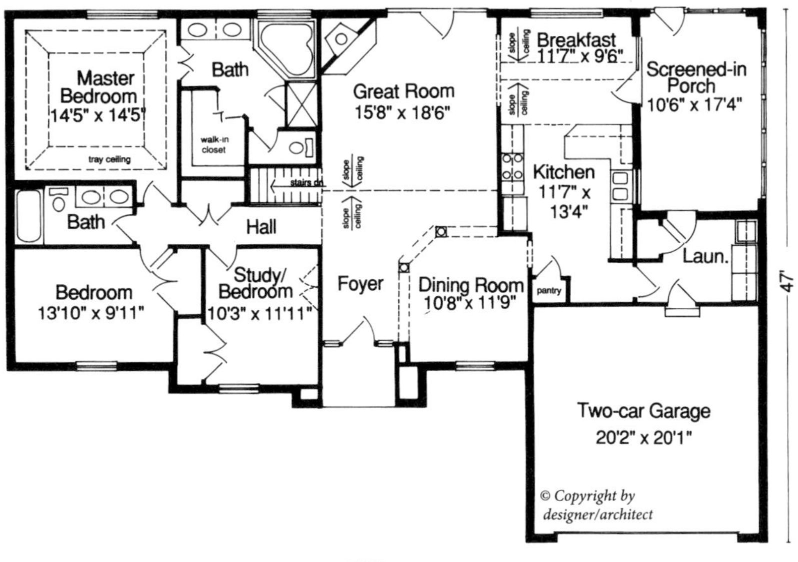

Plan #541-065L-0128 • Price Code D

Relaxing Solarium

- 2,283 total square feet of living area
- This one-level home with 9' ceiling heights throughout is designed with formal and informal spaces
- The open great room and dining room are defined by columns and dropped ceilings
- A corner fireplace and triple French doors highlight the great room
- 3 bedrooms, 2 baths, 2-car garage
- Basement foundation

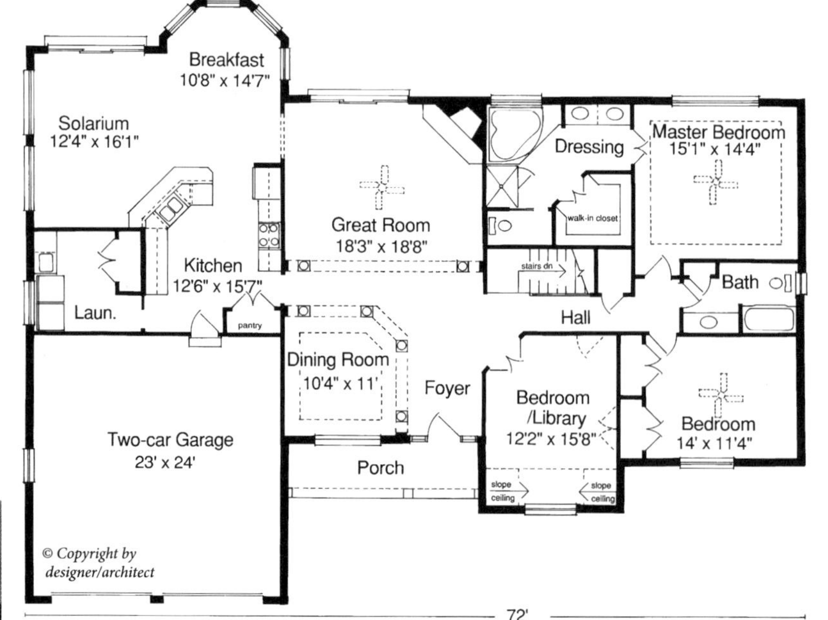

Plan #541-007D-0037 • Price Code A

Summer Home Or Year-Round

- 1,403 total square feet of living area
- Impressive living areas for a modest-sized home
- Special master/hall bath has linen storage, step-up tub and lots of window light
- Spacious closets everywhere you look
- 3 bedrooms, 2 baths, 2-car drive under garage
- Basement foundation

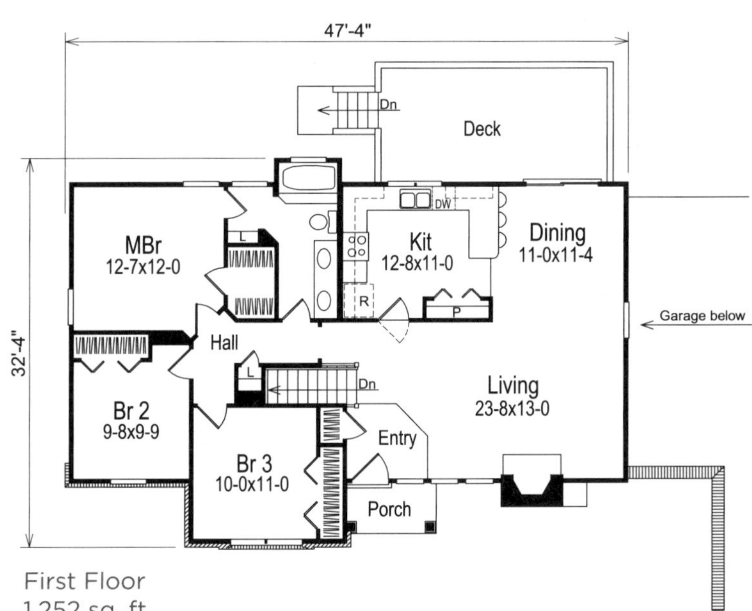

First Floor
1,252 sq. ft.

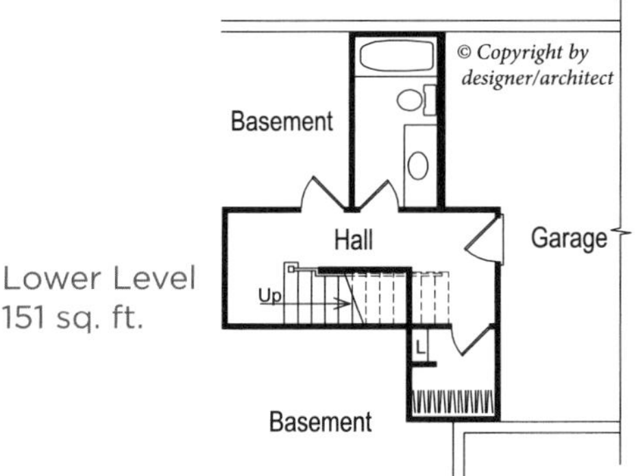

Lower Level
151 sq. ft.

Plan #541-122D-0001 • Price Code AAA

Energy Efficient Two-Story Berm Home

- 1,105 total square feet of living area
- Energy efficient home with 2" x 6" exterior walls
- This fresh, modern design enjoys sleek window lines and a stucco exterior making it truly a one-of-a-kind living experience
- The compact, yet efficient U-shaped kitchen offers a tremendous amount of counterspace within reach for all sort of kitchen tasks at hand
- A tall sloped ceiling in the two-story living room gives this home an open and spacious feel all those who enter will appreciate
- 2 bedrooms, 1 1/2 baths
- Slab foundation

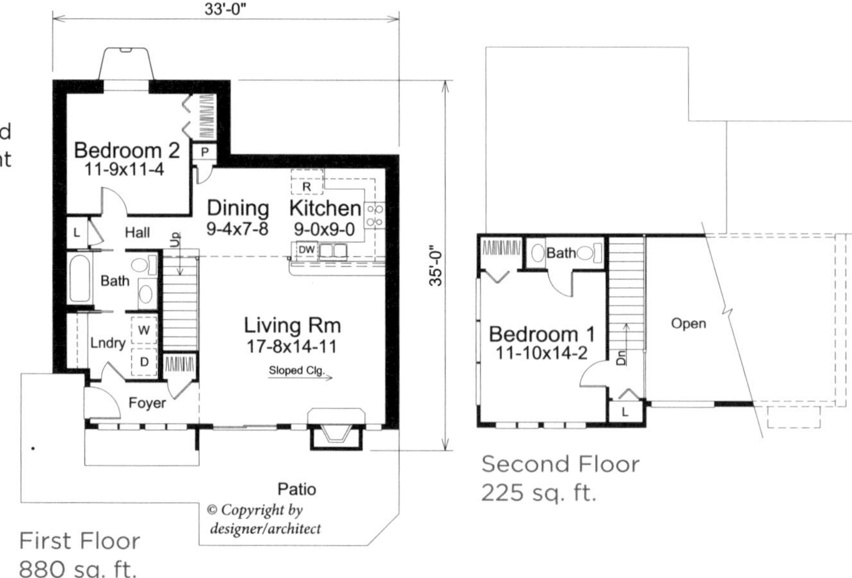

First Floor
880 sq. ft.

Second Floor
225 sq. ft.

• To Order See Page 288 or Call Toll-Free 1-877-379-3420

Economical Ranch For Easy Living

- 1,314 total square feet of living area
- Energy efficient home with 2" x 6" exterior walls
- Covered porch adds immediate appeal and welcoming charm
- Open floor plan combined with a vaulted ceiling offers spacious living
- Functional kitchen is complete with a pantry and eating bar
- Cozy fireplace in the living room
- Private master bedroom features a large walk-in closet and bath
- 3 bedrooms, 2 baths, 2-car garage
- Basement foundation

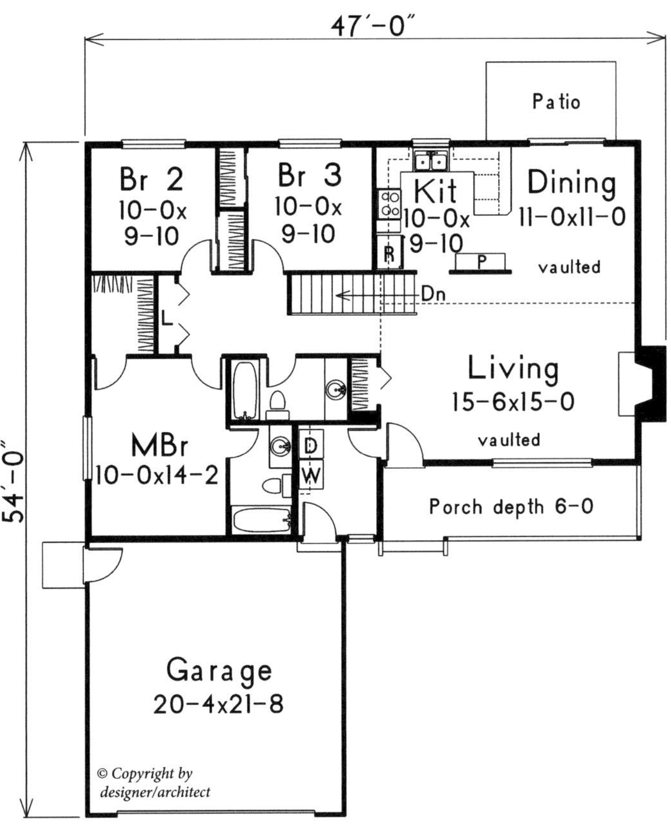

Plan #541-007D-0219 • Price Code B

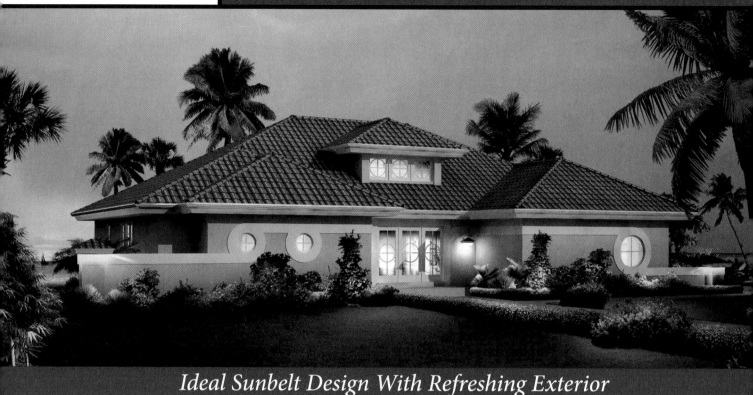

Ideal Sunbelt Design With Refreshing Exterior

- 1,939 total square feet of living area
- A grand entry has unique curved walls and flanking coat closets leading down a few steps into an enormous sunken great room
- The spacious kitchen with cabinets galore has a built-in pantry, functional island/snack bar and dining area with views of the covered patio nearby
- A laundry room, mechanical and coat closets are conveniently situated between the kitchen and garage
- The huge master bedroom features a luxury bath with separate shower, large walk-in closet and private covered patio
- 2 bedrooms, 2 baths, 2-car side garage
- Crawl space foundation

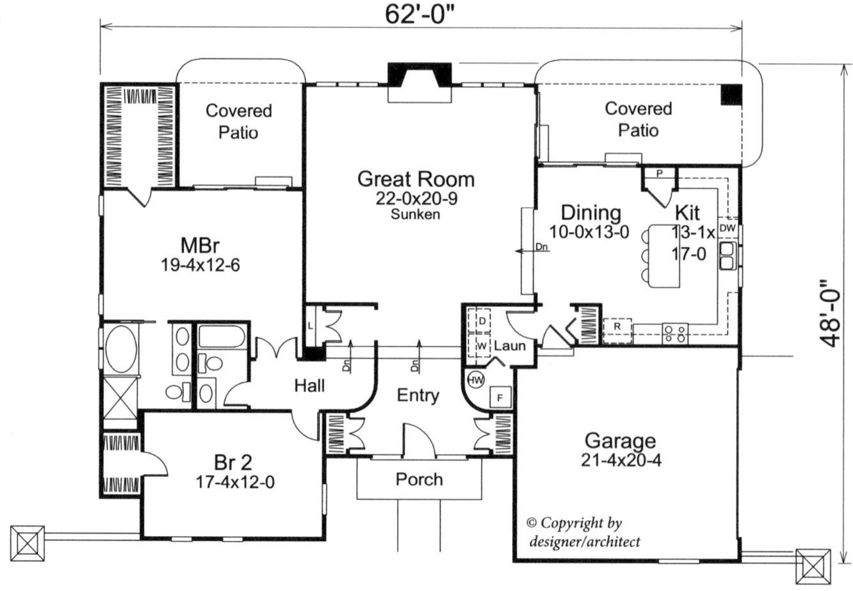

Plan #541-121D-0002 • Price Code B

Sophisticated Ranch With Split Bedrooms

- 2,025 total square feet of living area
- The cozy great room enjoys a 42" wood burning fireplace as the main focal point along with a vaulted ceiling and 12' wall
- The formal dining room enjoys a decorative column and beam system along with a vaulted ceiling for added spaciousness
- The vaulted kitchen has a versatile cooktop island with separate oven for great functionality
- An elegant coffered ceiling tops the private master bedroom
- 3 bedrooms, 2 1/2 baths, 2-car side entry garage
- Basement foundation

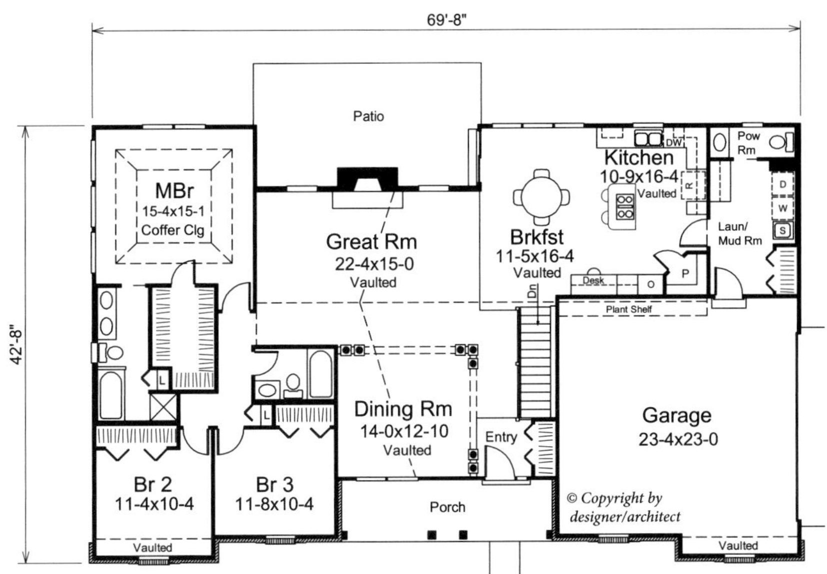

Plan #541-048D-0008 • Price Code C

Stately Covered Front Entry

- 2,089 total square feet of living area
- Family room features a fireplace, built-in bookshelves and triple sliders opening to the covered patio
- The kitchen overlooks the family room and features a pantry and desk
- Separated from the three secondary bedrooms, the master bedroom becomes a quiet retreat with patio access
- Master bedroom features an oversized bath with walk-in closet and corner tub
- 4 bedrooms, 3 baths, 2-car garage
- Slab foundation

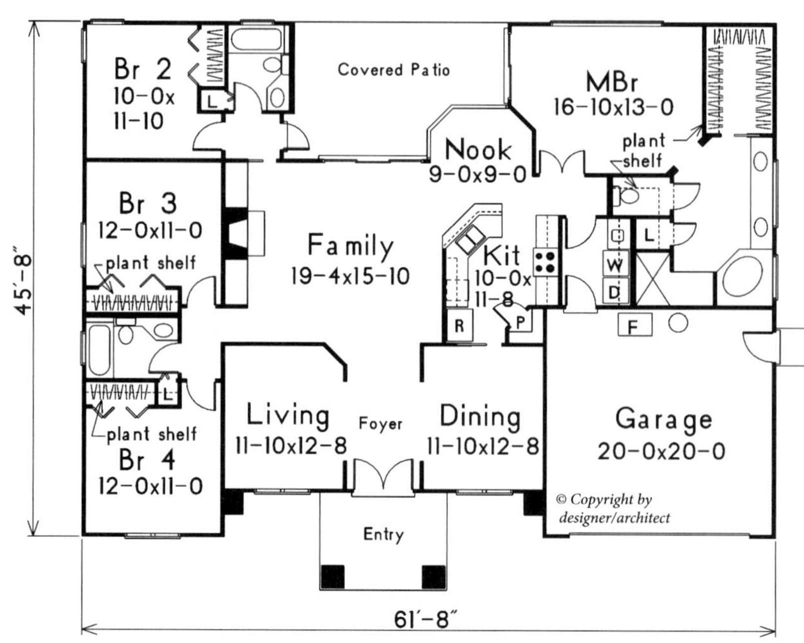

• To Order See Page 288 or Call Toll-Free 1-877-379-3420

Plan #541-008D-0068 • Price Code C

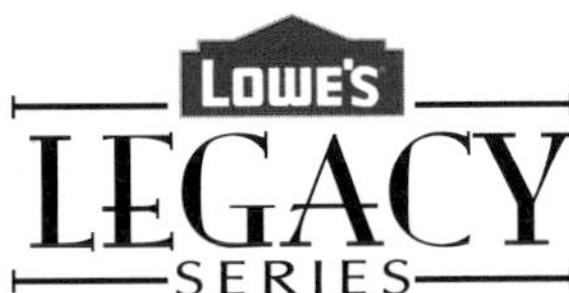

Floridian Style Home

- 1,932 total square feet of living area
- Large see-through fireplace warms and beautifies the entire home
- The spacious master bedroom enjoys a walk-in closet and direct access to the outdoors
- Sliding glass doors in the activity room and breakfast nook lead to a large, open deck
- 3 bedrooms, 2 baths, 2-car side entry garage
- Partial basement/crawl space foundation, drawings also include crawl space foundation

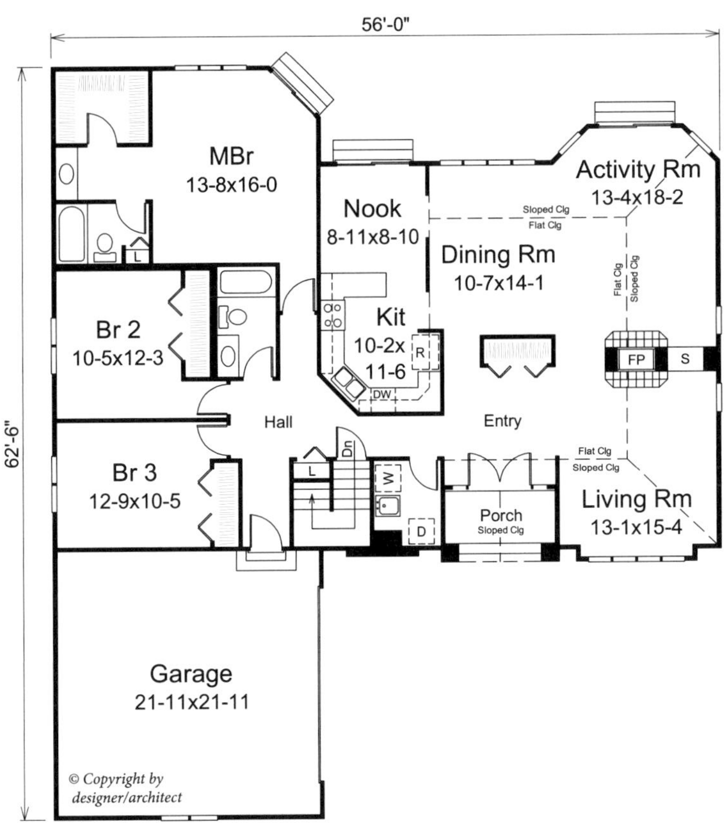

Plan #541-003D-0001 • Price Code C

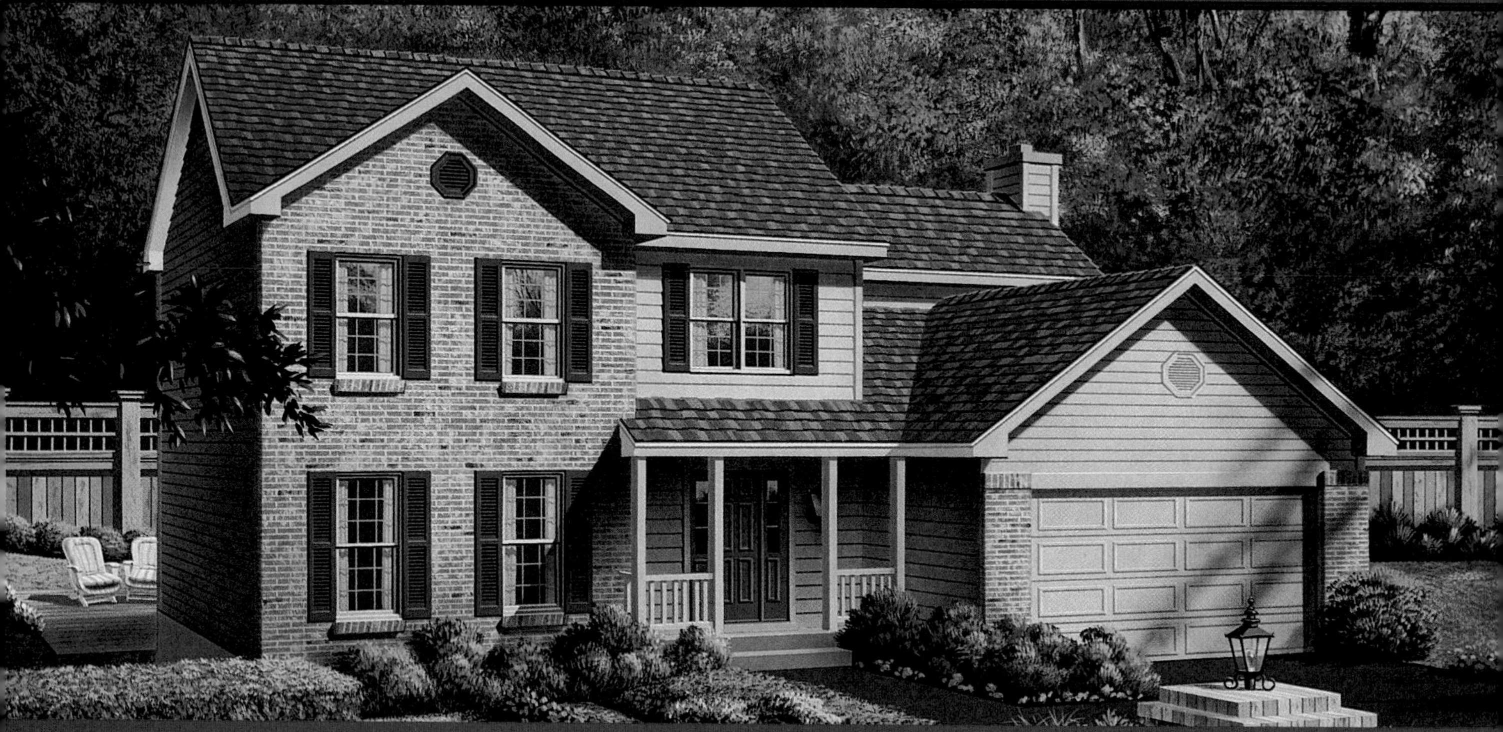

Practical Two-Story, Full Of Features

- 2,058 total square feet of living area
- Handsome two-story foyer with balcony creates a spacious entrance area
- Vaulted master bedroom has a private dressing area and large walk-in closet
- Skylights furnish natural lighting in the hall and master bath
- The laundry closet is conveniently located on the second floor near the bedrooms
- 3 bedrooms, 2 1/2 baths, 2-car garage
- Basement foundation, drawings also include slab and crawl space foundations

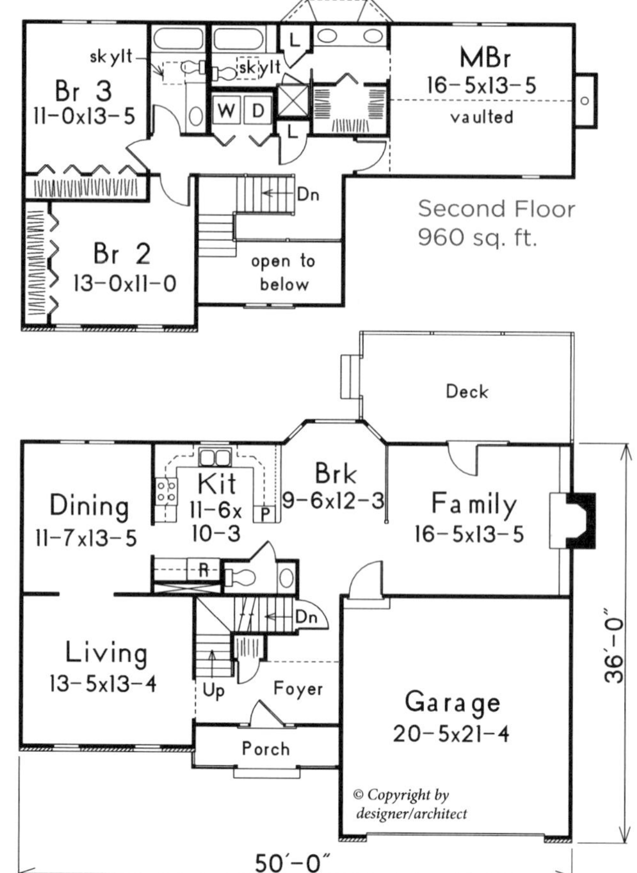

• To Order See Page 288 or Call Toll-Free 1-877-379-3420

Plan #541-007D-0055 • Price Code D

Country Home With Front Orientation

- 2,029 total square feet of living area
- Stonework, gables, roof dormer and double porches create a country flavor
- Kitchen enjoys extravagant cabinetry and counterspace in a bay, island snack bar, built-in pantry and cheery dining area with multiple tall windows
- Angled stairs descend from the large entry with wood columns and are open to a vaulted great room with corner fireplace
- 2" x 6" exterior walls available, please order plan #541-007E-0055
- Plan also available with energy efficient R-Control® SIPs (Structural Insulated Panels), please call 1-877-379-3420 for more information
- 3 bedrooms, 2 baths, 2-car side entry garage
- Basement foundation, drawings also include crawl space and slab foundations

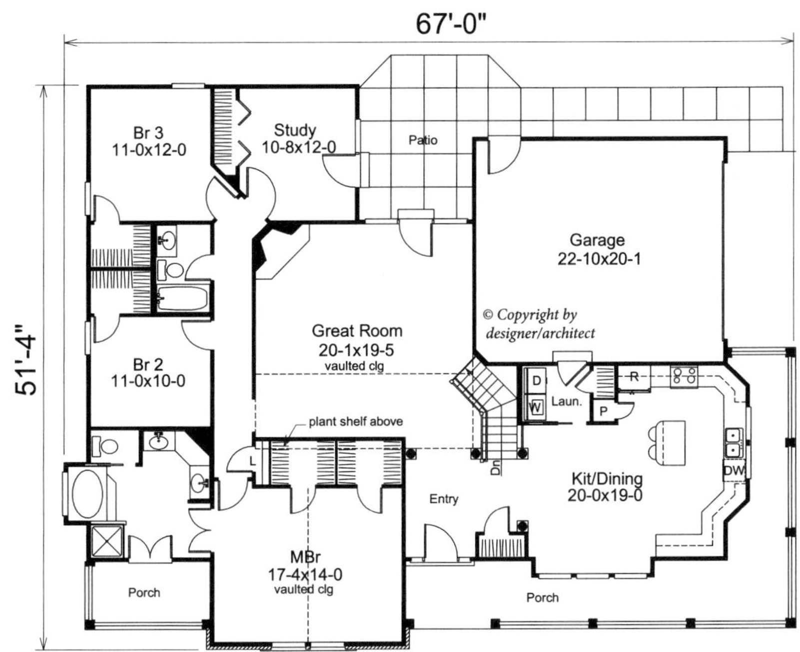

Plan #541-006D-0003 • Price Code B

Sculptured Roof Line And Facade Add Charm

- 1,674 total square feet of living area
- Vaulted great room, dining area and kitchen all enjoy a central fireplace and log bin
- Convenient laundry/mud room is located between the garage and the rest of the home with handy stairs to the basement
- Easily expandable screened porch and adjacent patio access the dining area
- Master bedroom features a full bath with tub, separate shower and walk-in closet
- 3 bedrooms, 2 baths, 2-car garage
- Basement foundation, drawings also include crawl space and slab foundations

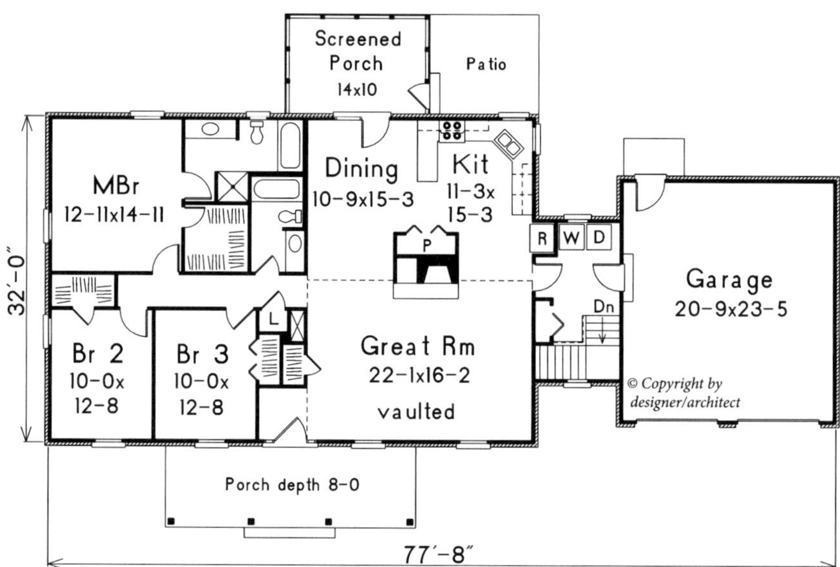

• To Order See Page 288 or Call Toll-Free 1-877-379-3420

Plan #541-055L-0026 • Price Code B

Bayed Dining Room

- 1,538 total square feetof living area
- Energy efficient home with 2" x 6" exterior walls
- Dining and great rooms are highlighted in this design
- Master suite has many amenities
- Traditional ranch facade looks great in any neighborhood
- 3 bedrooms, 2 baths, 2-car garage
- Slab, walk-out basement, basement, or crawl space foundation, please specify when ordering

Plan #541-055L-0158 • Price Code C

Open Living Areas

- 1,636 total square feet of living area
- The grilling porch is large enough for outdoor cooking and entertaining
- The bar with seating in the kitchen is great for serving snacks
- Columns separate the dining room from the rest of the house without enclosing it
- 3 bedrooms, 2 baths, 2-car garage
- Slab or crawl space foundation, please specify when ordering

• To Order See Page 288 or Call Toll-Free 1-877-379-3420

Plan #541-007D-0232 • Price Code D

Country Home With Charm And Great Planning

- 1,915 total square feet of living area
- A wrap-around porch invites you into a home with many pleasant surprises
- The great room enjoys a separate entry, large dining area, corner fireplace and awesome views of the rear veranda through three glass sliding doors
- Several corner windows brighten the sink area in the kitchen which also features a built-in pantry and center island/snack bar
- Off the hall is the vaulted master bedroom with two walk-in closets, a luxury bath and private porch
- A half bath with coat closet and workbench area with window are included in the oversized garage
- 3 bedrooms, 2 1/2 baths, 3-car side entry garage
- Slab foundation

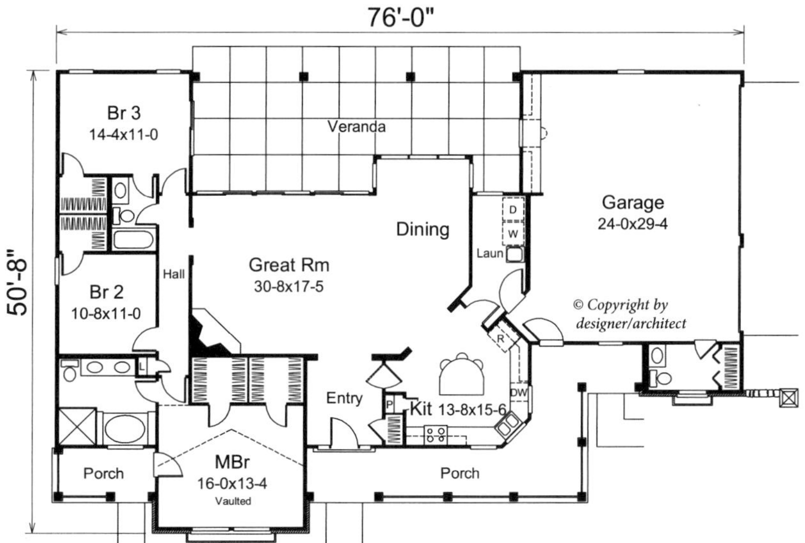

LOWE'S LEGACY SERIES

Plan #541-007D-0085 • Price Code B

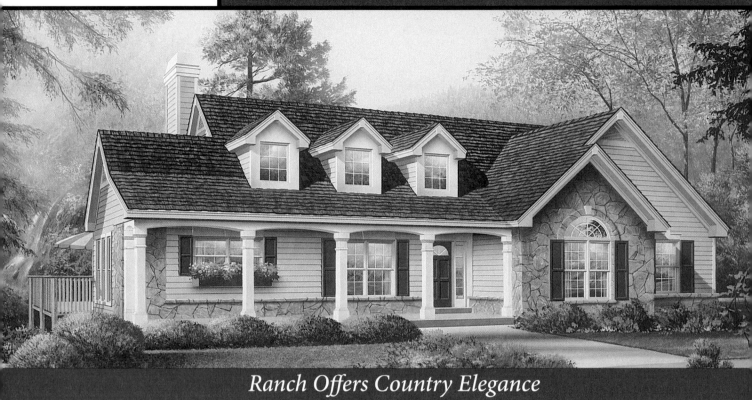

Ranch Offers Country Elegance

- 1,787 total square feet of living area
- Large great room with fireplace and vaulted ceiling features three large skylights and windows galore
- Cooking is sure to be a pleasure in this L-shaped well-appointed kitchen that includes a bayed breakfast area with access to the rear deck
- Every bedroom offers a spacious walk-in closet with a convenient laundry room just steps away
- 415 square feet of optional living area available on the lower level
- 3 bedrooms, 2 baths, 2-car drive under rear entry garage
- Walk-out basement foundation

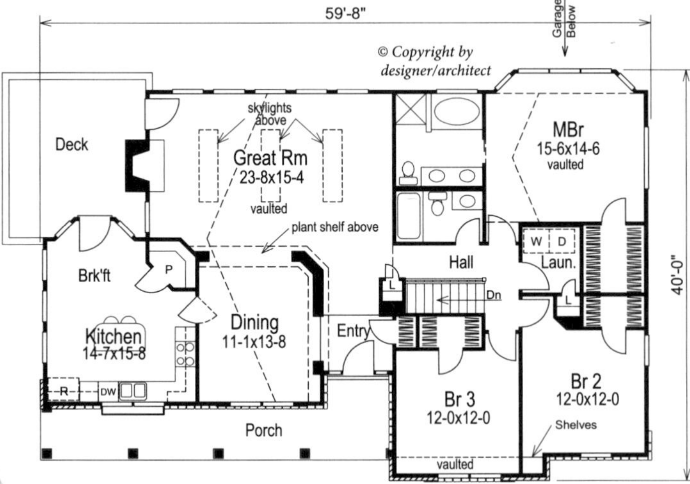

• To Order See Page 288 or Call Toll-Free 1-877-379-3420

Plan #541-029D-0002 • Price Code B

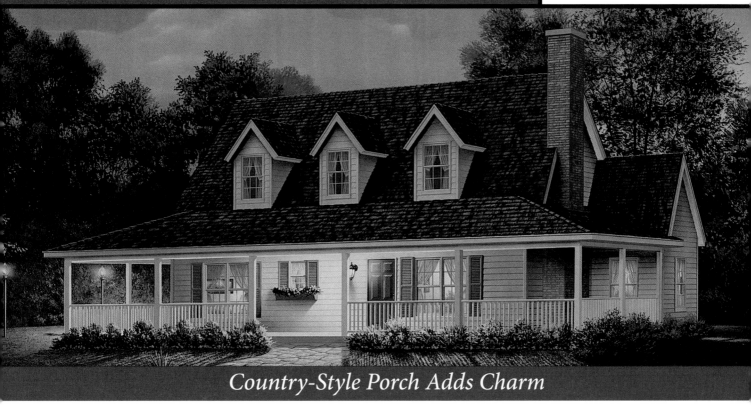

Country-Style Porch Adds Charm

- 1,619 total square feet of living area
- Private second floor bedroom and bath
- Kitchen features a snack bar and adjacent dining area
- Master bedroom has a private bath
- Centrally located washer and dryer
- 3 bedrooms, 3 baths
- Basement foundation, drawings also include crawl space and slab foundations

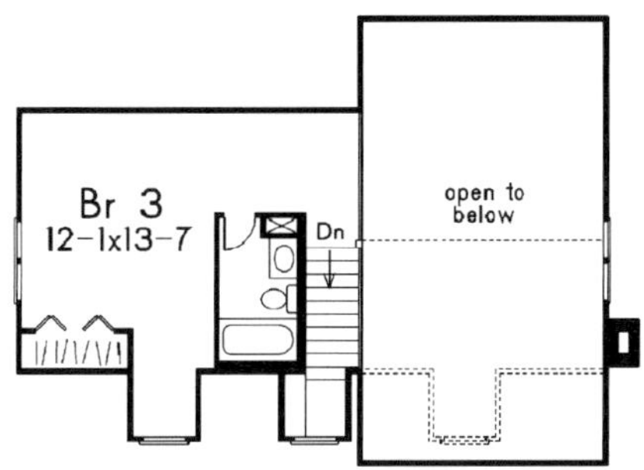

Second Floor
360 sq. ft.

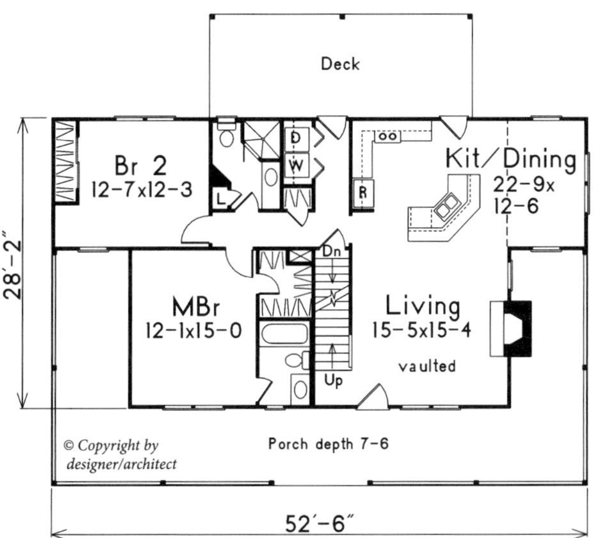

First Floor
1,259 sq. ft.

Plan #541-057D-0010 • Price Code A

Split-Bedroom Floor Plan

- 1,242 total square feet of living area
- Energy efficient home with 2" x 6" exterior walls
- The wide foyer opens to the living room for a spacious atmosphere and grand first impression
- The centrally located kitchen easily serves the large dining and living rooms
- The split-bedroom design allows privacy for the homeowners who will love spending time in their master bedroom retreat
- 3 bedrooms, 2 baths, 2-car garage
- Basement foundation

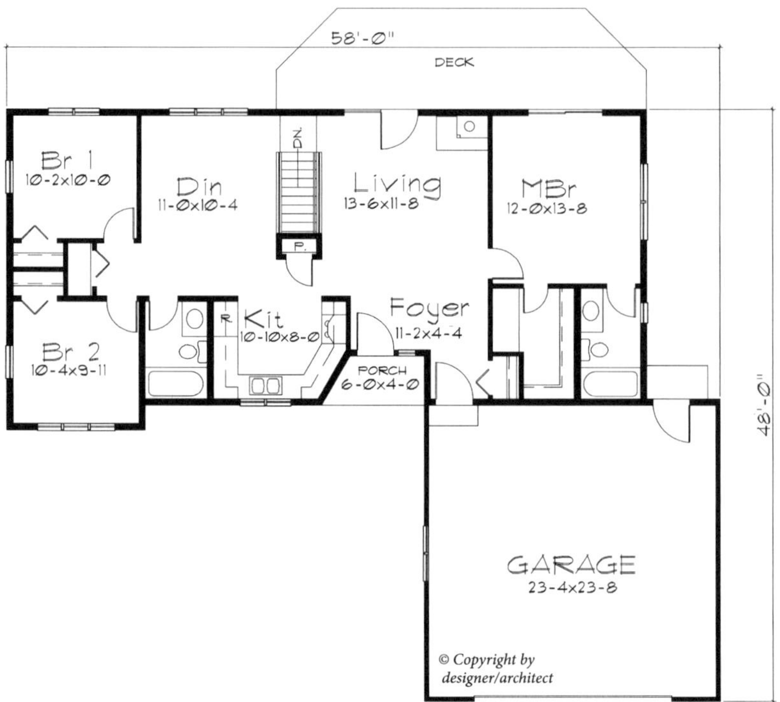

To Order See Page 288 or Call Toll-Free 1-877-379-3420

Plan #541-007D-0124 • Price Code C

Country Ranch Enjoys Large Great Room

- 1,944 total square feet of living area
- Spacious surrounding porch, covered patio and stone fireplace create an expansive ponderosa appearance
- The large entry leads to a grand-sized great room featuring a vaulted ceiling, fireplace, wet bar and access to the porch through three patio doors
- The U-shaped kitchen is open to the hearth room and enjoys a snack bar, fireplace and patio access
- A luxury bath, walk-in closet and doors to the porch are a few of the amenities of the master bedroom
- 3 bedrooms, 2 baths, 3-car detached garage
- Basement foundation

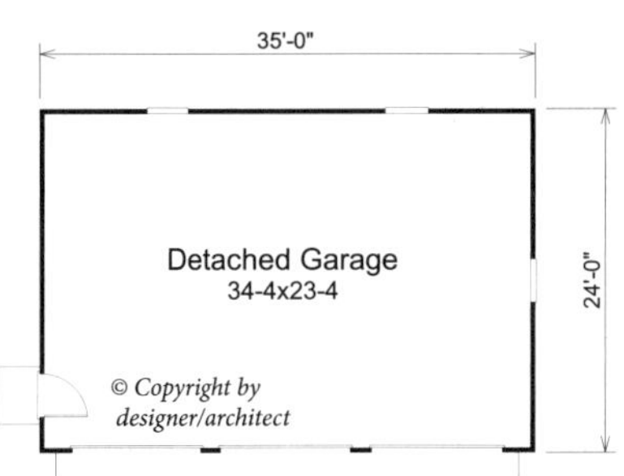

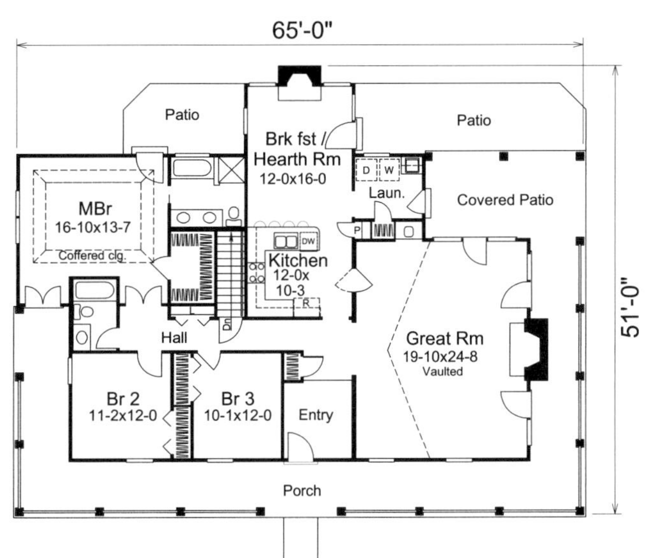

Plan #541-033D-0009 • Price Code C

Charming Two-Story With Dormers And Porch

- 1,711 total square feet of living area
- U-shaped kitchen joins the breakfast and family rooms for an open living atmosphere
- Master bedroom has a secluded covered porch and private bath
- The balcony overlooks the family room that features a fireplace and accesses the deck
- 3 bedrooms, 2 1/2 baths, 2-car garage
- Basement foundation

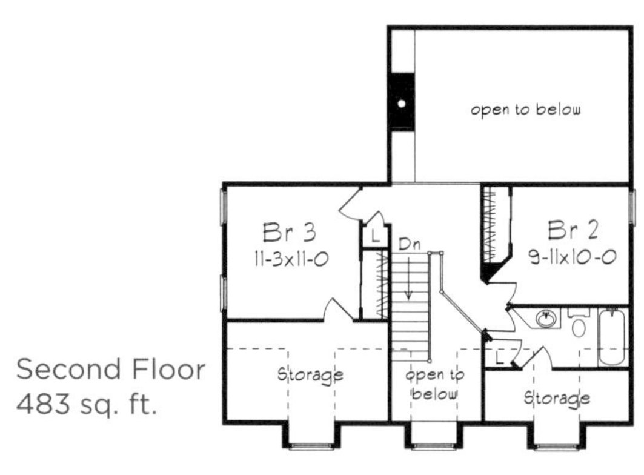

Second Floor
483 sq. ft.

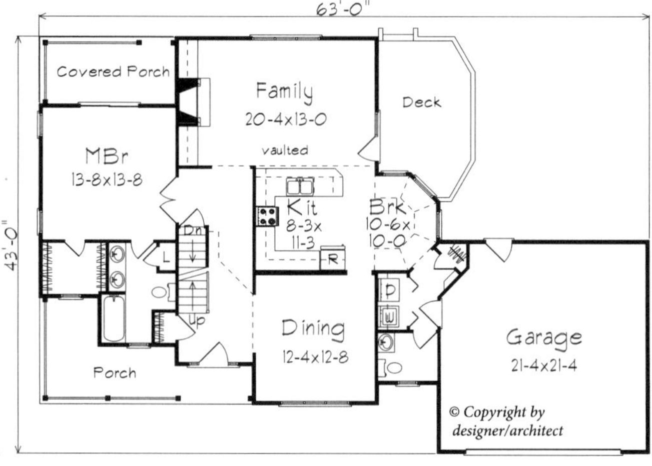

First Floor
1,228 sq. ft.

• To Order See Page 288 or Call Toll-Free 1-877-379-3420

Plan #541-021D-0004 • Price Code D

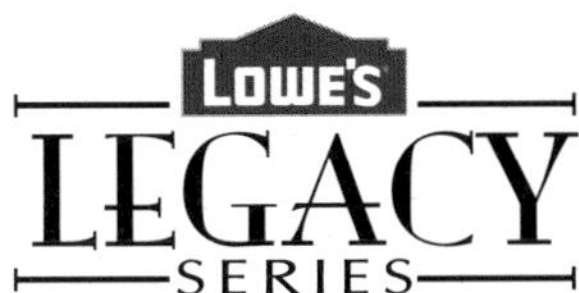

Full Pillared Porch Makes A Grand Entrance

- 1,800 total square feet of living area
- Energy efficient home with 2″ x 6″ exterior walls
- The stylish kitchen and breakfast area feature large windows that allow a great view outdoors
- Covered front and rear porches provide an added dimension to this home's living space
- Generous storage areas and a large utility room add to this spacious design
- Large separate master bedroom with adjoining bath has a large tub and corner shower
- 3 bedrooms, 2 baths, 2-car garage
- Crawl space foundation, drawings also include slab foundation

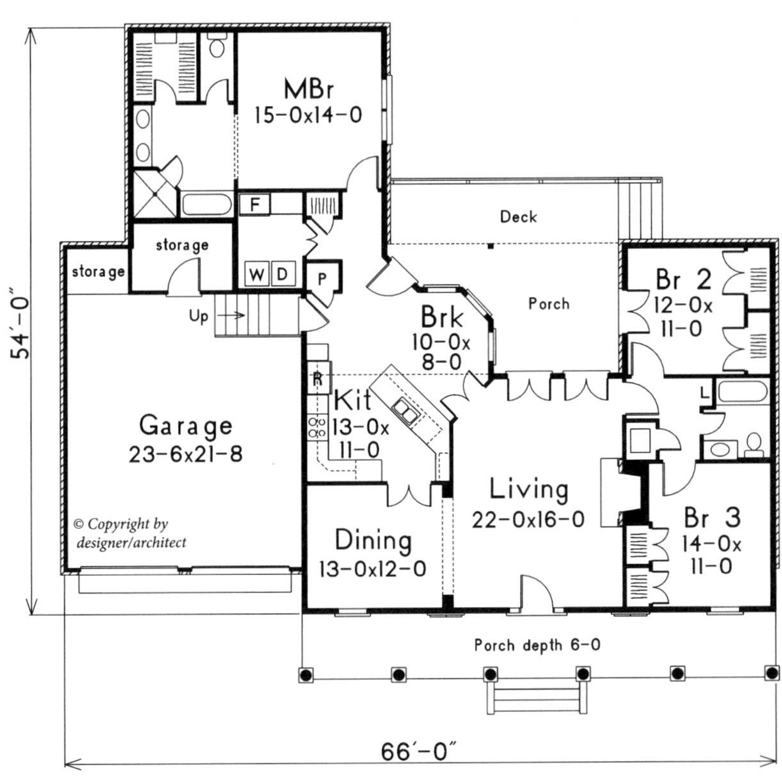

Plan #541-007D-0218 • Price Code C

Classic English Tudor With Room To Grow

- 1,828 total square feet of living area
- The large entry has a generous guest closet and leads into the sunken living areas at the rear of the home
- A corner fireplace, 9' sliding doors to the rear patio and an open dining area with bay window are a few features of the sensational great room
- The first floor bedroom and full bath are the perfect answer to having overnight guests, a child home from college or a visiting in-law
- A 20' x 13' unfinished room behind the garage is ideal for a workshop, office, art studio, family room, game room or expanding any way you wish
- The second floor has a large master bedroom with two walk-in closets, a luxury bath, 9' wide patio doors to a private outdoor balcony plus a secondary bedroom and half bath
- 3 bedrooms, 2 1/2 baths, 2-car garage
- Crawl space foundation

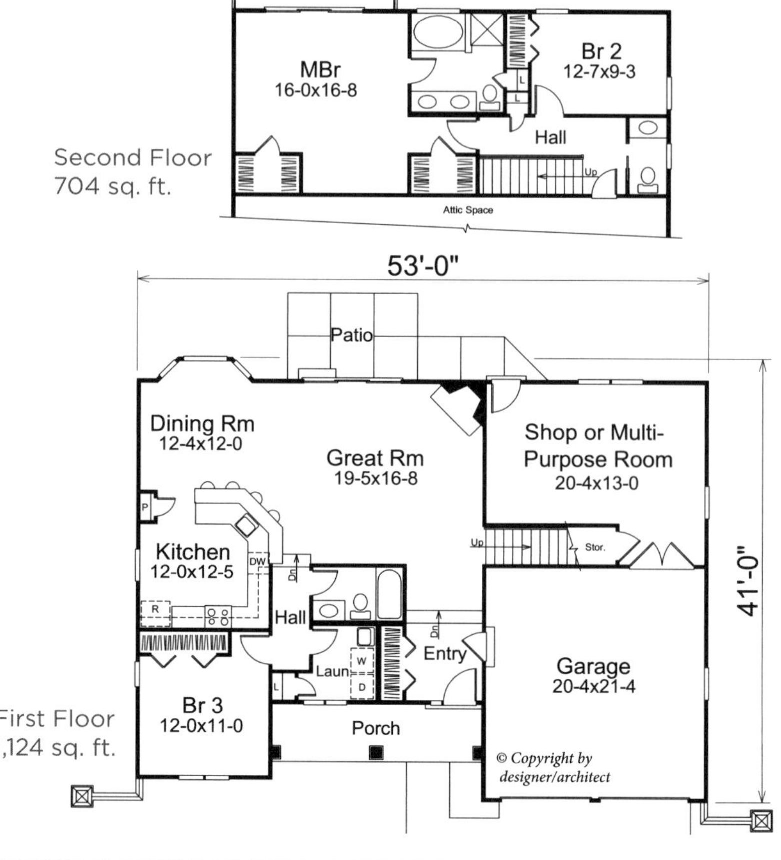

Second Floor
704 sq. ft.

First Floor
1,124 sq. ft.

To Order See Page 288 or Call Toll-Free 1-877-379-3420

Plan #541-037D-0003 • Price Code D

Garden Courtyard Lends Distinction And Privacy

- 1,996 total square feet of living area
- The large, covered rear porch enjoys direct access to the master bedroom suite and the living room
- The sculptured entrance has artful plant shelves and a special niche in the foyer
- Master bedroom boasts French doors, a garden tub, desk with bookshelves and generous storage
- Plant shelves and a high ceiling grace the hallway
- 3 bedrooms, 2 baths, 2-car side entry garage
- Slab foundation, drawings also include crawl space foundation

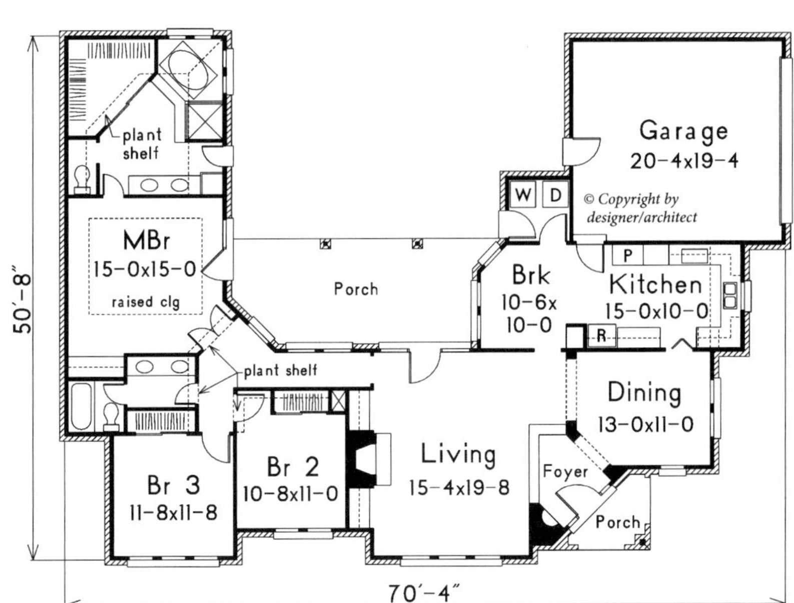

• To Order See Page 288 or Call Toll-Free 1-877-379-3

Plan #541-005D-0001 • Price Code B

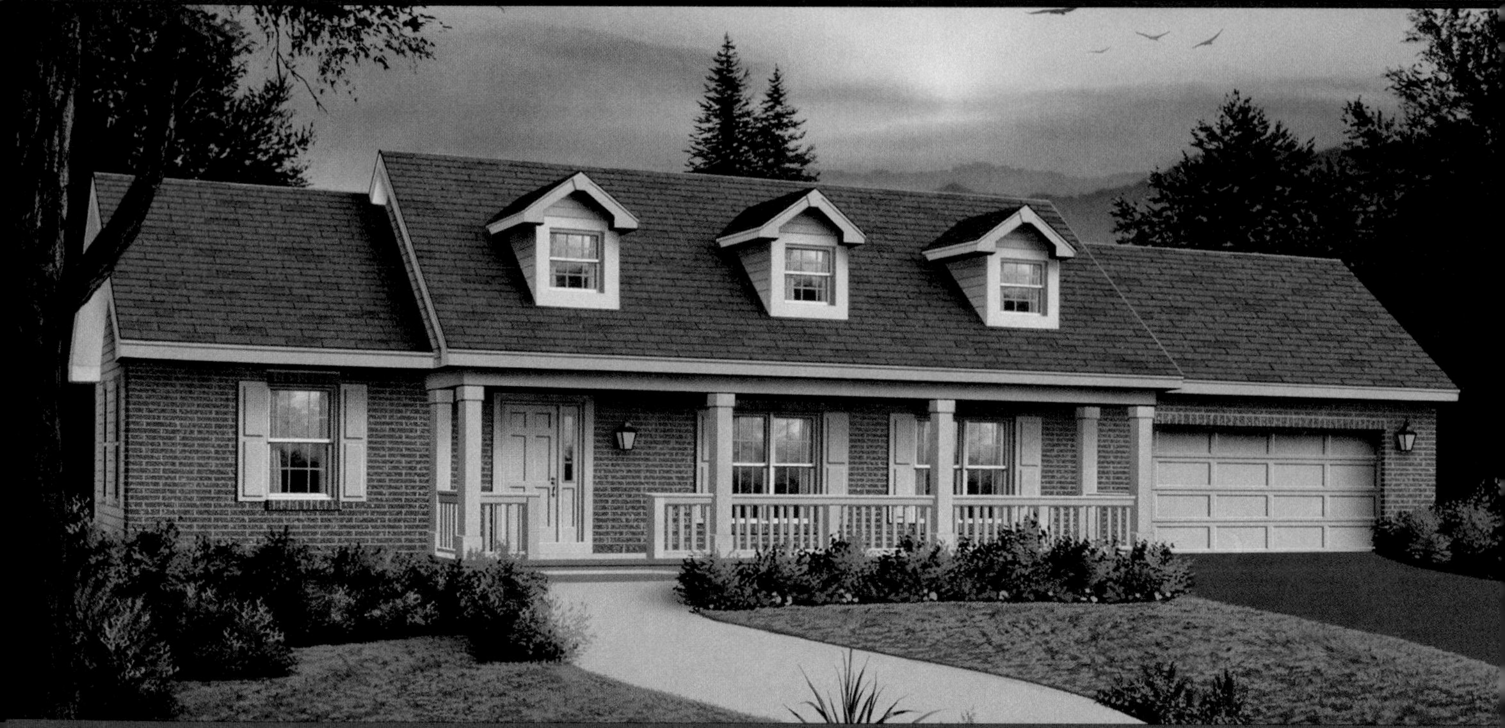

Classic Ranch Has Grand Appeal With Expansive Porch

- 1,400 total square feet of living area
- Master bedroom is secluded for privacy
- The large utility room has additional cabinet space
- Covered porch provides an outdoor seating area
- Roof dormers add great curb appeal
- Living room and master bedroom feature vaulted ceilings
- Oversized two-car garage has storage space
- Plan also available with energy efficient R-Control® SIPs (Structural Insulated Panels), please call 1-877-379-3420 for more information
- 3 bedrooms, 2 baths, 2-car garage
- Basement foundation, drawings also include crawl space foundation

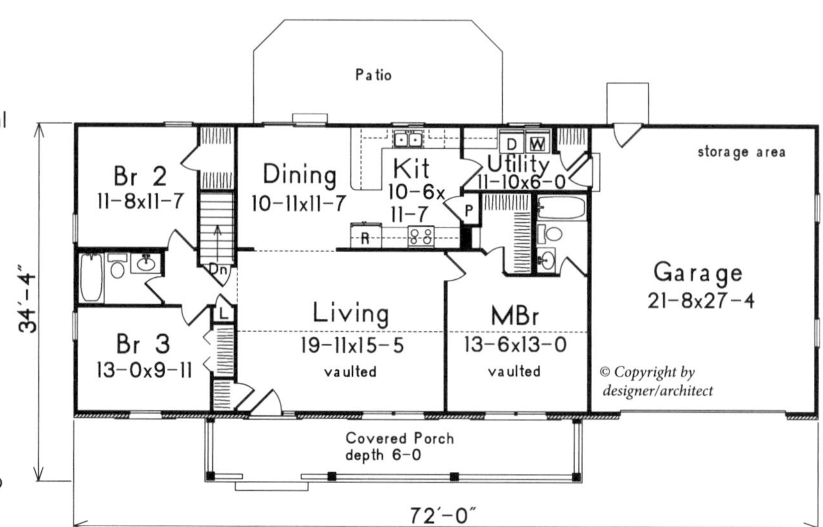

Plan #541-077L-0043 • Price Code D

Split-Bedroom, Family Design

- 1,752 total square feet of living area
- The gas fireplace is framed by elegant built-in cabinets
- The media/hobby room is a great workspace and overlooks the front yard
- The large island in the kitchen provides extra counterspace as well as a snack bar for casual meals
- 3 bedrooms, 2 baths, 2-car side entry garage
- Slab foundation, drawings also include basement and crawl space foundations

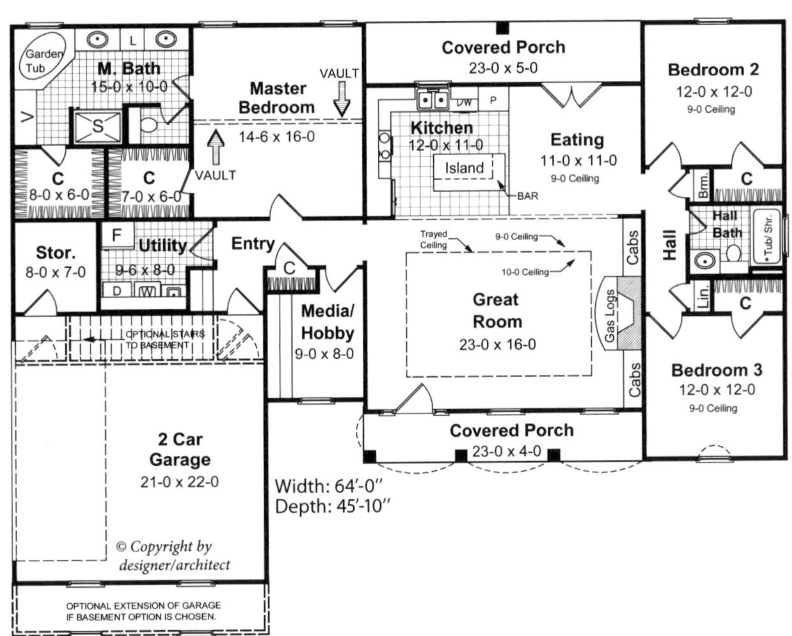

Plan #541-007D-0017 • Price Code C

Organized Kitchen Is The Center Of Activity

- 1,882 total square feet of living area
- Handsome brick facade
- The spacious great room and dining area combination is brightened by unique corner windows and patio access
- Well-designed kitchen incorporates a breakfast bar peninsula, sweeping casement window above sink and a walk-in pantry island
- Master bedroom features a large walk-in closet and private bath with bay window
- Plan also available with energy efficient R-Control® SIPs (Structural Insulated Panels), please call 1-877-379-3420 for more information
- 4 bedrooms, 2 baths, 2-car side entry garage
- Basement foundation

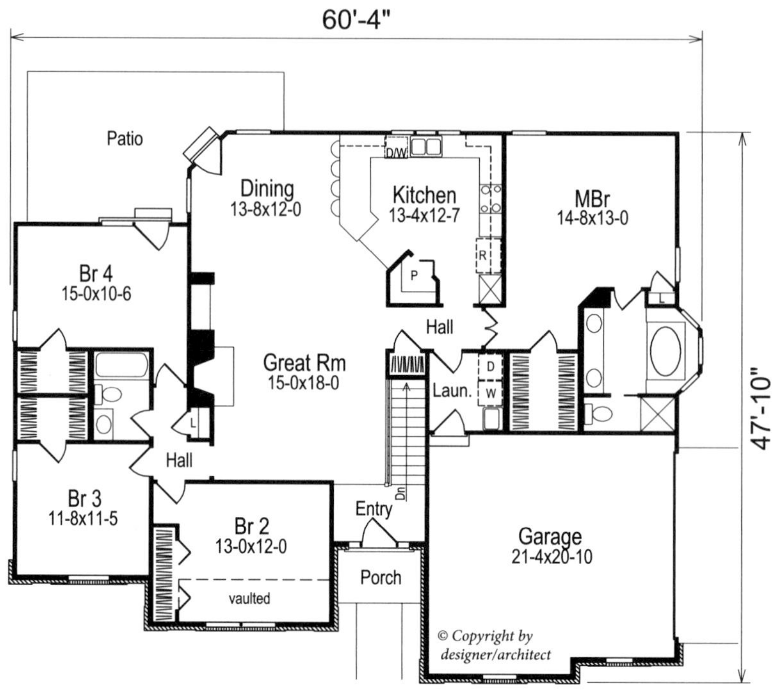

• To Order See Page 288 or Call Toll-Free 1-877-379-3420

Plan #541-003D-0005 • Price Code B

Private Breakfast Room Provides Casual Dining

- 1,708 total square feet of living area
- Massive family room is enhanced with several windows, a fireplace and access to the porch
- Deluxe master bath is accented by a step-up corner tub flanked by double vanities
- Closets throughout maintain organized living
- Bedrooms are isolated from living areas
- 3 bedrooms, 2 baths, 2-car garage
- Basement foundation, drawings also include crawl space foundation

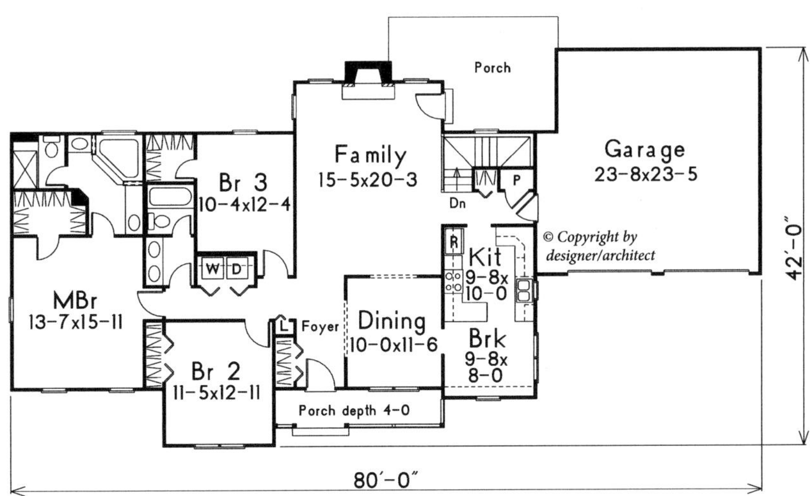

Plan #541-058D-0006 • Price Code A

Year-Round Or Weekend Getaway Home

- 1,339 total square feet of living area
- Full-length covered porch enhances front facade
- Vaulted ceiling and stone fireplace add drama to the family room
- Walk-in closets in the bedrooms provide ample storage space
- Combined kitchen/dining area adjoins the family room for the perfect entertaining space
- 2" x 6" exterior walls available, please order plan #541-058D-0072
- 3 bedrooms, 2 1/2 baths
- Crawl space foundation

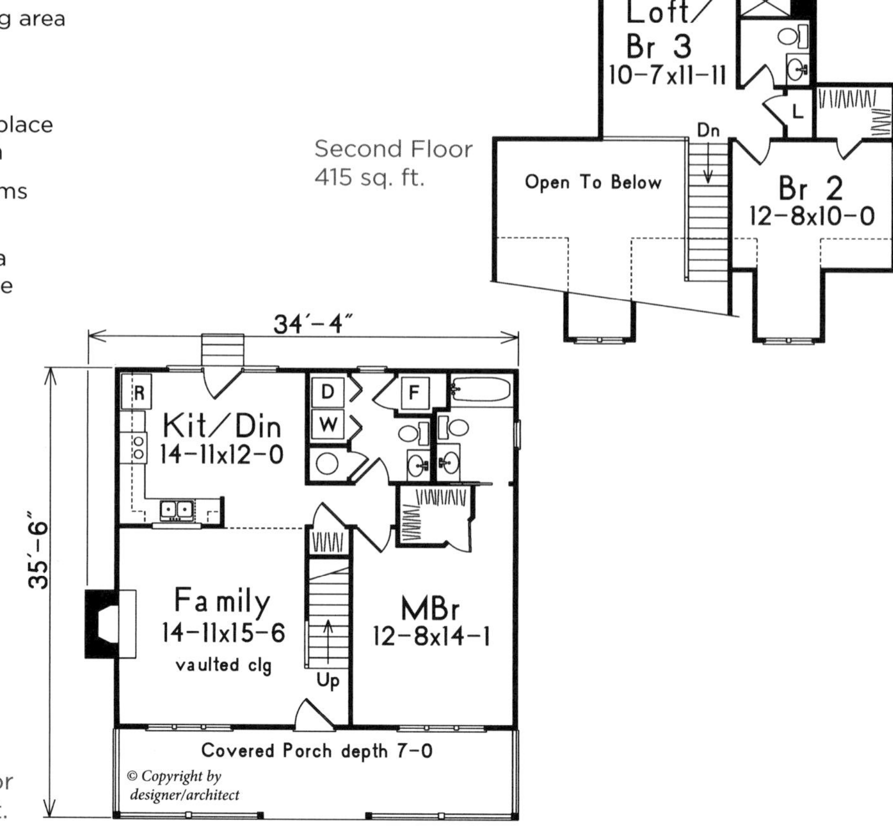

Second Floor
415 sq. ft.

First Floor
924 sq. ft.

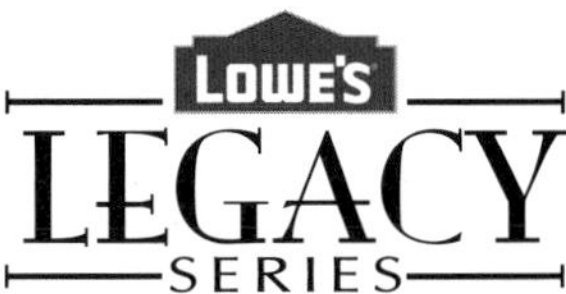

Plan #541-013L-0014 • Price Code C

LOWE'S LEGACY SERIES

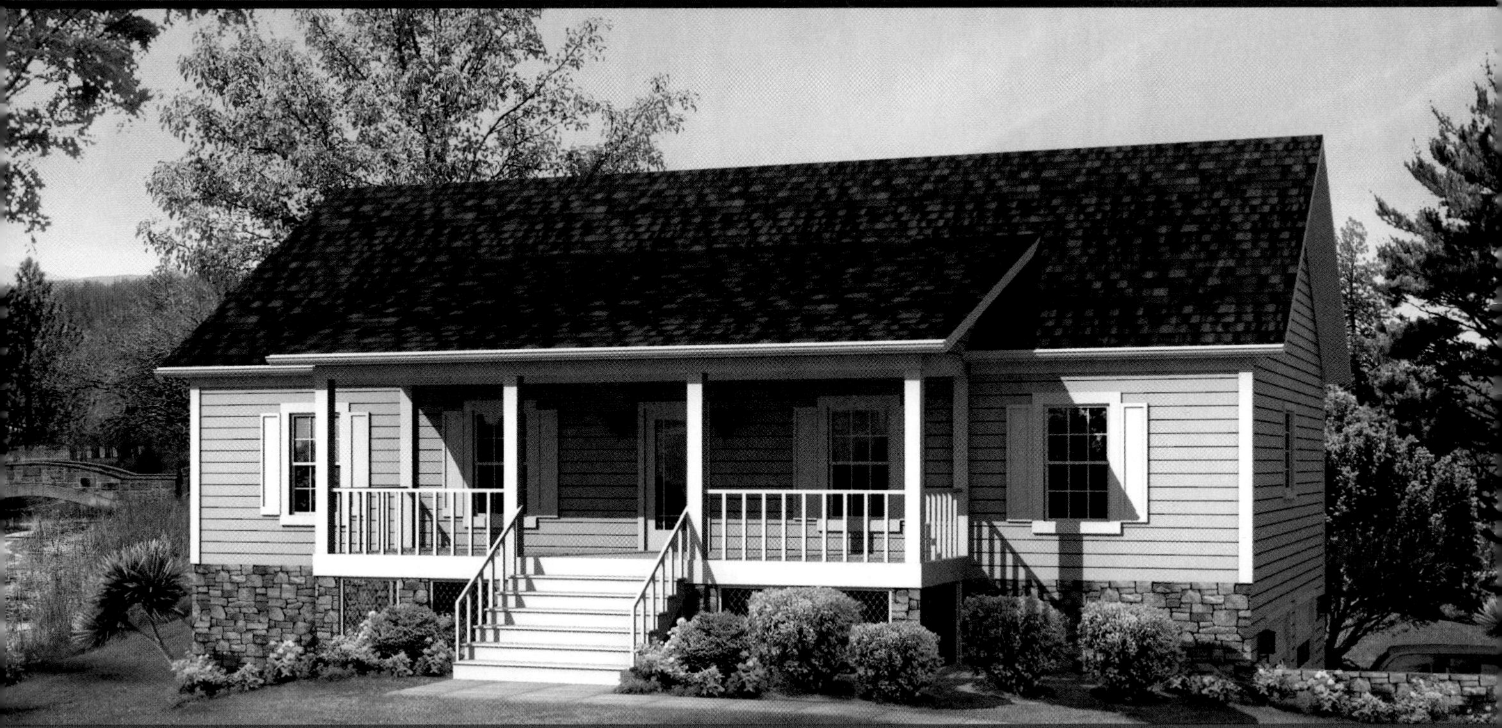

A Rustic Drive Under Ranch

- 1,728 total square feet of living area
- Large entry leads to the family room featuring a corner fireplace and a window wall overlooking an enormous deck
- Master bedroom is adorned with a dramatic bath featuring an angled entry and a corner tub
- 3 bedrooms, 2 baths, 2-car drive under side entry garage
- Basement foundation, drawings also include crawl space foundation

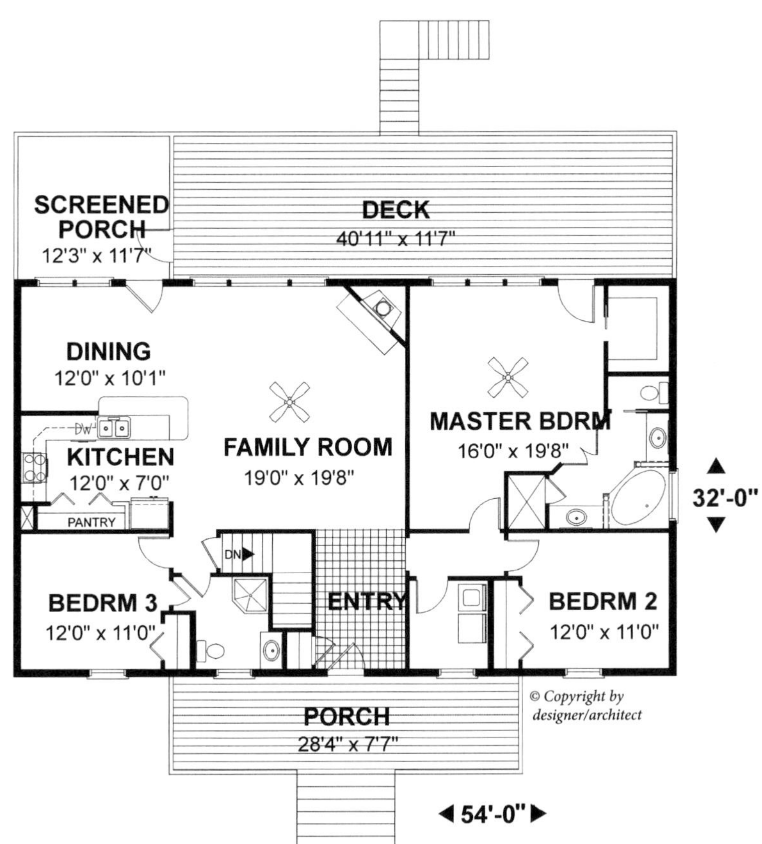

Plan #541-068D-0005 • Price Code A

Spacious Living In This Ranch

- 1,433 total square feet of living area
- Vaulted living room includes a cozy fireplace and an oversized entertainment center
- Bedrooms #2 and #3 share a full bath
- Master bedroom has a full bath and large walk-in closet
- 3 bedrooms, 2 baths, 2-car garage
- Basement foundation, drawings also include crawl space and slab foundations

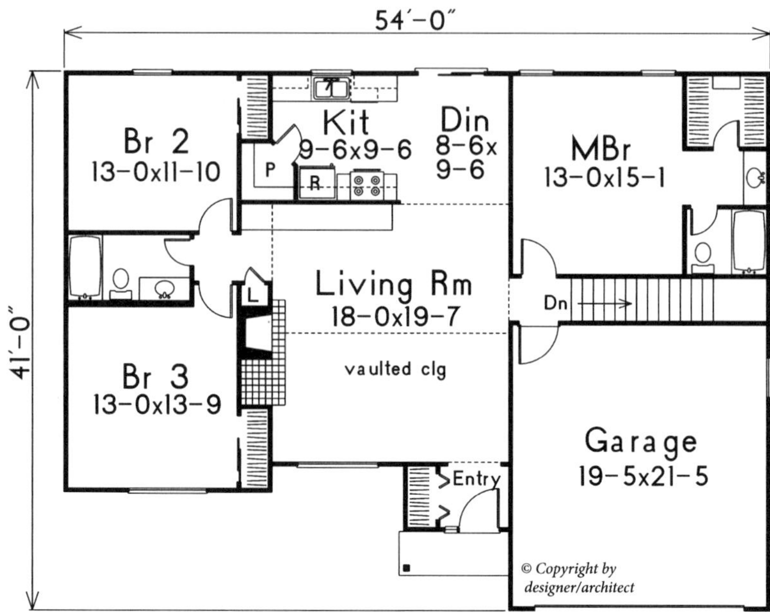

• To Order See Page 288 or Call Toll-Free 1-877-379-3420

Plan #541-001D-0018 • Price Code AA

Front Porch And Center Gable Add Style To This Ranch

- 988 total square feet of living area
- Pleasant covered porch entry
- The kitchen, living and dining areas are combined to maximize space
- The entry has a convenient coat closet
- The laundry closet is located adjacent to the bedrooms
- 3 bedrooms, 1 bath, 1-car garage
- Basement foundation, drawings also include crawl space foundation

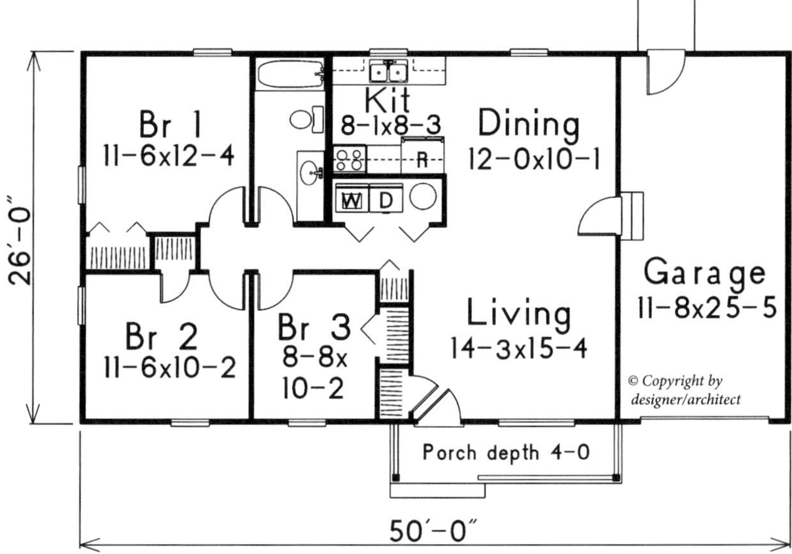

Plan #541-014D-0011 • Price Code C

Elegant Exterior

- 2,106 total square feet of living area
- Energy efficient home with 2" x 6" exterior walls
- 9' ceilings throughout home
- Large two-story foyer features open staircase and plant ledge
- Kitchen with centrally located eating bar offers double pantries for additional storage
- An arch with columns on either side separates dining and living rooms
- Master bath includes plush dressing area, double sinks, a spa tub, linen cabinet and a separate room with toilet and shower
- 3 bedrooms, 2 1/2 baths, 2-car garage
- Basement foundation

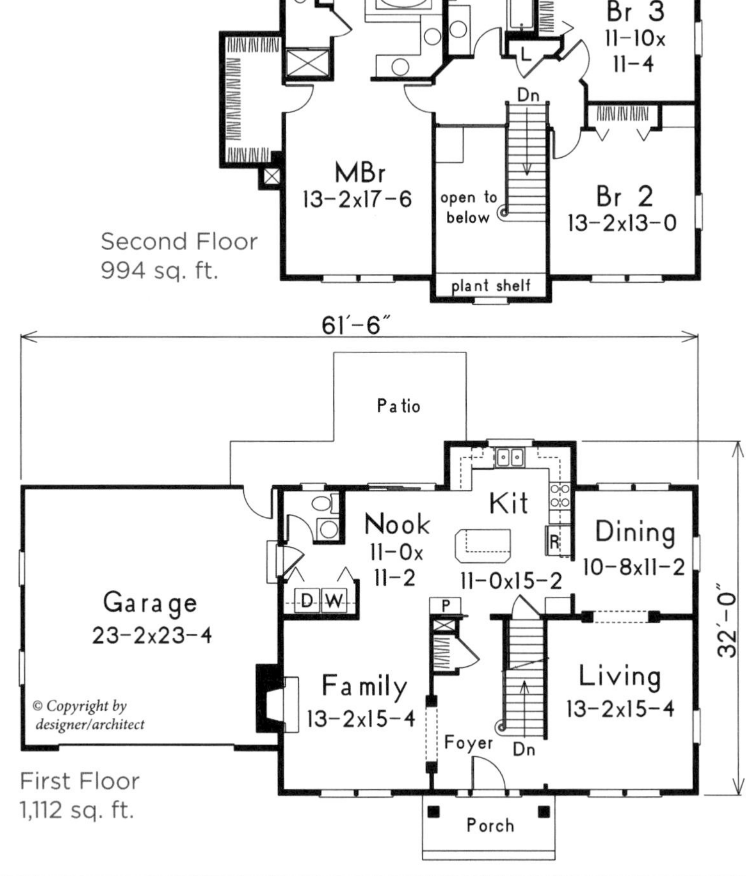

• To Order See Page 288 or Call Toll-Free 1-877-379-3420

Plan #541-057D-0019 • Price Code C

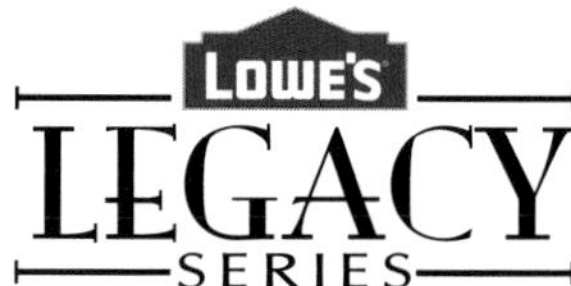

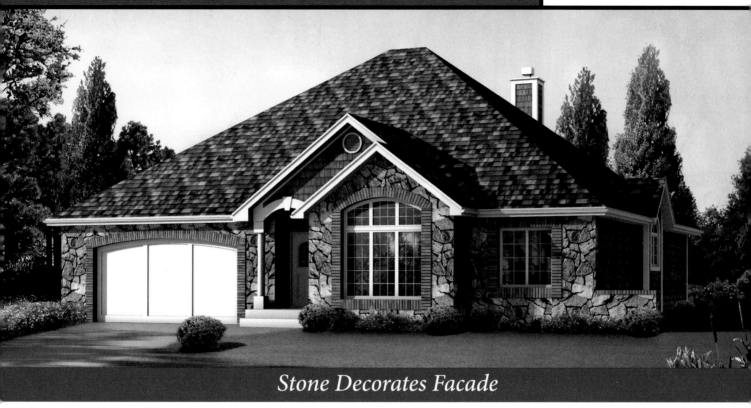

Stone Decorates Facade

- 1,838 total square feet of living area
- Energy efficient home with 2" x 6" exterior walls
- The angled great room features a corner fireplace, French doors to the rear deck and connects to the dining room for a spacious atmosphere
- The wrap-around kitchen counter offers plenty of workspace and room for casual meals
- Retreat to the master bedroom where a deluxe bath, walk-in closet and deck access will pamper the homeowners
- 3 bedrooms, 2 baths, 2-car garage
- Crawl space foundation, drawings also include basement foundation

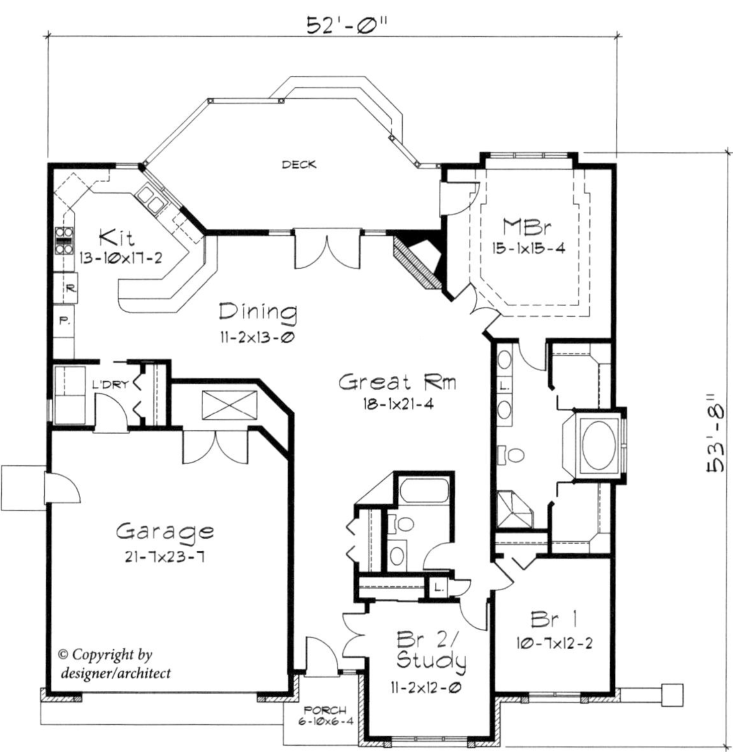

Plan #541-077L-0045 • Price Code D

Plush Master Bedroom Retreat

- 1,799 total square feet of living area
- The vaulted ceiling in the great room creates a dynamic living space
- The garage offers an extra storage area with room to create a shop, bonus room or separate porch
- The bonus room with half bath has the potential to be a great guest room or play room and provides an additional 394 square feet of living area
- 3 bedrooms, 2 1/2 baths, 2-car garage
- Crawl space foundation, drawings also include slab foundation

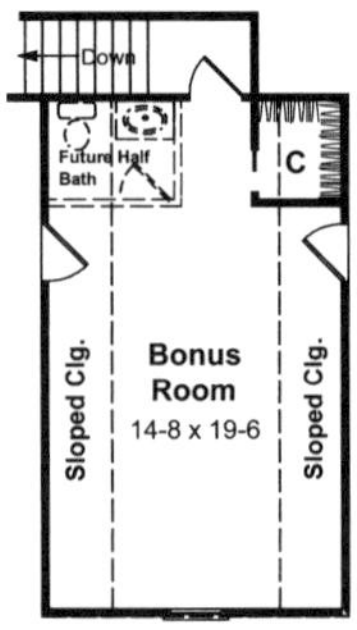

Future Half Bath
C
Sloped Clg.
Bonus Room
14-8 x 19-6
Sloped Clg.

Optional
Second Floor

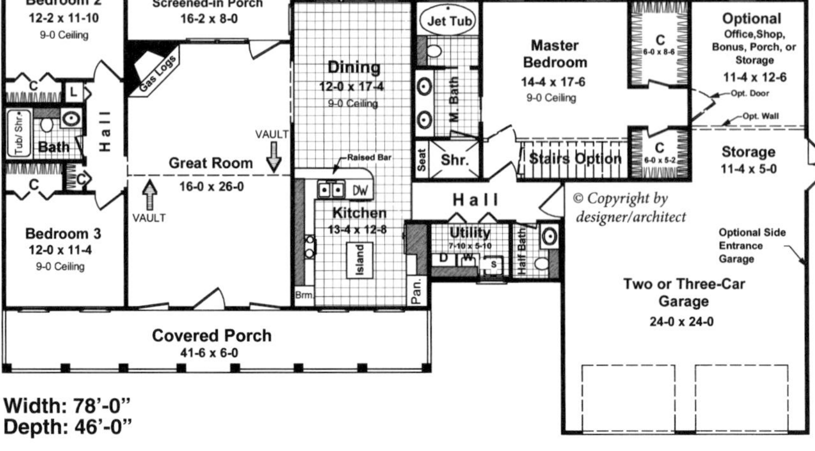

Width: 78'-0"
Depth: 46'-0"

First Floor
1,799 sq. ft.

• To Order See Page 288 or Call Toll-Free 1-877-379-3420

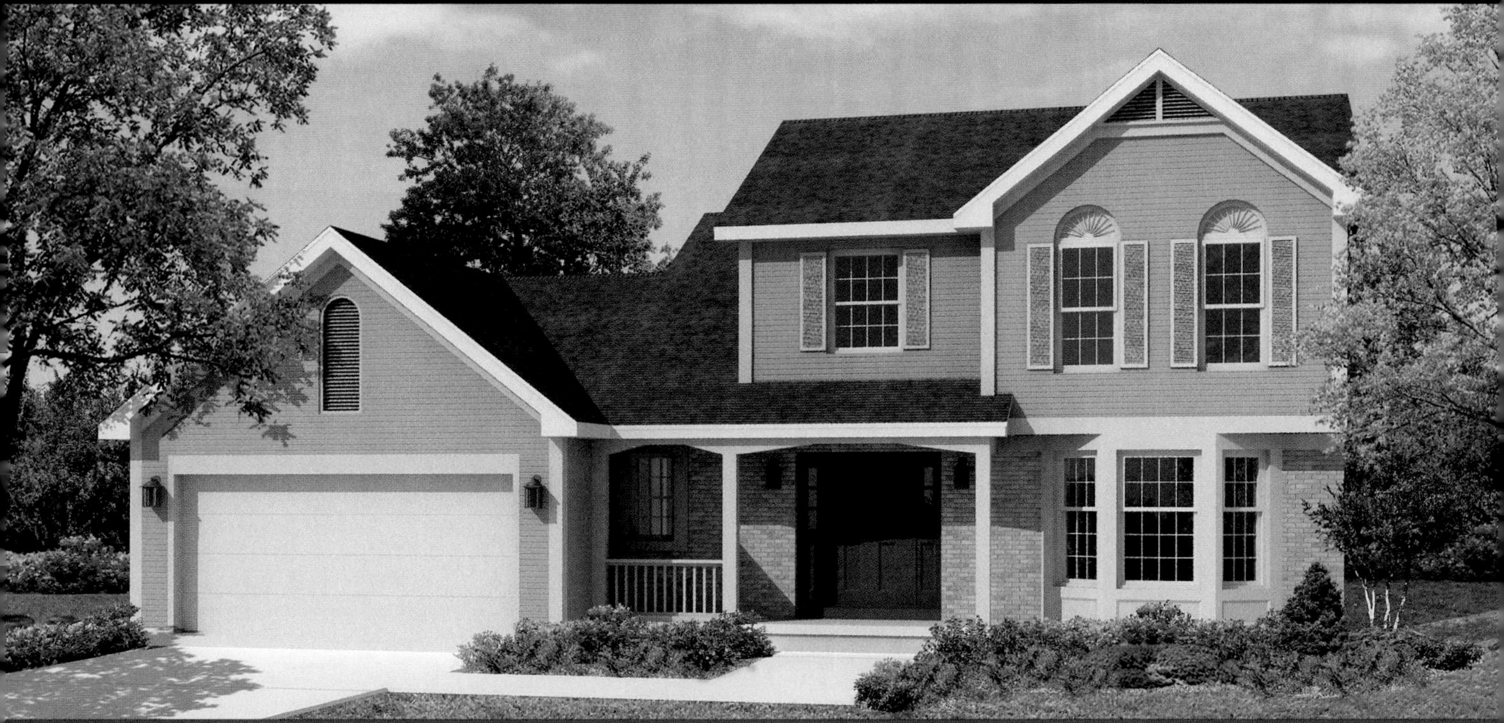

Great Plan For Formal And Informal Entertaining

- 1,813 total square feet of living area
- Bedrooms are located on the second floor for privacy
- Living room with large bay window joins the dining room for expansive formal entertaining
- The family room, dinette and kitchen combine for an impressive living area
- Two-story foyer and L-shaped stairs create a dramatic entry
- Inviting covered porch
- 3 bedrooms, 2 1/2 baths, 2-car garage
- Basement foundation

Second Floor
719 sq. ft.

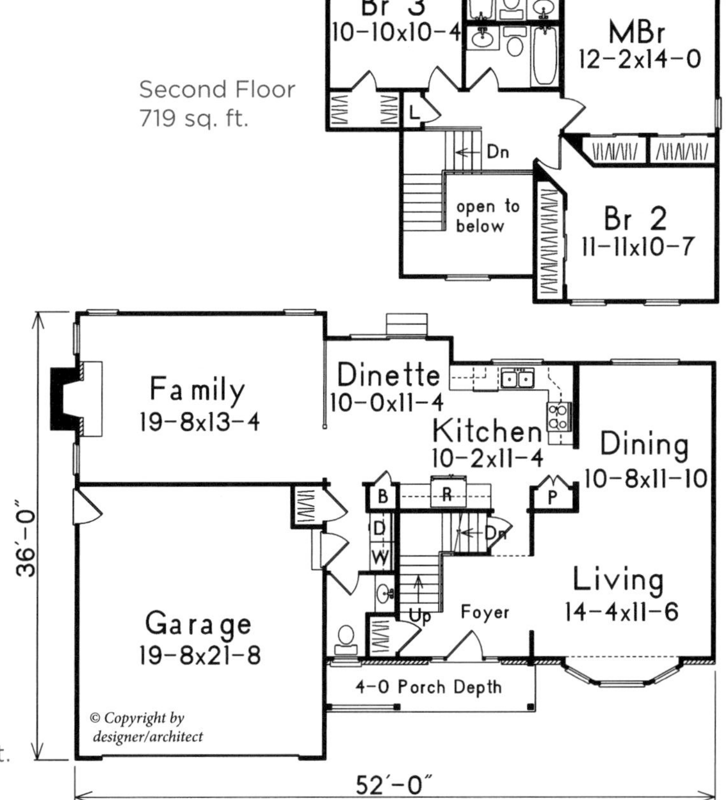

First Floor
1,094 sq. ft.

Plan #541-001D-0024 • Price Code A

Functional Layout For Comfortable Living

- 1,360 total square feet of living area
- Kitchen/dining room features an island workspace and plenty of dining area
- Master bedroom has a large walk-in closet and private bath
- Laundry room is adjacent to the kitchen for easy access
- Convenient workshop in garage
- Large closets in secondary bedrooms maintain organization
- Plan also available with energy efficient R-Control® SIPs (Structural Insulated Panels), please call 1-877-379-3420 for more information
- 3 bedrooms, 2 baths, 2-car side entry garage
- Basement foundation, drawings also include crawl space and slab foundations

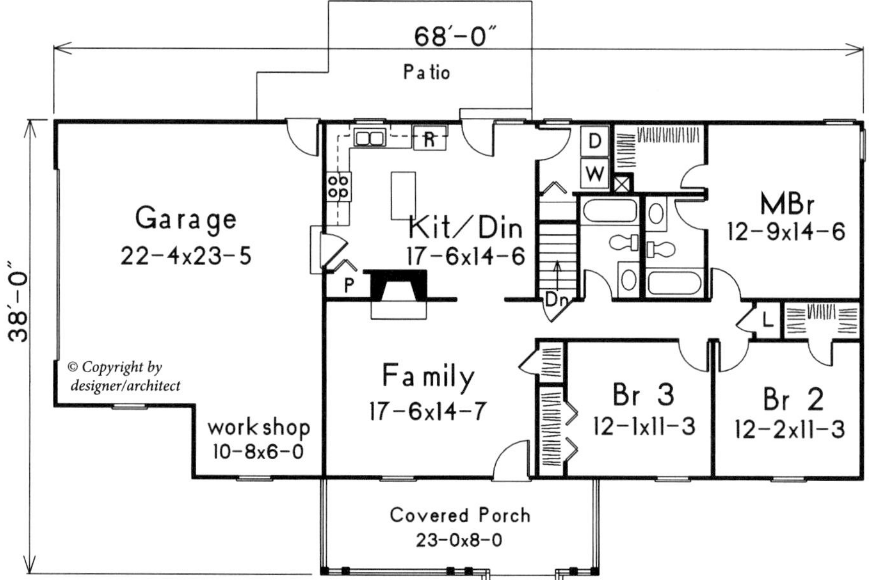

• To Order See Page 288 or Call Toll-Free 1-877-379-3420

Plan #541-007D-0049 • Price Code C

Classic Exterior Employs Innovative Planning

- 1,791 total square feet of living area
- Vaulted great room and octagon-shaped dining area enjoy a spectacular view of the covered patio
- Kitchen features a pass-through to the dining area, center island, large walk-in pantry and breakfast area with large bay window
- The master bedroom enjoys a vaulted ceiling and a sitting area
- The garage includes extra storage space
- 2″ x 6″ exterior walls available, please order plan #541-007E-0049
- Plan also available with energy efficient R-Control® SIPs (Structural Insulated Panels), please call 1-877-379-3420 for more information
- 4 bedrooms, 2 baths, 2-car garage
- Basement foundation, drawings also include crawl space and slab foundations

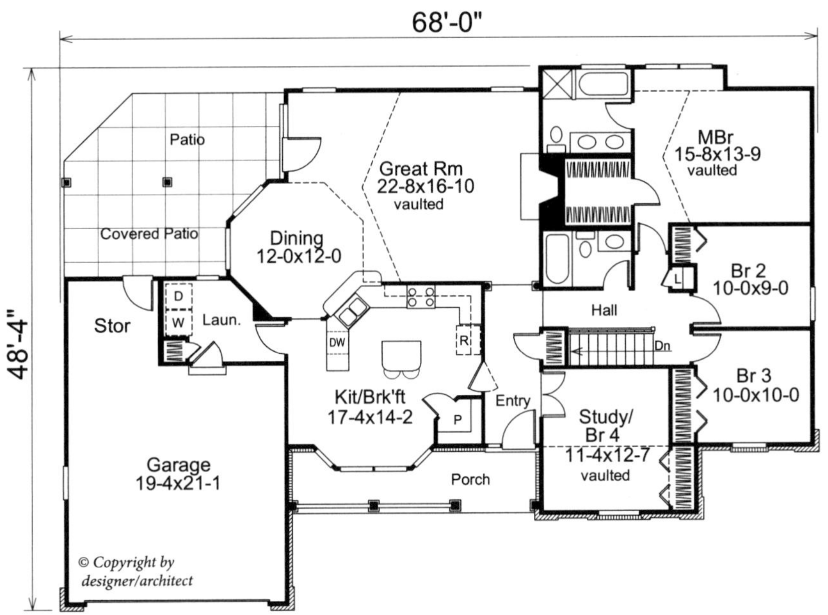

Plan #541-065L-0022 • Price Code B

Spacious Foyer Welcomes Guests

- 1,593 total square feet of living area
- This home is designed with an insulated foundation system featuring pre-mounted insulation on concrete walls providing a drier, warmer and smarter structure
- The rear porch is a pleasant surprise and perfect for enjoying the outdoors
- Great room is filled with extras such as a corner fireplace, sloping ceiling and view to the outdoors
- A large island with seating separates the kitchen from the dining area
- 3 bedrooms, 2 baths, 2-car garage
- Basement foundation

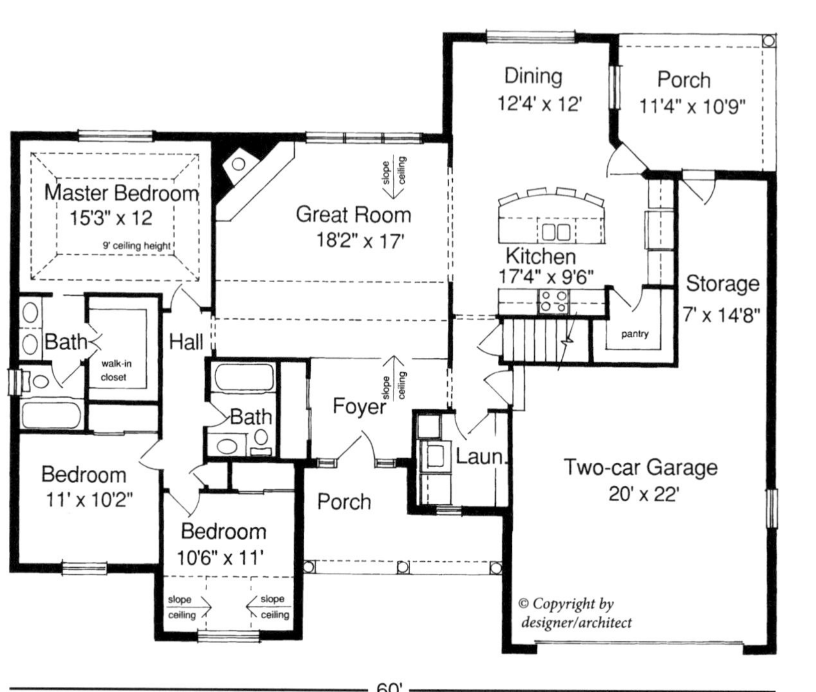

• To Order See Page 288 or Call Toll-Free 1-877-379-3420

Plan #541-048D-0011 • Price Code B

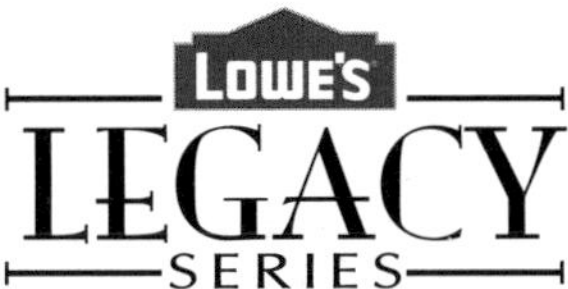

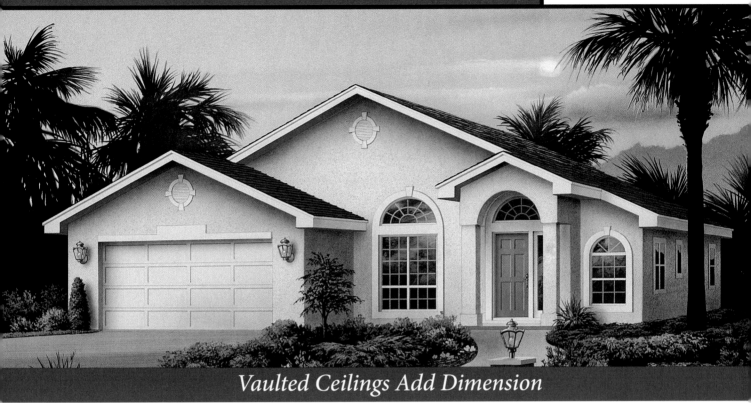

Vaulted Ceilings Add Dimension

- 1,550 total square feet of living area
- Alcove in the family room can be used as a cozy corner fireplace or as a media center
- Master bedroom features a large walk-in closet, skylight and separate tub and shower
- Convenient laundry closet
- Kitchen with pantry and breakfast bar connects to the family room
- Family room and master bedroom access the covered patio
- 3 bedrooms, 2 baths, 2-car garage
- Slab foundation

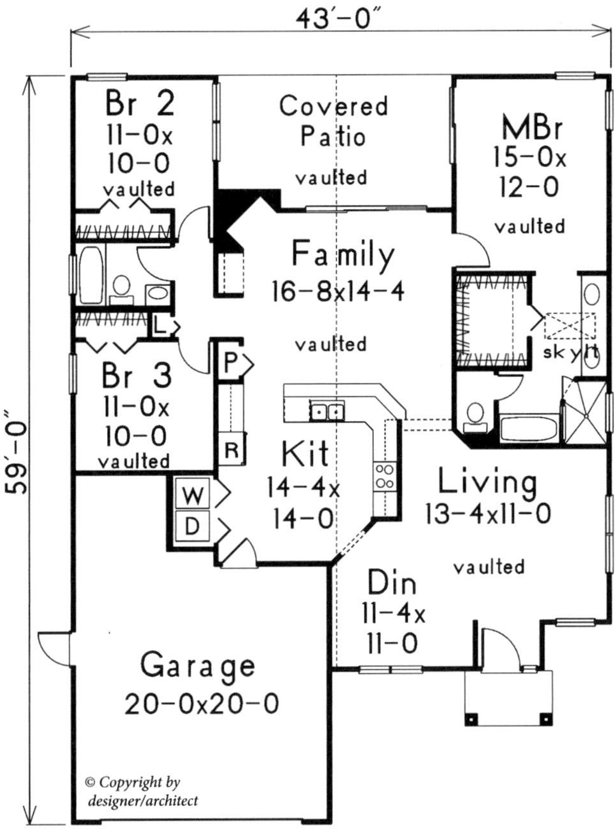

Plan #541-022D-0002 • Price Code A

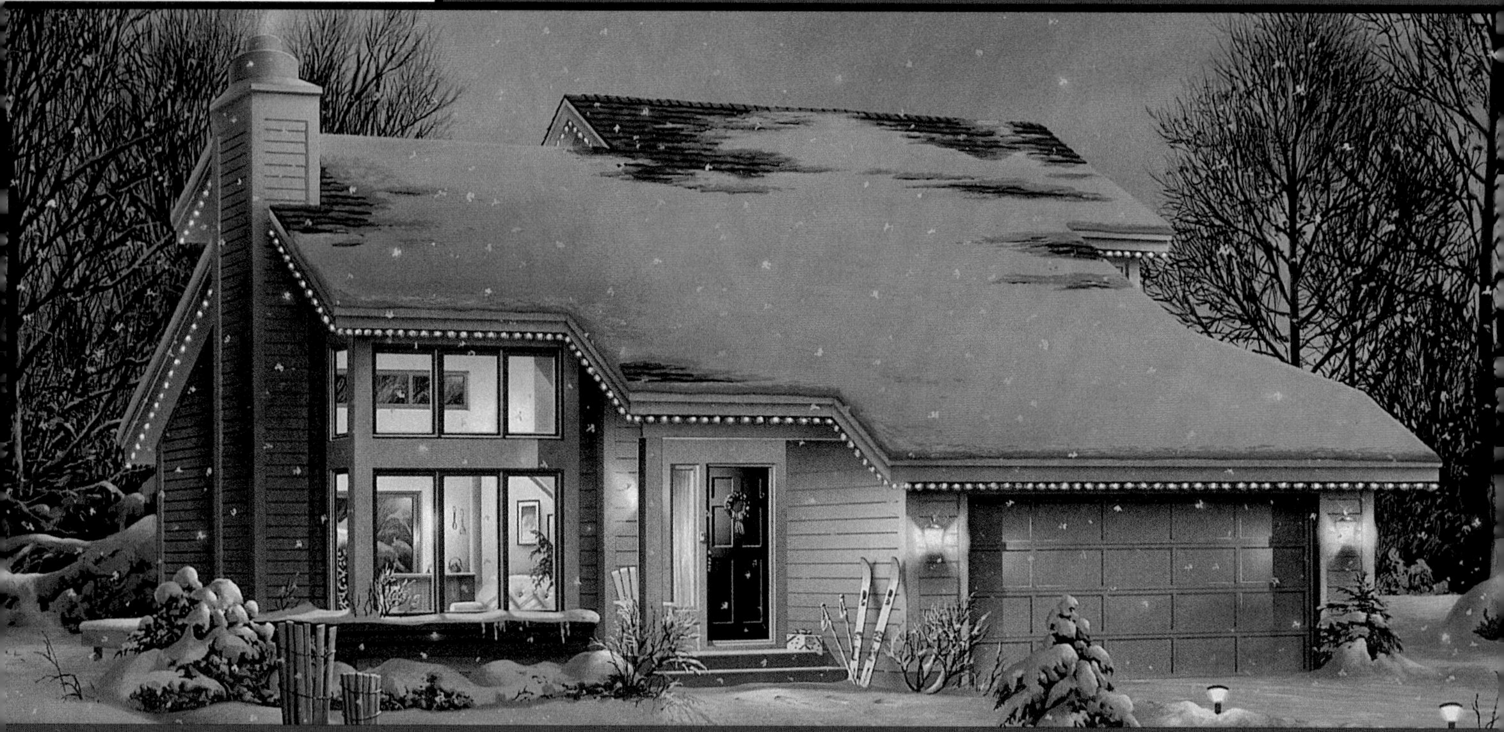

Floor-To-Ceiling Window Expands Compact Two-Story

- 1,246 total square feet of living area
- Corner living room window adds openness and light
- Out-of-the-way kitchen with dining area accesses the outdoors
- Private first floor master bedroom has interesting corner windows
- Large walk-in closet is located in bedroom #3
- Easily built perimeter allows economical construction
- 3 bedrooms, 2 baths, 2-car garage
- Basement foundation

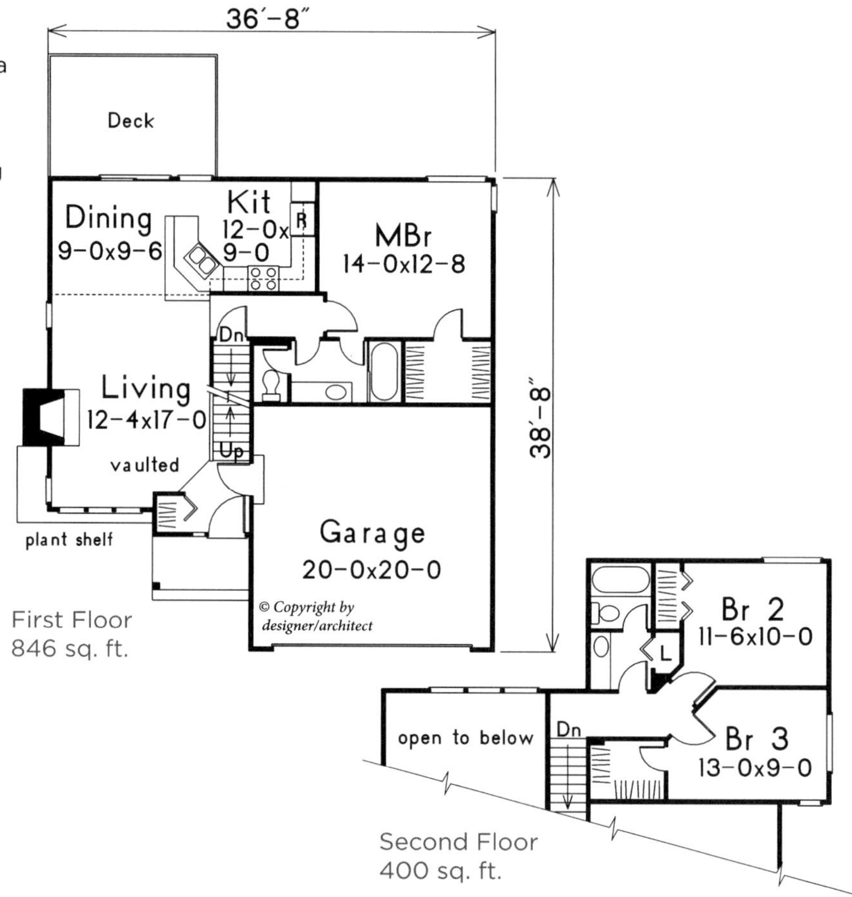

• To Order See Page 288 or Call Toll-Free 1-877-379-3420

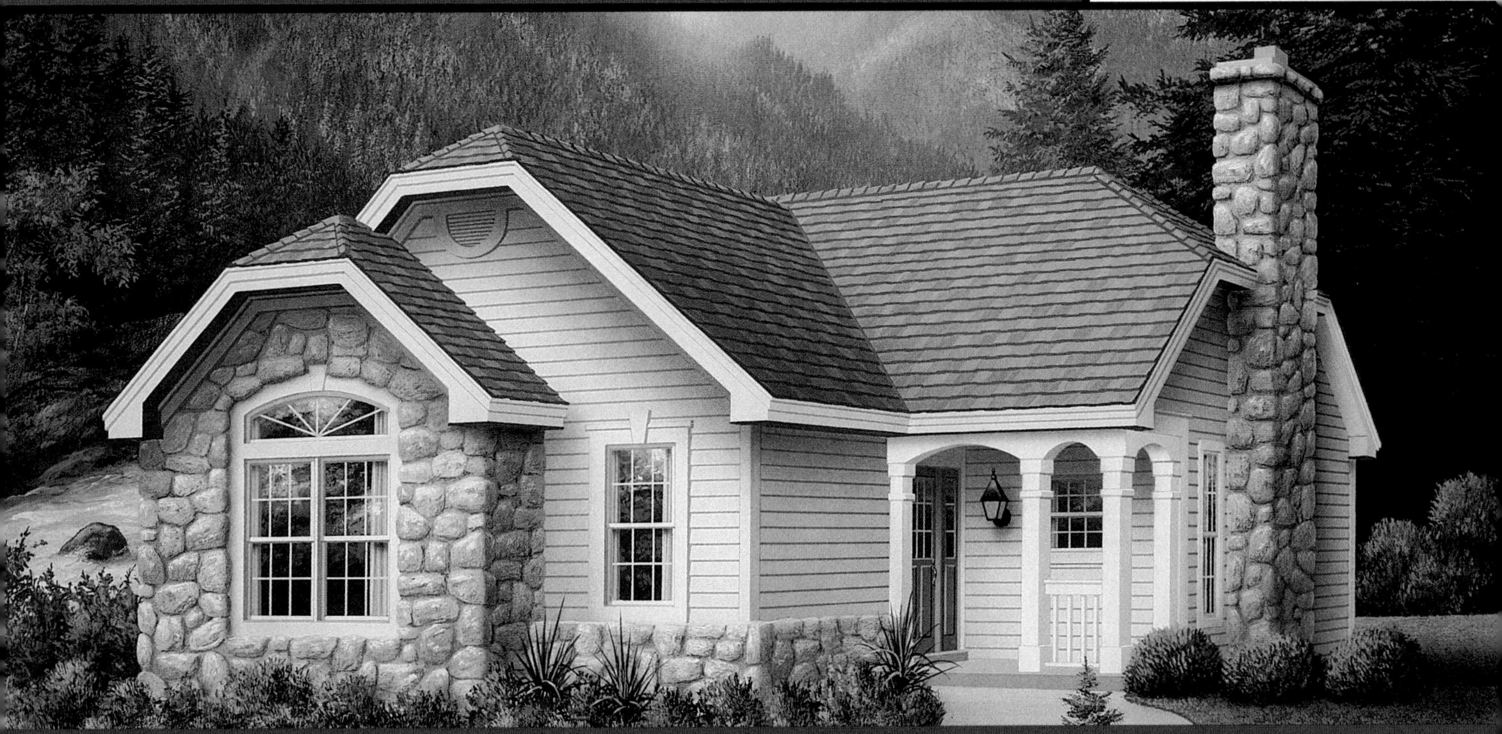

Atrium Living For Views On A Narrow Lot

- 1,547 total square feet of living area
- Dutch gables and stone accents provide an enchanting appearance
- The spacious living room offers a masonry fireplace, atrium with window wall and is open to a dining area with bay window
- Kitchen has a breakfast counter, lots of cabinet space and glass sliding doors to a balcony
- 2 bedrooms, 2 baths, 1-car drive under rear entry garage
- Walk-out basement foundation

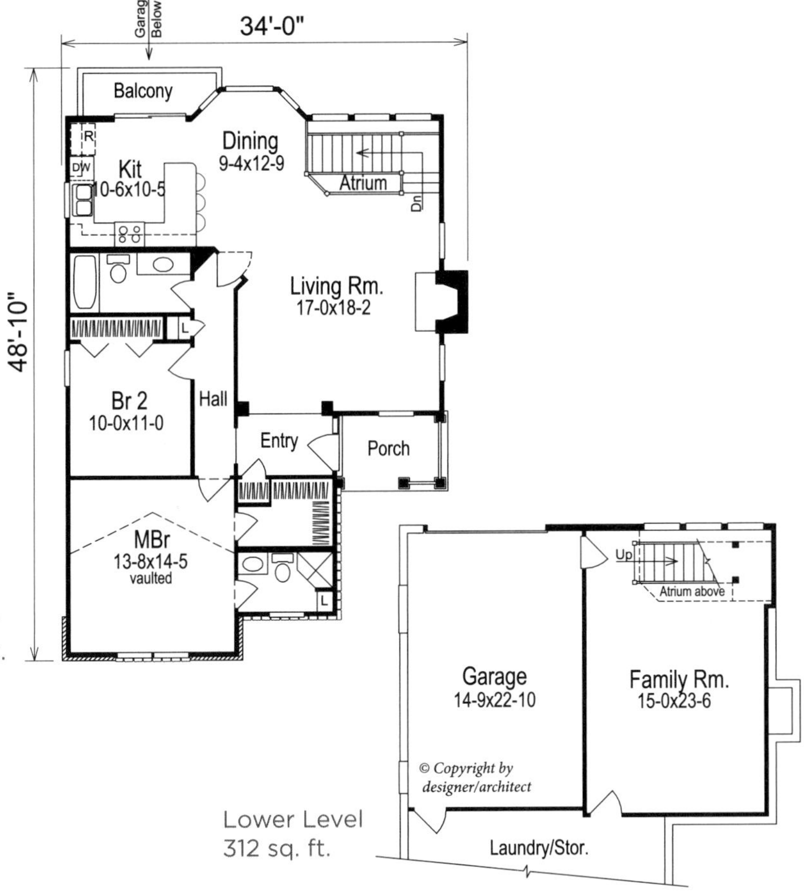

First Floor
1,235 sq. ft.

Lower Level
312 sq. ft.

Plan #541-008D-0078 • Price Code C

Wonderful Victorian Styling

- 1,971 total square feet of living area
- Great room, kitchen and breakfast area unite to provide a central living space
- Unique parlor offers a place for conversation off the dining area
- Deluxe master bedroom has a walk-in closet and sunny master bath
- 3 bedrooms, 2 1/2 baths, optional 2-car garage
- Basement foundation

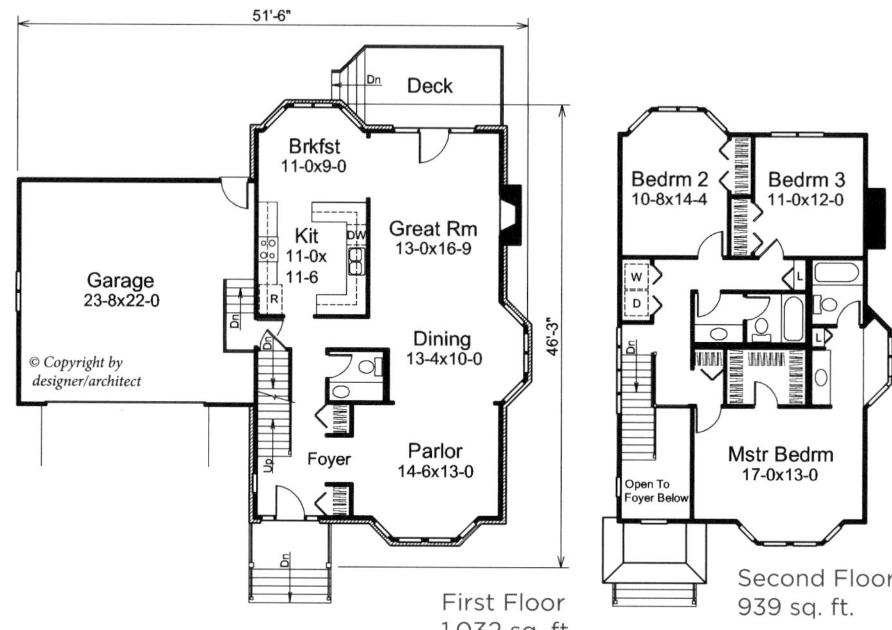

First Floor
1,032 sq. ft.

Second Floor
939 sq. ft.

• To Order See Page 288 or Call Toll-Free 1-877-379-3420

Plan #541-057D-0036 • Price Code AAA

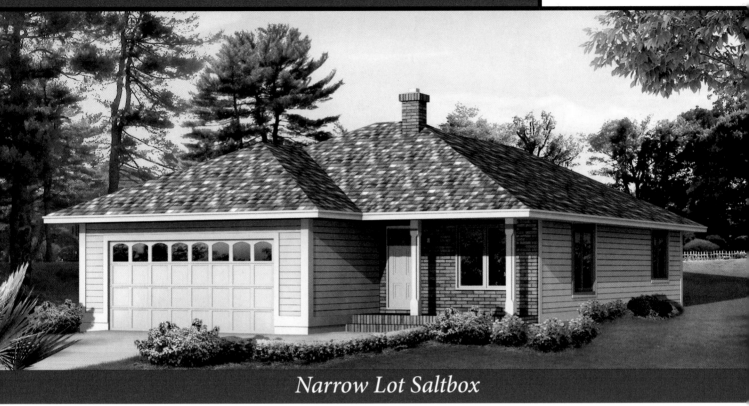

Narrow Lot Saltbox

- 1,042 total square feet of living area
- Attractive covered porch graces entryway
- The kitchen/dining area serves as a great family oriented space
- Generous closet space throughout the home
- 2 bedrooms, 1 bath, 2-car garage
- Basement foundation

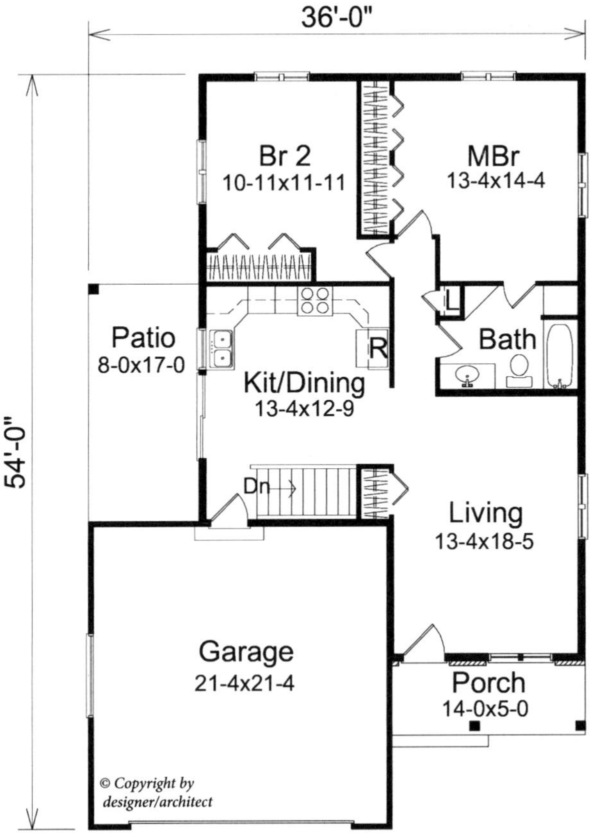

Plan #541-007D-0240 • Price Code C

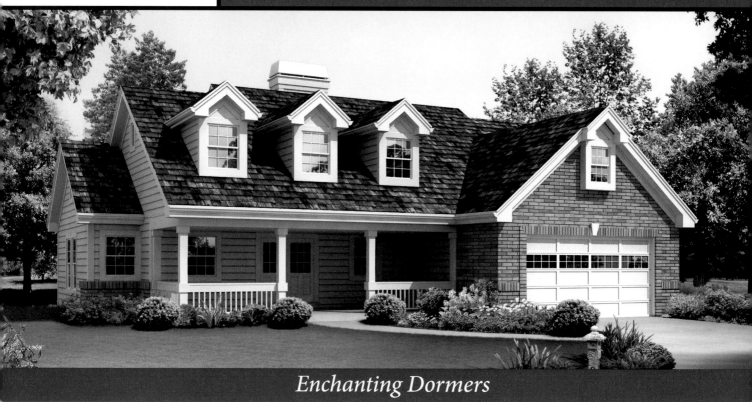

Enchanting Dormers

- 1,663 total square feet of living area
- A large country porch with decorative railing welcomes you into the spacious entrance foyer through double doors
- The great room of grand scale offers wonderful views through a 30' wide window wall, floor-to-ceiling brick fireplace and a vaulted ceiling
- A snack bar, built-in pantry and vaulted ceiling are a few features of the efficient U-shaped kitchen
- The master bedroom has a vaulted ceiling, showcase windows, walk-in closet and roomy bath with separate shower
- 3 bedrooms, 2 baths, 2-car garage
- Basement foundation, drawings also include crawl space and slab foundations

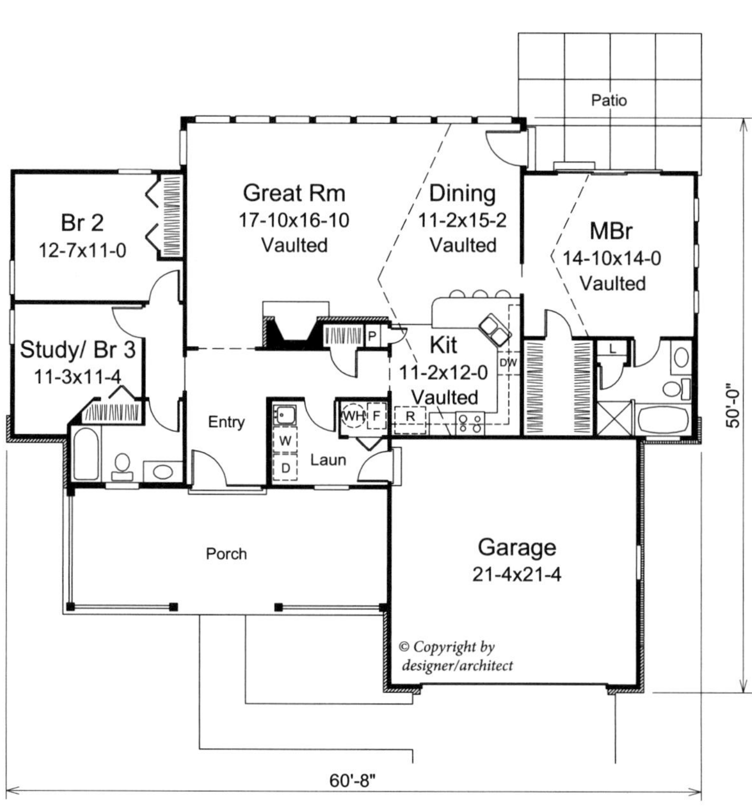

• To Order See Page 288 or Call Toll-Free 1-877-379-3420

Plan #541-021D-0015 • Price Code C

Stucco Finish And Authentic Southern Home Styling

- 1,700 total square feet of living area
- Energy efficient home with 2" x 6" exterior walls
- Fully appointed kitchen features a center island with eating bar and wine rack
- Laundry chute from the second floor bath to the utility room is a handy feature
- Master bath includes a raised marble tub and a sloped ceiling
- 3 bedrooms, 2 1/2 baths, 2-car detached carport
- Crawl space foundation, drawings also include basement and slab foundations

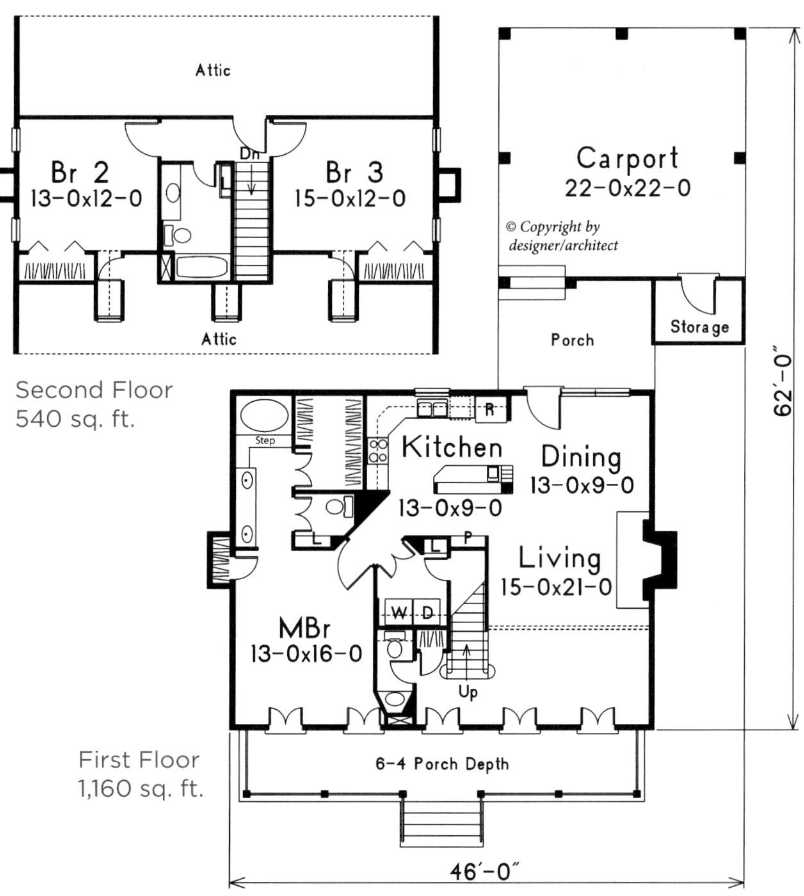

Second Floor
540 sq. ft.

First Floor
1,160 sq. ft.

Plan #541-121D-0005 • Price Code A

Cozy Corner Fireplace In Great Room

- 1,562 total square feet of living area
- The formal dining room is graced with an open feeling thanks to the beautiful vaulted ceiling and decorative corner columns
- A wrap-around breakfast bar has enough seating for five people and overlooks the large and spacious great room
- All the bedrooms are located near each other for convenient family living
- 3 bedrooms, 2 baths, 2-car garage
- Basement foundation

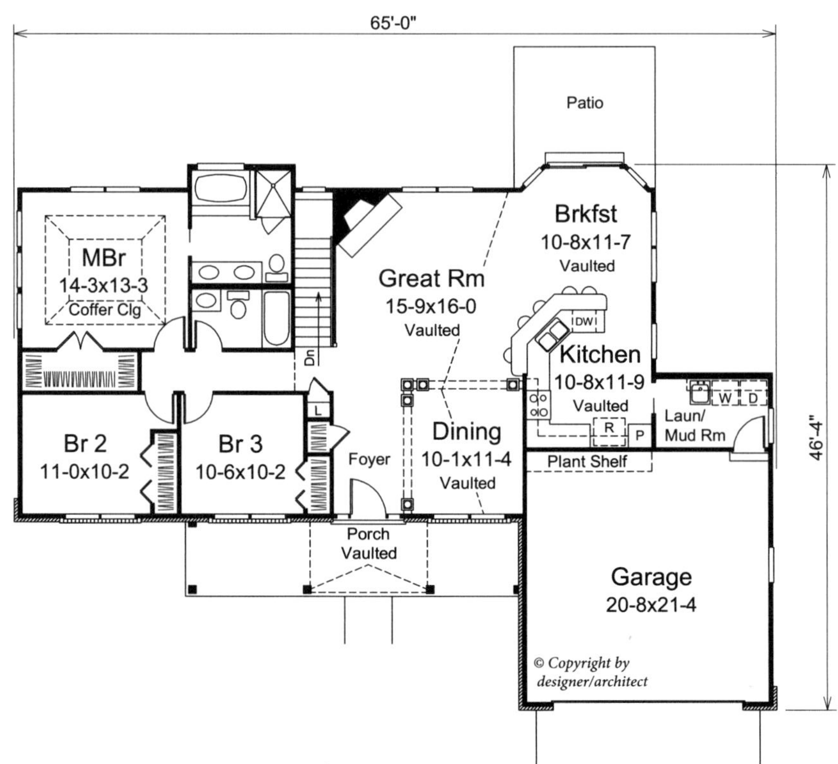

• To Order See Page 288 or Call Toll-Free 1-877-379-3420

Plan #541-007D-0135 • Price Code AAA

Two Bedroom Cottage With Garage And Shop

- 801 total square feet of living area
- A wrap-around porch, roof dormer and fancy stonework all contribute to a delightful and charming exterior
- The living room enjoys a separate entry, a stone fireplace, vaulted ceiling and lots of windows
- The well-equipped kitchen has a snack bar and dining area with bay which offers access to the rear patio
- An oversized two-car garage features a large vaulted room ideal for a shop, studio, hobby room or office with built-in cabinets and access to the porch
- 2 bedrooms, 1 bath, 2-car side entry garage
- Slab foundation

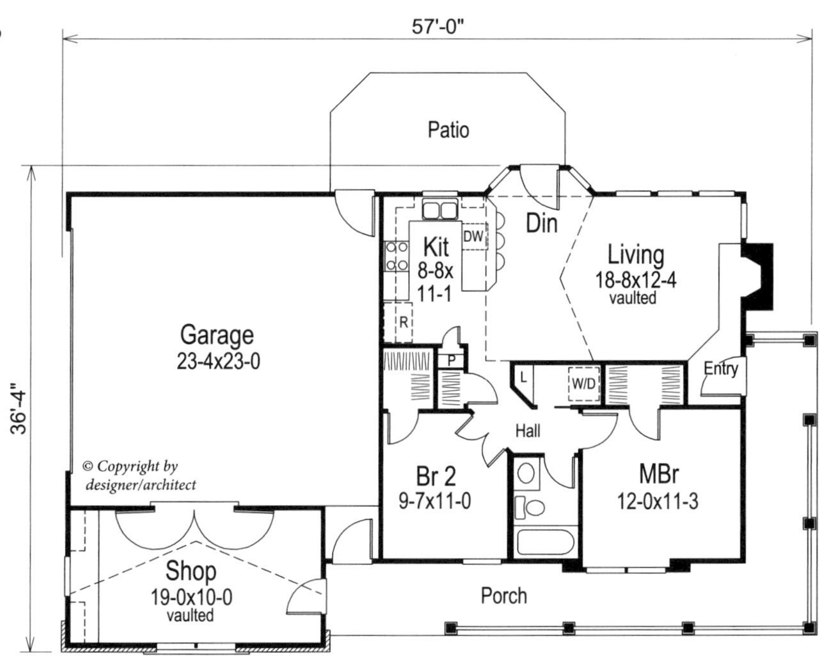

Plan #541-013L-0156 • Price Code B

Angled Suite Adds Interest

- 1,800 total square feet of living area
- Many lovely window accents are found throughout the home providing a warm glow and plenty of natural light
- Highly functional ceiling fans are located in the screen porch, master suite and the family room
- Bedrooms #2 and #3 each contain ample closet space and immediate access to a full bath
- The bonus room above the garage has an additional 503 square feet of living space
- 3 bedrooms, 3 baths, 3-car side entry garage
- Crawl space foundation

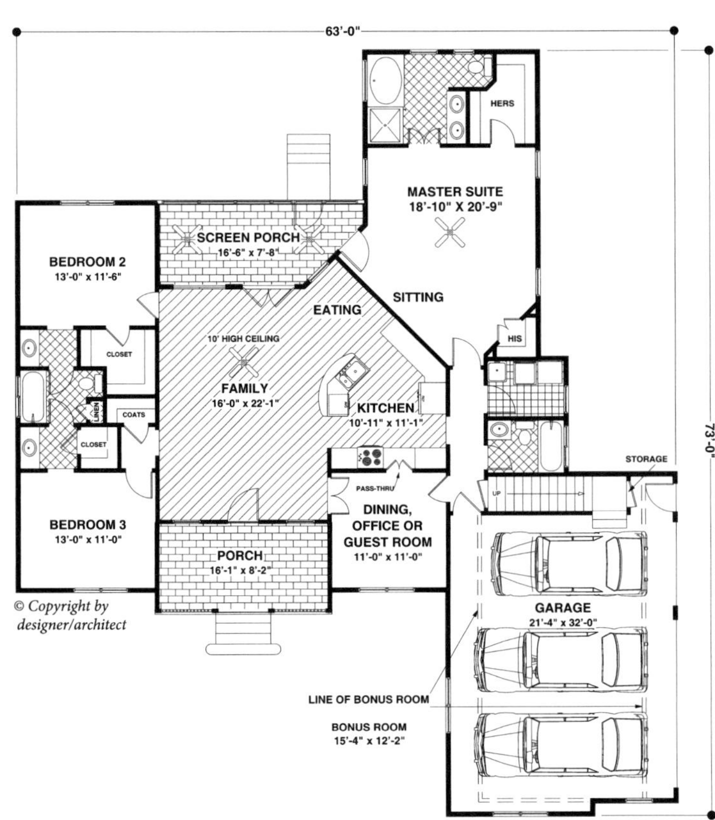

• To Order See Page 288 or Call Toll-Free 1-877-379-3420

Plan #541-055L-0526 • Price Code D

Classic Tudor Features Highlight This Craftsman Home

- 2,146 total square feet of living area
- The extended counter in the kitchen features enough casual dining space for three people to comfortably dine
- The stunning great room has a center fireplace and direct access to the grilling porch
- The private master bath includes both a large corner whirlpool tub and a separate shower
- 3 bedrooms, 2 1/2 baths, 2-car rear entry garage
- Crawl space or slab foundation, please specify when ordering

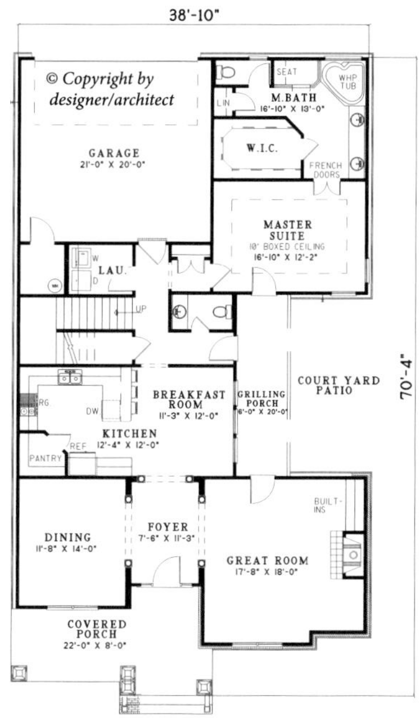

First Floor
1,654 sq. ft.

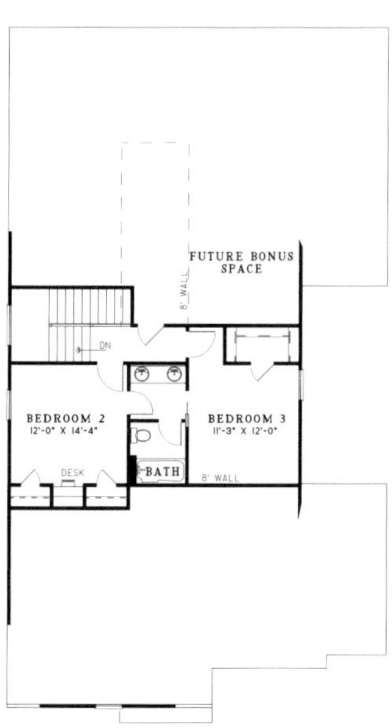

Second Floor
492 sq. ft.

Plan #541-010D-0001 • Price Code B

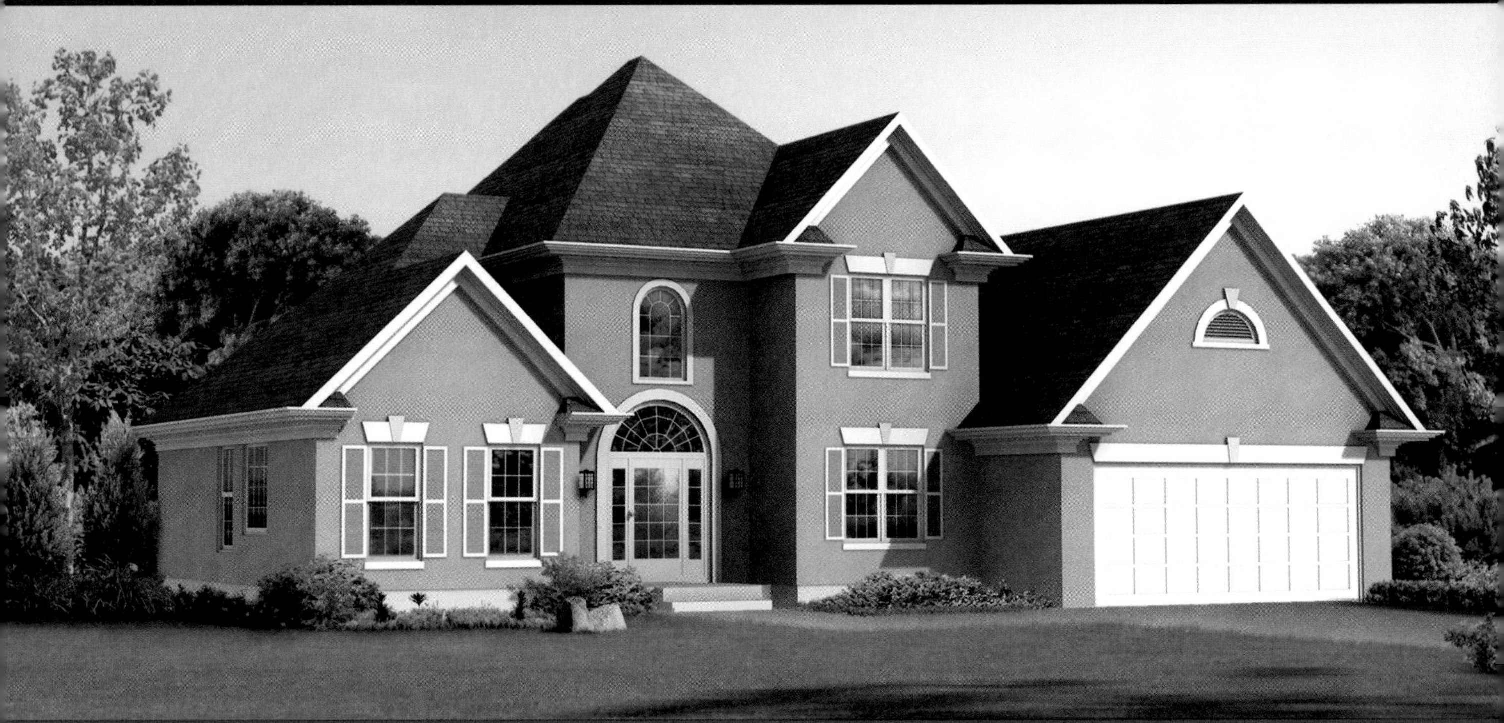

Circle-Top Windows Adorn The Foyer

- 1,516 total square feet of living area
- On the second floor the stairway looks out over the living room
- The master bedroom enjoys first floor privacy and a luxurious bath
- Kitchen has easy access to the deck, laundry closet and garage
- 3 bedrooms, 2 1/2 baths, 2-car garage
- Basement foundation

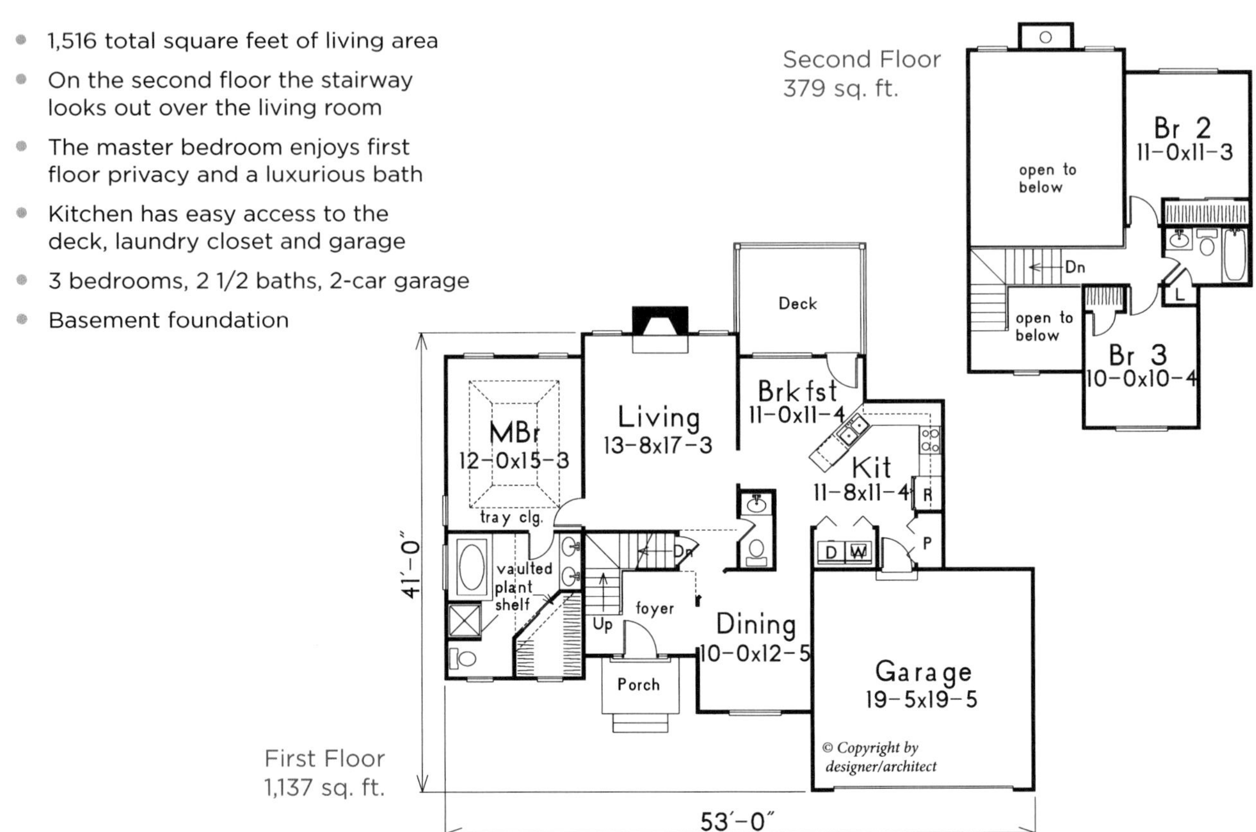

• To Order See Page 288 or Call Toll-Free 1-877-379-3420

Plan #541-121D-0007 • Price Code AA

Spacious Great Room

- 1,308 total square feet of living area
- A lovely bay window and access to the rear patio are some of the features of the vaulted kitchen/dining area
- A tall ceiling and warming fireplace in the great room appeals to every homeowner
- The vaulted master bedroom showcases a large walk-in closet, bay window and private bath
- 3 bedrooms, 2 baths, 2-car detached garage
- Basement foundation

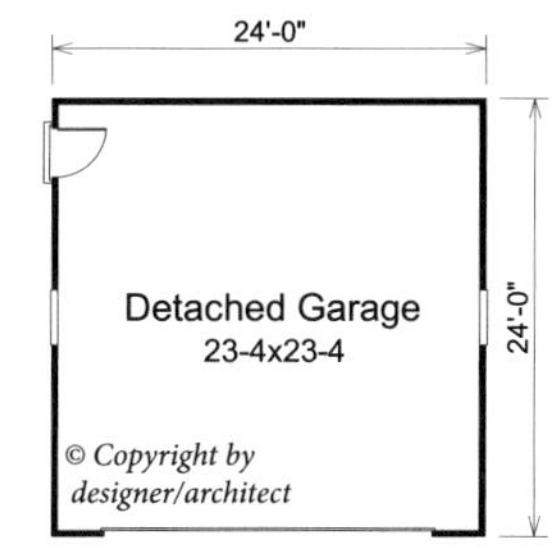

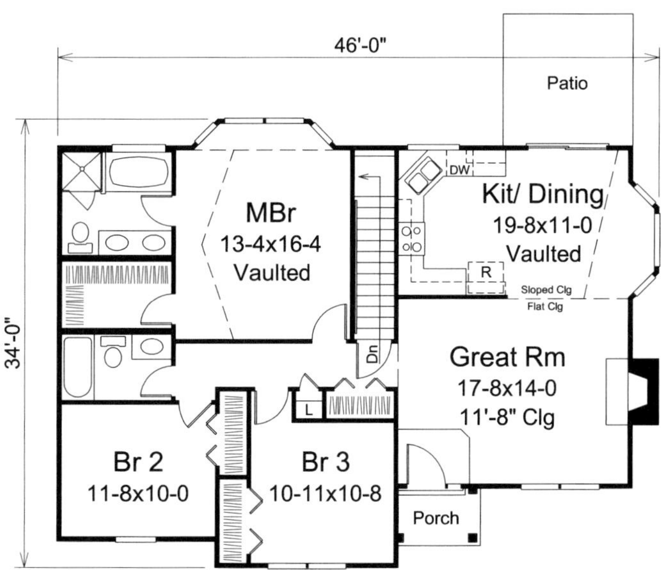

Plan #541-040D-0027 • Price Code C

Country Style With Wrap-Around Porch

- 1,597 total square feet of living area
- Spacious family room includes a fireplace and coat closet
- Open kitchen and dining room provide a breakfast bar and access to the outdoors
- Convenient laundry area is located near the kitchen
- Secluded master bedroom enjoys a walk-in closet and private bath
- 4 bedrooms, 2 1/2 baths, 2-car detached garage
- Basement foundation

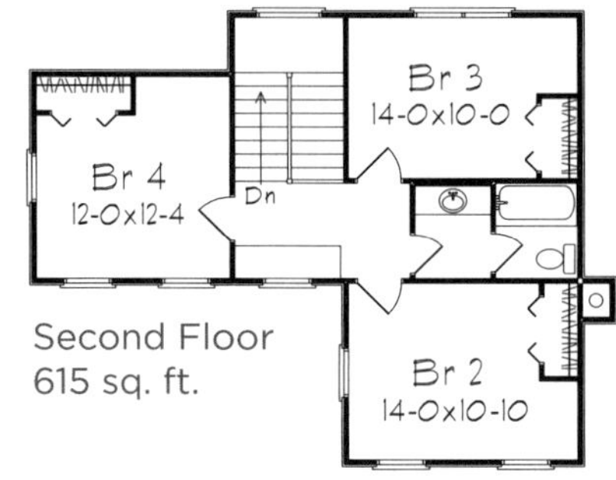

Second Floor
615 sq. ft.

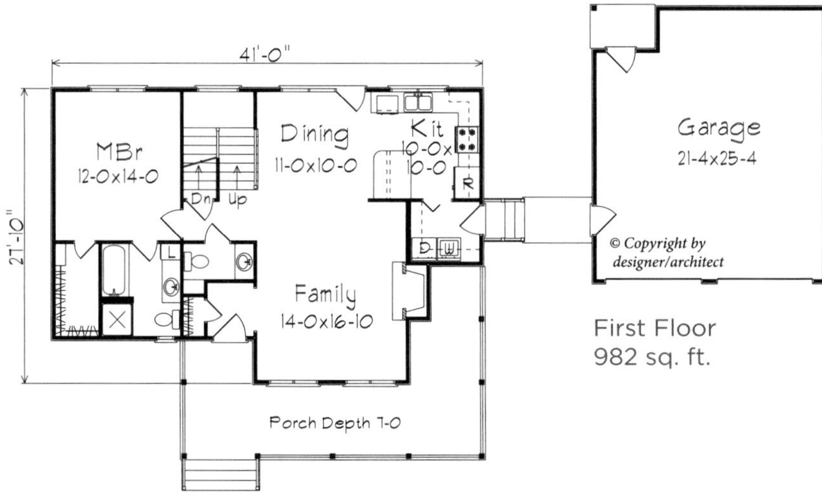

First Floor
982 sq. ft.

• To Order See Page 288 or Call Toll-Free 1-877-379-3420

Plan #541-055L-0530 • Price Code D

Bungalow Home With Stylish Roof Dormers

- 2,237 total square feet of living area
- The stunning open great room has a center fireplace and a corner wet bar with sink and refrigerator
- The private master bath includes a large corner whirlpool tub and a separate shower plus a large walk-in closet for organization
- The peninsula in the kitchen features enough casual dining space for two people to comfortably dine
- 3 bedrooms, 2 1/2 baths, 2-car rear entry garage
- Crawl space or slab foundation, please specify when ordering

First Floor
1,708 sq. ft.

Second Floor
529 sq. ft.

Plan #541-014D-0007 • Price Code A

High-Style Vaulted Ranch

- 1,453 total square feet of living area
- Energy efficient home with 2" x 6" exterior walls
- Decorative vents, window trim, shutters and brick blend to create dramatic curb appeal
- Kitchen opens to the living area and includes a salad sink in the island as well as a pantry and handy laundry room
- Exquisite master bedroom is highlighted by a vaulted ceiling, dressing area with walk-in closet, private bath and spa tub/shower
- 3 bedrooms, 2 baths, 2-car garage
- Basement foundation, drawings also include crawl space foundation

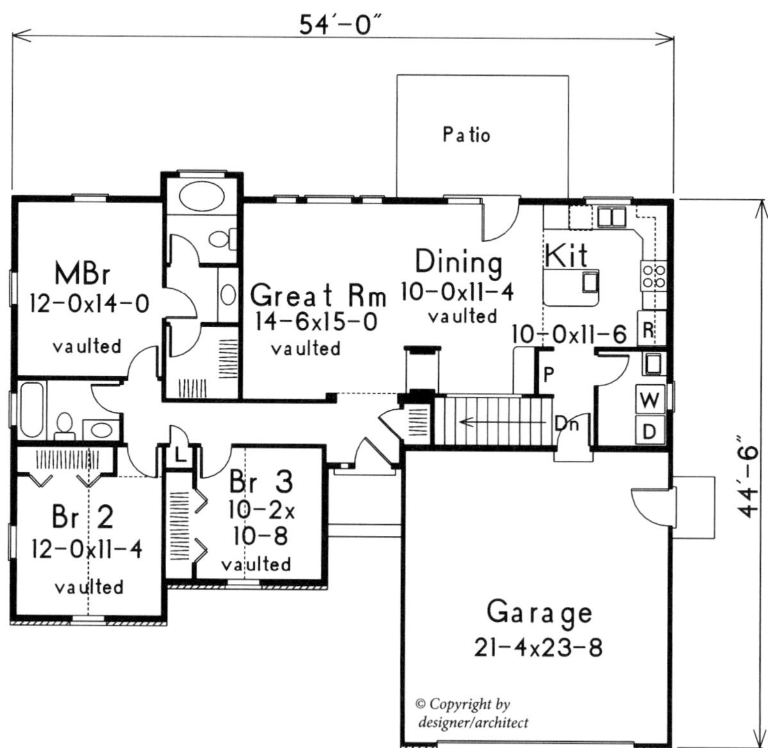

• To Order See Page 288 or Call Toll-Free 1-877-379-3420

Plan #541-010D-0006 • Price Code AA

Brick And Siding Enhance This Traditional Home

- 1,170 total square feet of living area
- Master bedroom enjoys privacy at the rear of this home
- Kitchen has an angled bar that overlooks the great room and breakfast area
- Living areas combine to create a greater sense of spaciousness
- Great room has a cozy fireplace
- 3 bedrooms, 2 baths, 2-car garage
- Slab foundation

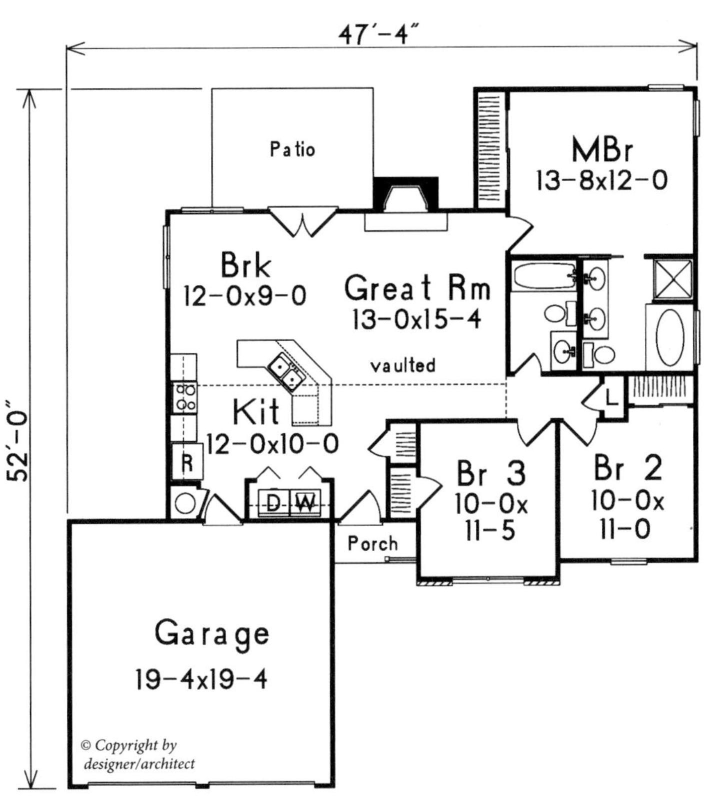

Plan #541-004D-0002 • Price Code C

Well-Designed Ranch With Wrap-Around Porch

- 1,823 total square feet of living area
- Vaulted living room is spacious and easily accesses the dining area
- The master bedroom boasts a tray ceiling, large walk-in closet and a private bath with a corner whirlpool tub
- Cheerful dining area is convenient to the U-shaped kitchen and also enjoys patio access
- Centrally located laundry room connects the garage to the living areas
- 3 bedrooms, 2 baths, 2-car garage
- Basement foundation

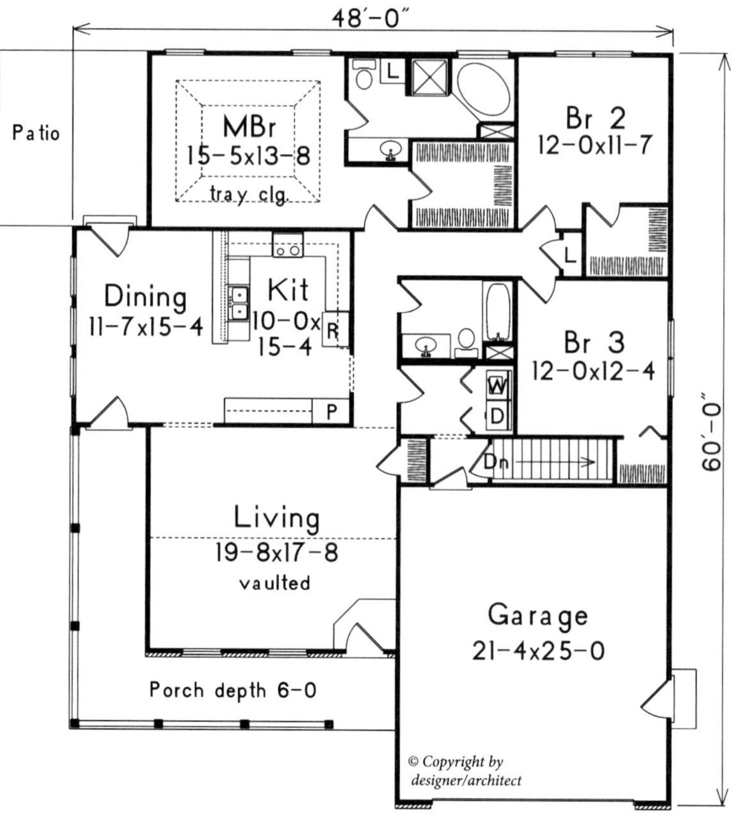

• To Order See Page 288 or Call Toll-Free 1-877-379-3420

Plan #541-013L-0043 • Price Code B

LOWE'S LEGACY SERIES

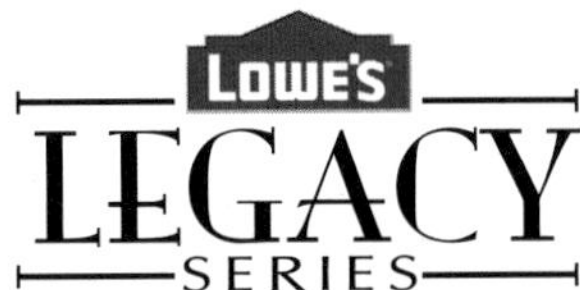

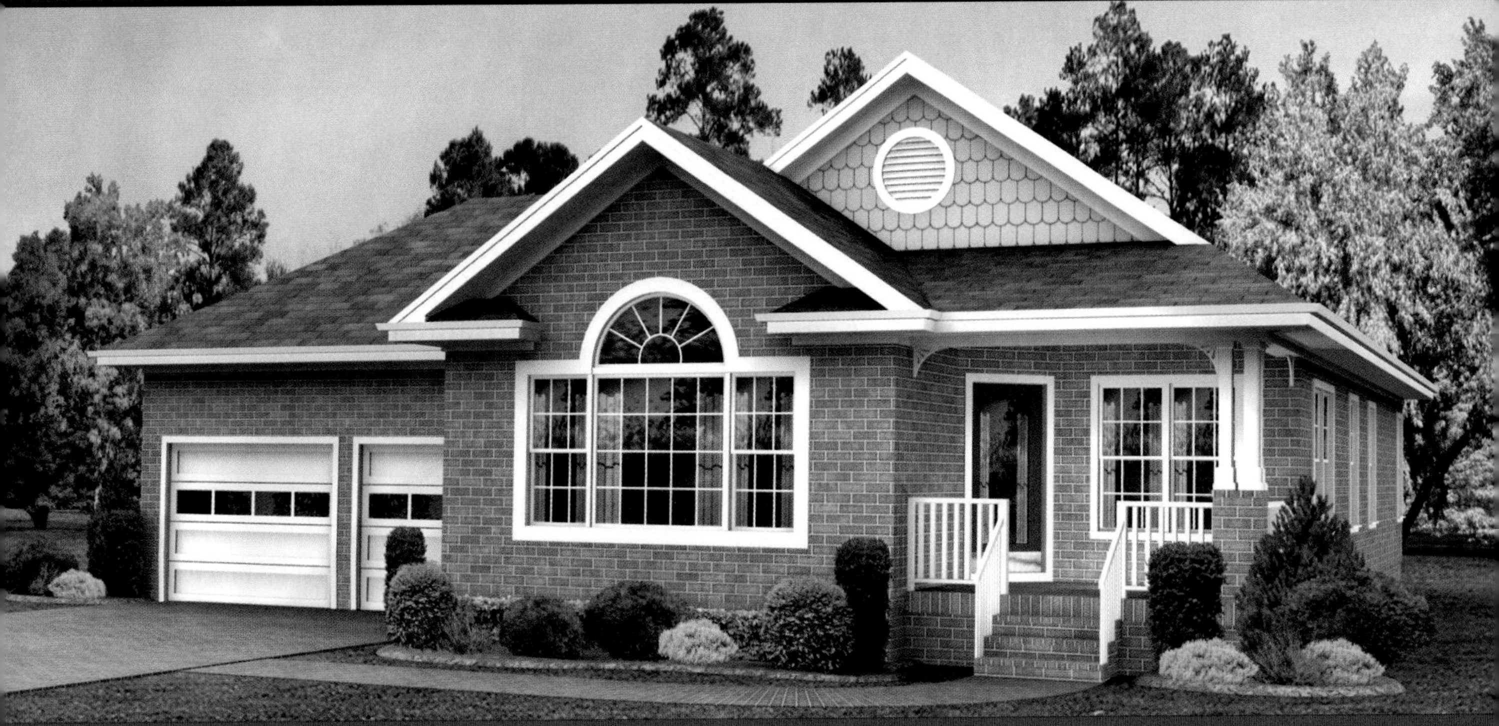

A Lovely Layout For Casual Family Living

- 1,343 total square feet of living area
- Large front window and high ceiling create an open family room
- Kitchen has plenty of counterspace for dining and preparing food
- A screened porch is connected to the master suite for an open air feel
- Laundry room is centrally located between all bedrooms
- 3 bedrooms, 2 baths, 2-car garage
- Basement foundation, drawings also include slab foundation

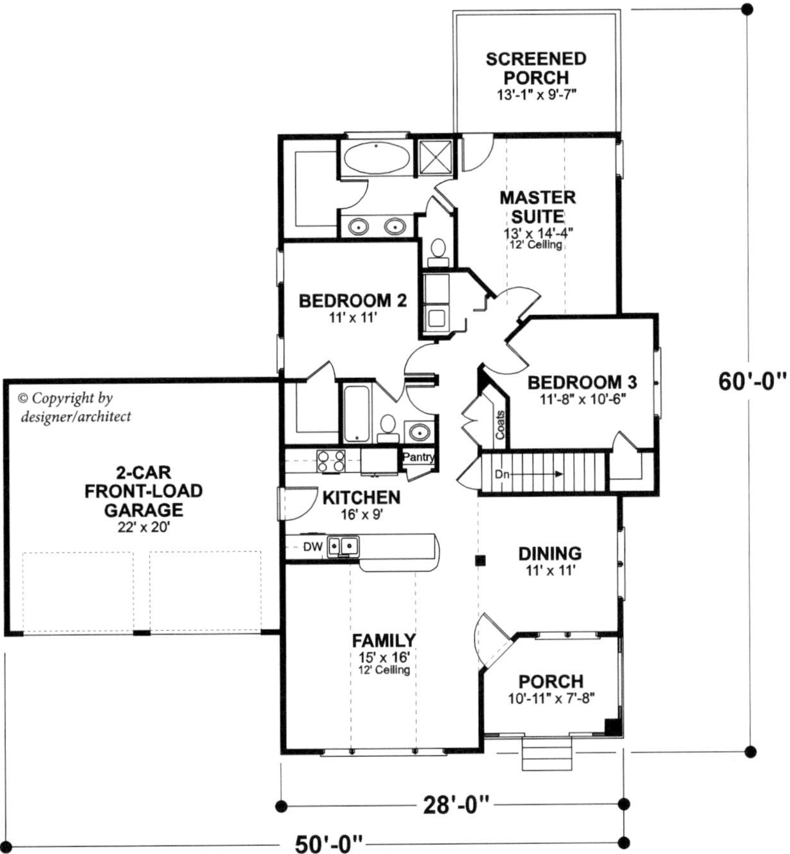

Plan #541-013L-0050 • Price Code D

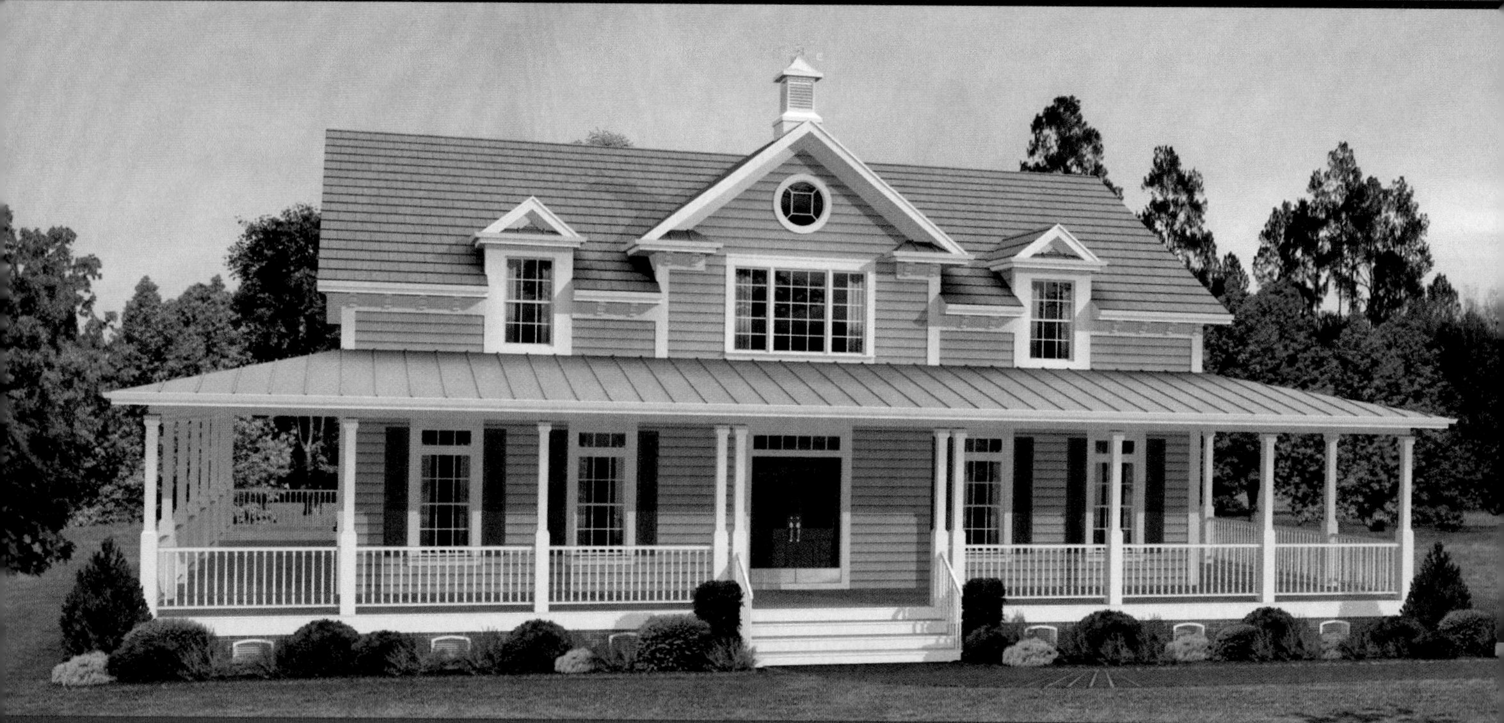

Beautiful Country Porch

- 2,098 total square feet of living area
- Energy efficient home with 2″ x 6″ exterior walls
- Covered porch wraps around the entire house, leading to the deck and screened porch in the back
- Spacious country kitchen has plenty of cabinet space as well as counterspace
- Convenient laundry chute is located near the second floor bathroom
- 3 bedrooms, 2 1/2 baths, 3-car side entry detached garage
- Crawl space foundation, drawings also include basement foundation

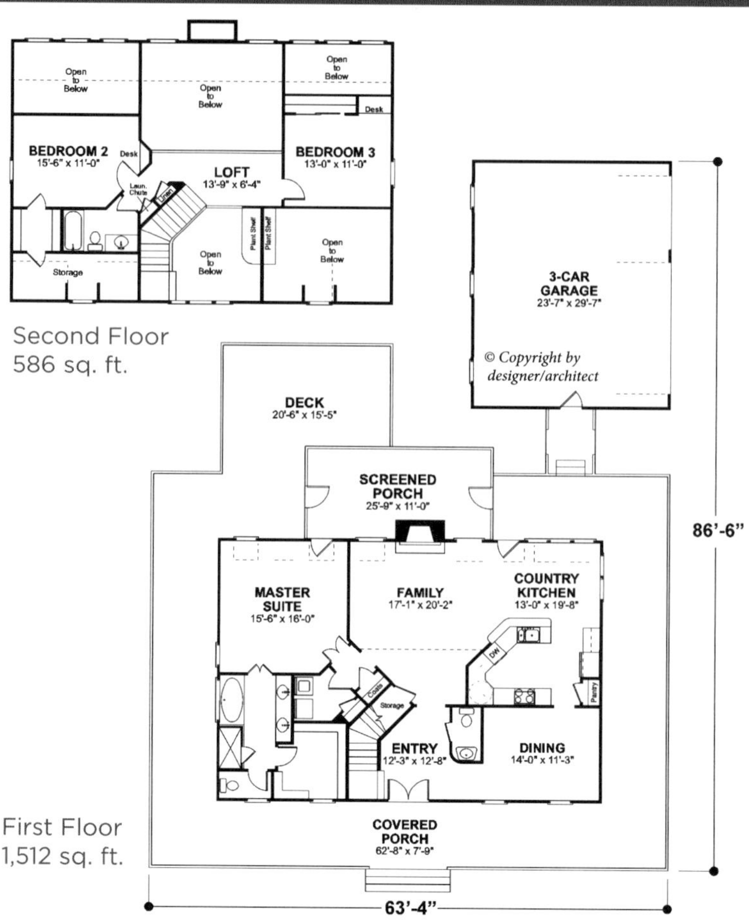

• To Order See Page 288 or Call Toll-Free 1-877-379-3420

Plan #541-007D-0249 • Price Code C

Country Ranch With Room to Grow

- 1,740 total square feet of living area
- Protective covered porch and separate entry with guest closet invite you into the vast open living areas
- The great room offers a vaulted ceiling, a fireplace and is open to a semi-formal dining area
- A laundry room with coat closet, walk-in pantry, island with snack bar and glass sliding doors to rear patio are some of the many features of the vaulted kitchen/breakfast area
- Decorative windows above the bed wall add sunlight to the master bedroom that also enjoys a luxury bath and large walk-in closet
- 3 bedrooms, 2 baths, 2-car garage
- Basement foundation

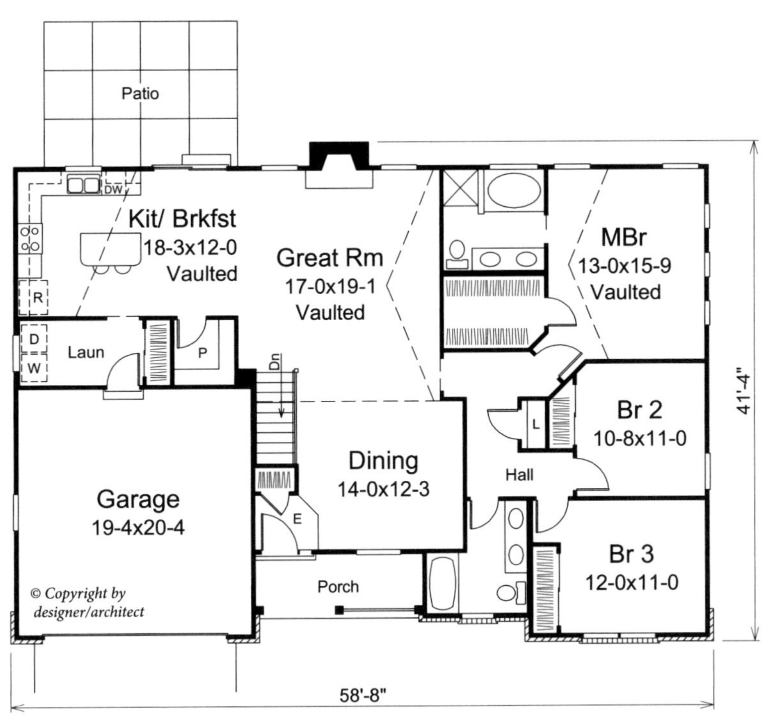

Plan #541-010D-0002 • Price Code B

Stone Entry Accents This Stately Two-Story

- 1,776 total square feet of living area
- Master bedroom has a double-door entry into the formal living room
- Large foyer has plenty of room for greeting guests
- Great room is open to the second floor and features a fireplace flanked by windows
- 3 bedrooms, 2 1/2 baths, 2-car side entry garage
- Walk-out basement foundation

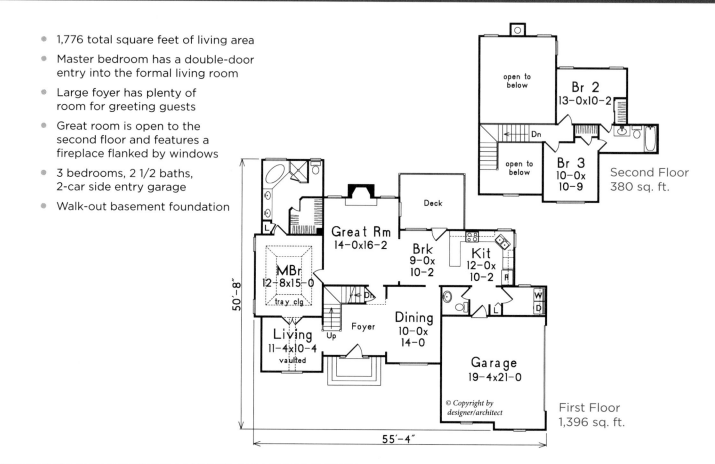

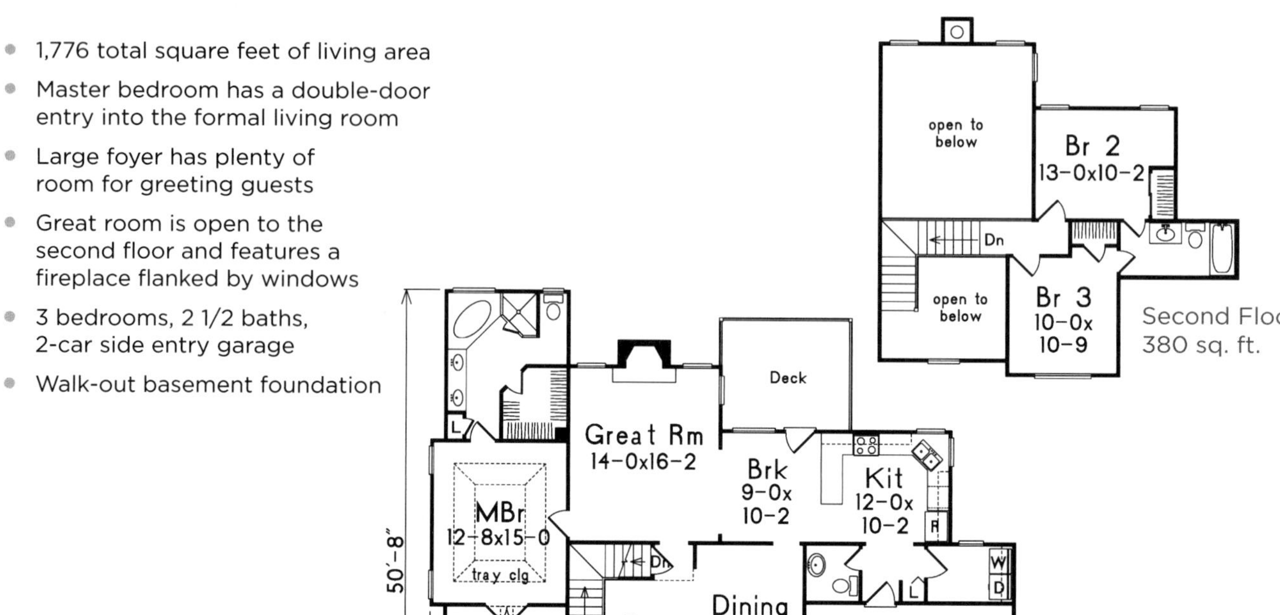

Second Floor
380 sq. ft.

First Floor
1,396 sq. ft.

• To Order See Page 288 or Call Toll-Free 1-877-379-3420

Plan #541-077L-0128 • Price Code E

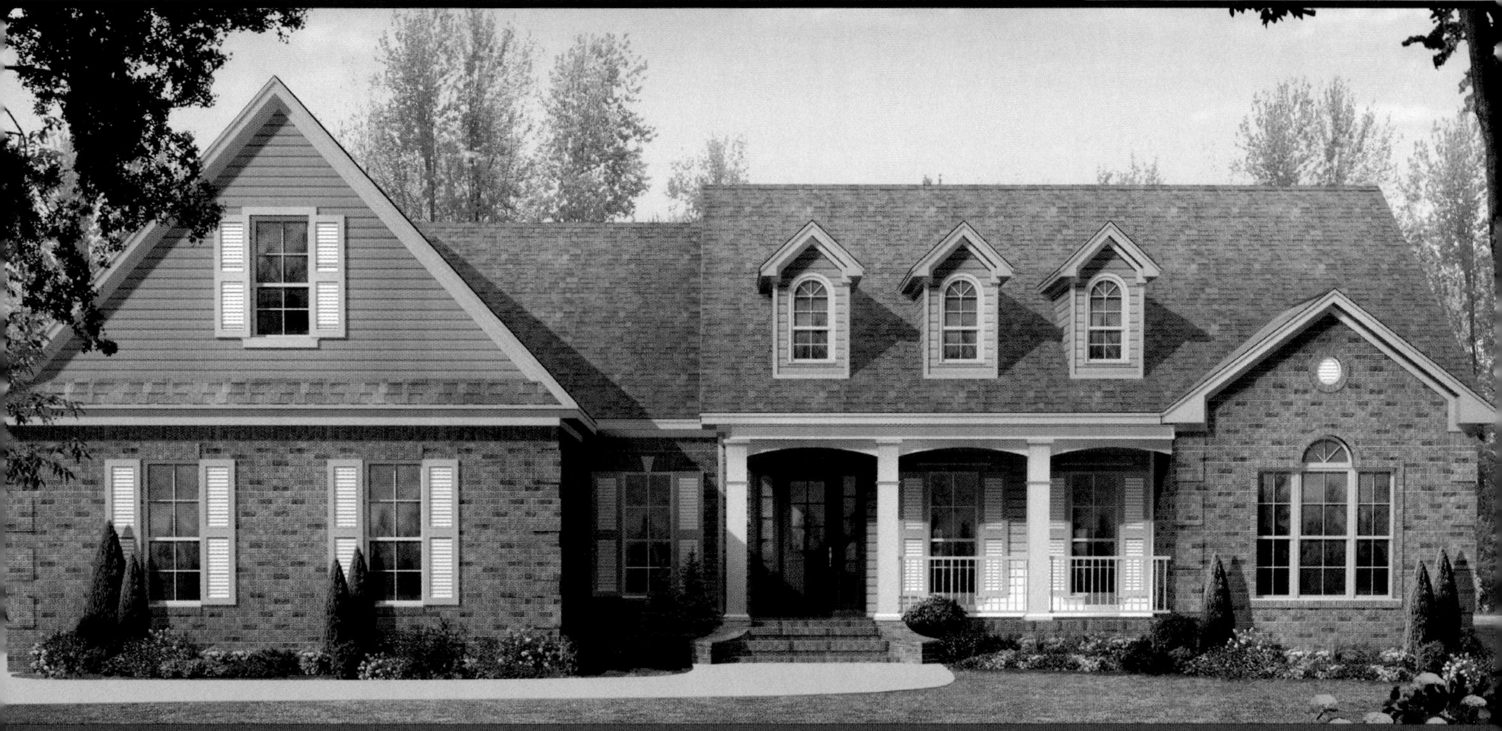

Open Floor Plan For Family Living

- 2,000 total square feet of living area
- A popular outdoor kitchen is incorporated into the covered rear porch perfect for year-round outdoor enjoyment with family and friends
- Enter double doors off the great room to find a media/hobby room with plenty of storage space
- Double walk-in closets in the master bedroom and bath help keep the homeowners organized
- The bonus room above the garage has an additional 359 square feet of living area
- 3 bedrooms, 2 1/2 baths, 2-car side entry garage
- Slab foundation, drawings also include crawl space and basement foundations

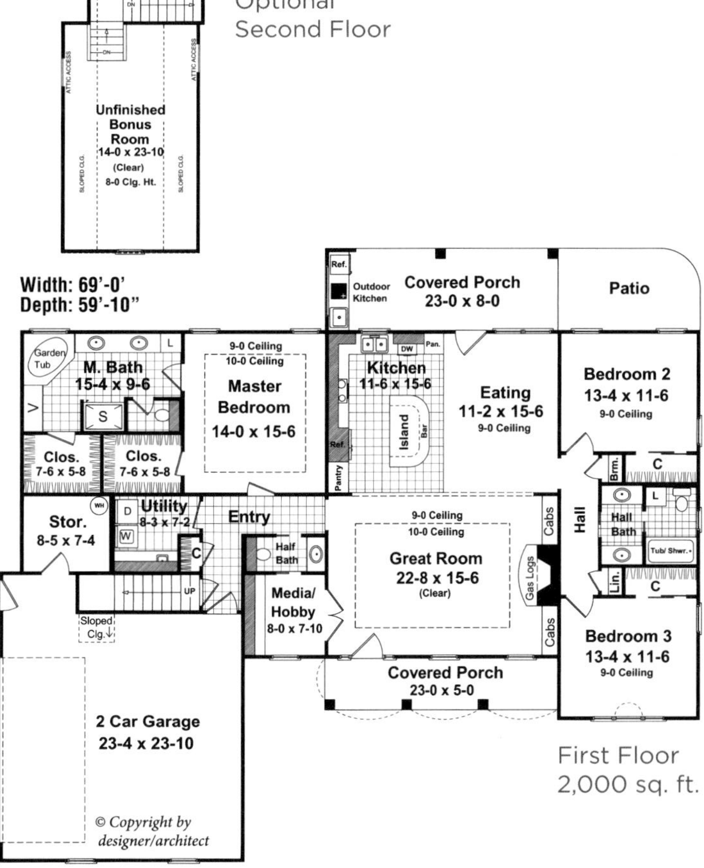

Plan #541-033D-0012 • Price Code C

Central Living Area Keeps Bedrooms Private

- 1,546 total square feet of living area
- Spacious, open rooms create a casual atmosphere
- Master bedroom is secluded for privacy
- Dining room features a large bay window
- Kitchen and dinette combine for added space and include access to the outdoors
- Large laundry room includes a convenient sink
- 3 bedrooms, 2 baths, 2-car garage
- Basement foundation

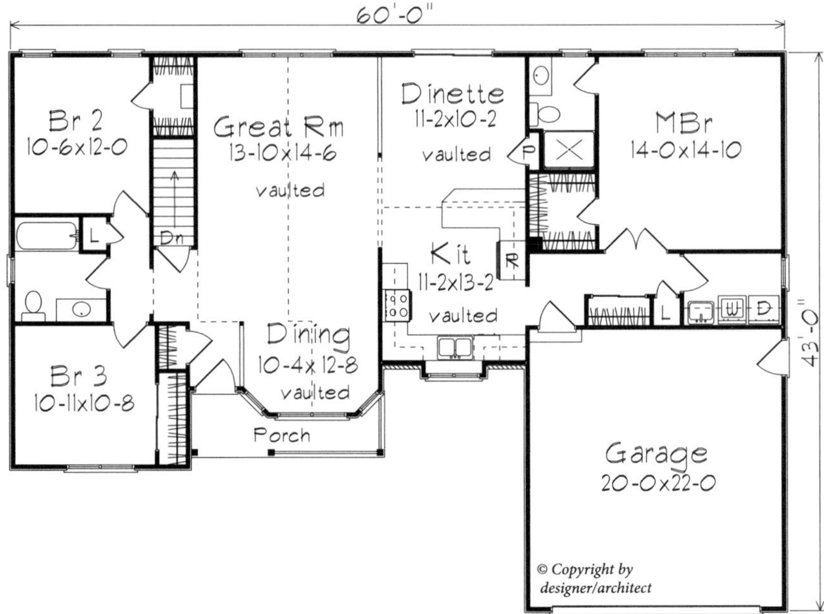

• To Order See Page 288 or Call Toll-Free 1-877-379-3420

Plan #541-007D-0031 • Price Code AA

Innovative Ranch Has Cozy Corner Patio

- 1,092 total square feet of living area
- A box window and inviting porch with dormers create a charming facade
- Eat-in kitchen offers a pass-through breakfast bar, corner window wall to patio, pantry and convenient laundry room with half bath
- Master bedroom features a double-door entry and walk-in closet
- 3 bedrooms, 1 1/2 baths, 1-car garage
- Basement foundation, drawings also include crawl space and slab foundations

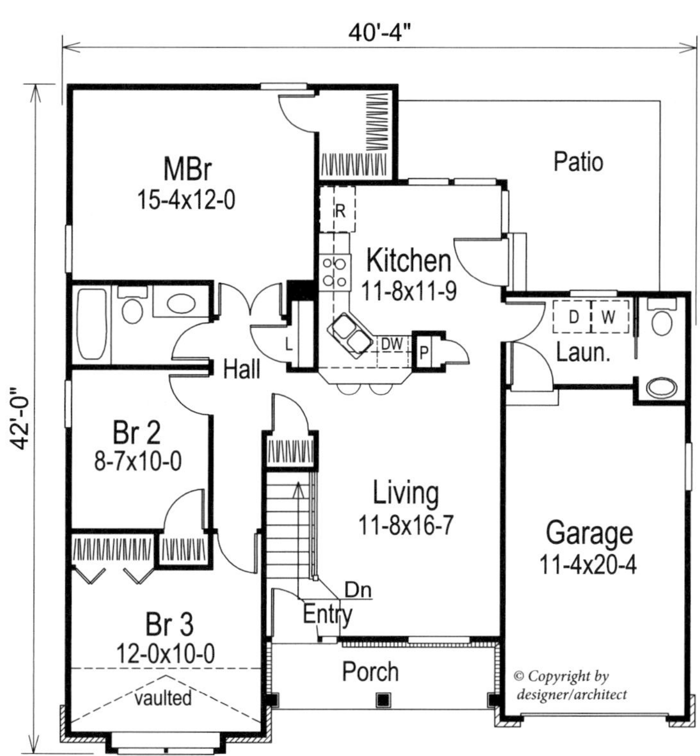

Plan #541-040D-0007 • Price Code D

Vaulted Ceilings Enhance Spacious Home

- 2,073 total square feet of living area
- Family room provides an ideal gathering area with a fireplace, large windows and vaulted ceiling
- Private first floor master bedroom enjoys a vaulted ceiling and luxury bath
- Kitchen features an angled bar connecting it to the breakfast area
- 4 bedrooms, 2 1/2 baths, 2-car side entry garage
- Basement foundation

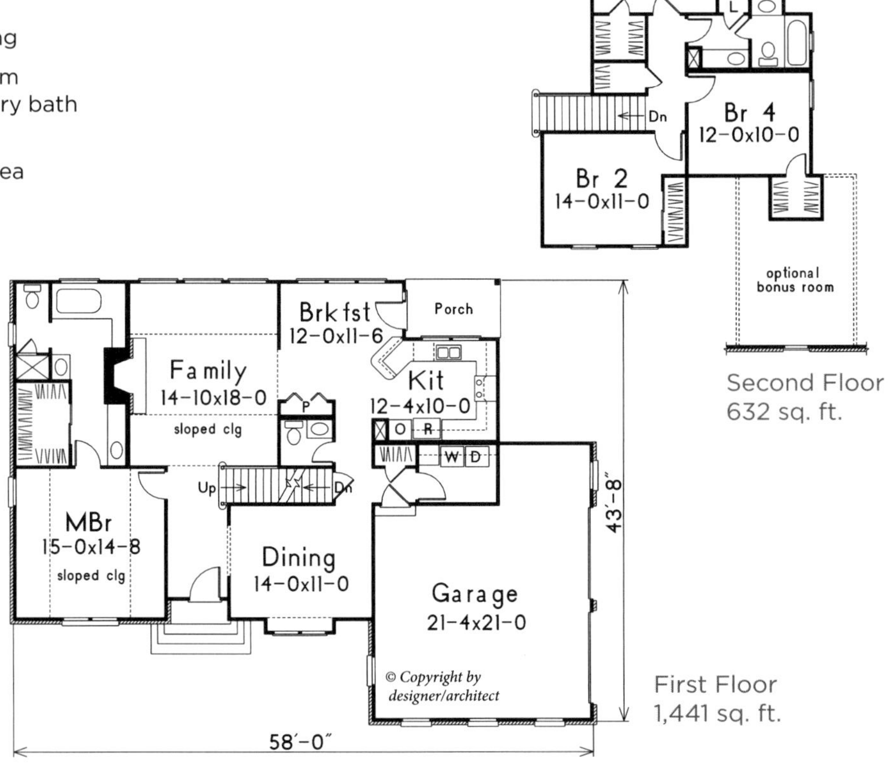

Second Floor
632 sq. ft.

First Floor
1,441 sq. ft.

• To Order See Page 288 or Call Toll-Free 1-877-379-3420

Plan #541-072L-0555 • Price Code E

LOWE'S LEGACY SERIES

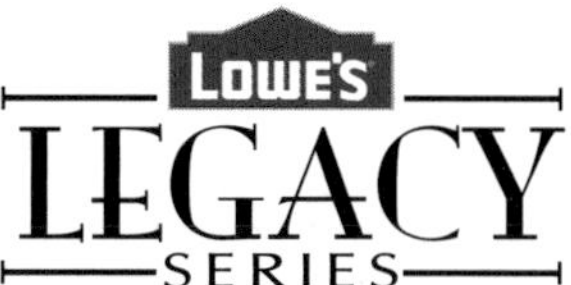

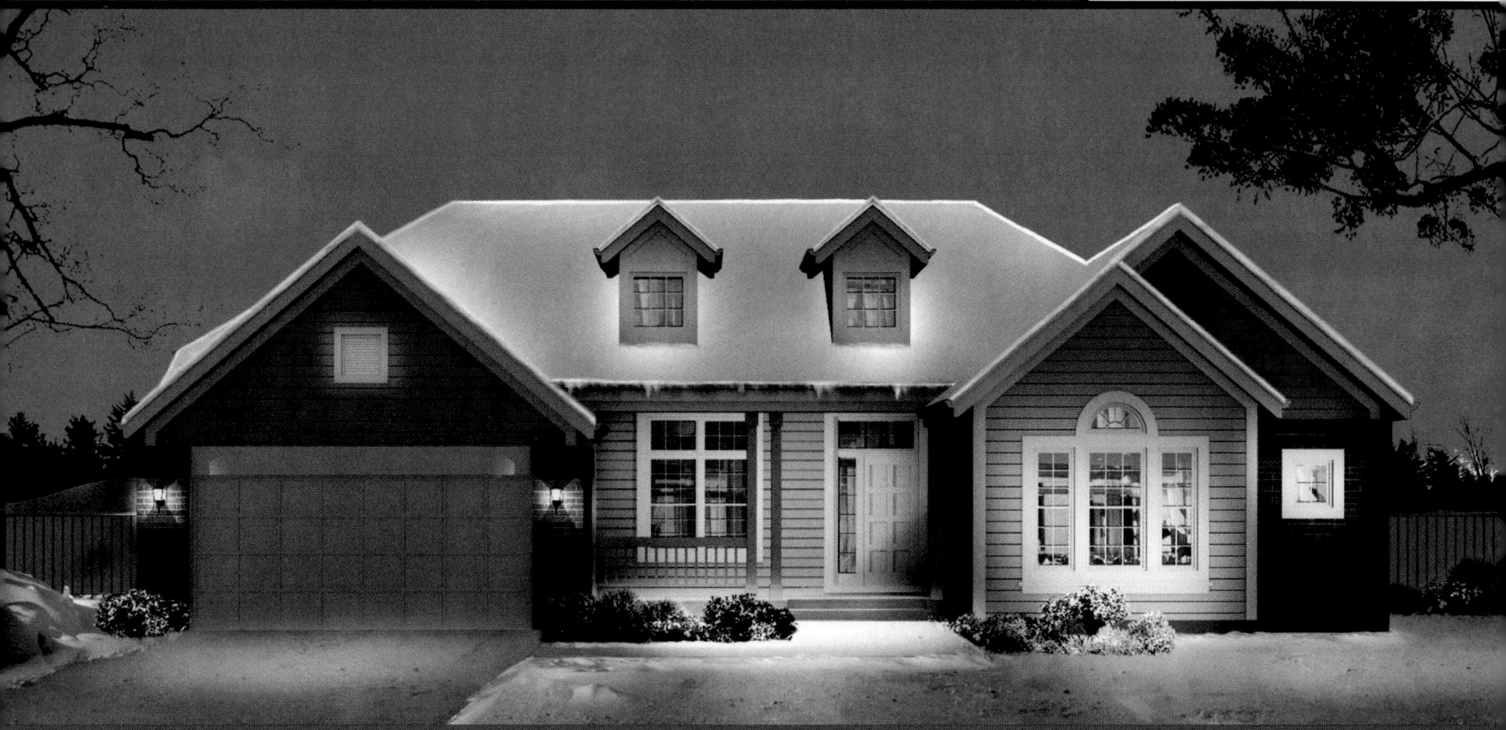

Welcoming Porch

- 2,025 total square feet of living area
- The kitchen/breakfast area has a handy center island great for family gatherings
- The master bedroom features lovely windows and a large walk-in closet
- A corner tub, double sinks and a walk-in shower are included in the appealing master bath
- 3 bedrooms, 2 baths, 2-car garage
- Basement foundation

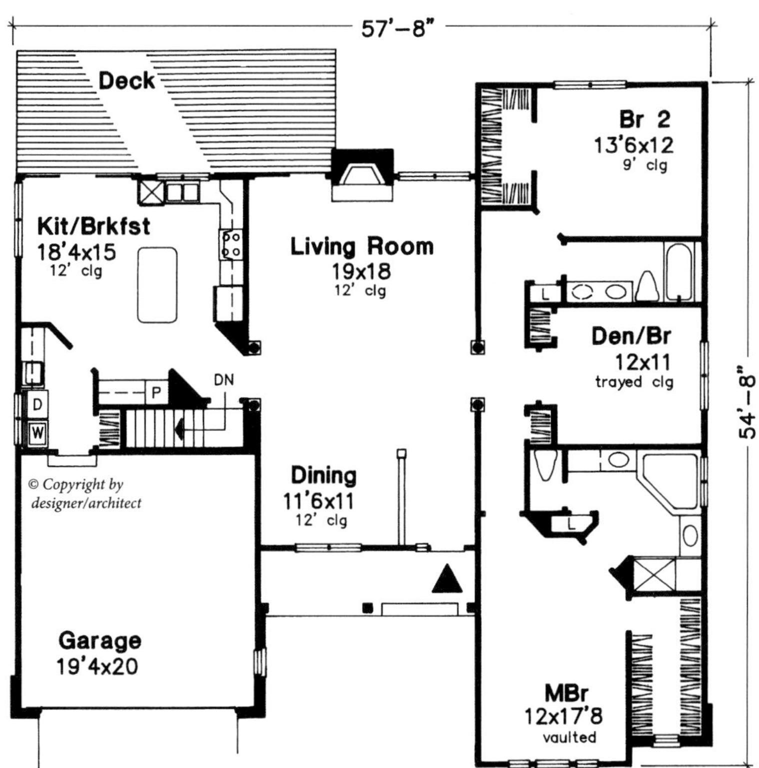

Plan #541-058D-0067 • Price Code B

Luxurious Master Bedroom

- 1,587 total square feet of living area
- The spacious family room features a vaulted ceiling, fireplace and convenient coat closet
- The kitchen/breakfast area is brightened by a large window and includes a convenient pantry
- Secondary bedrooms are generously sized and share a full bath
- 3 bedrooms, 2 baths, 2-car garage
- Basement foundation

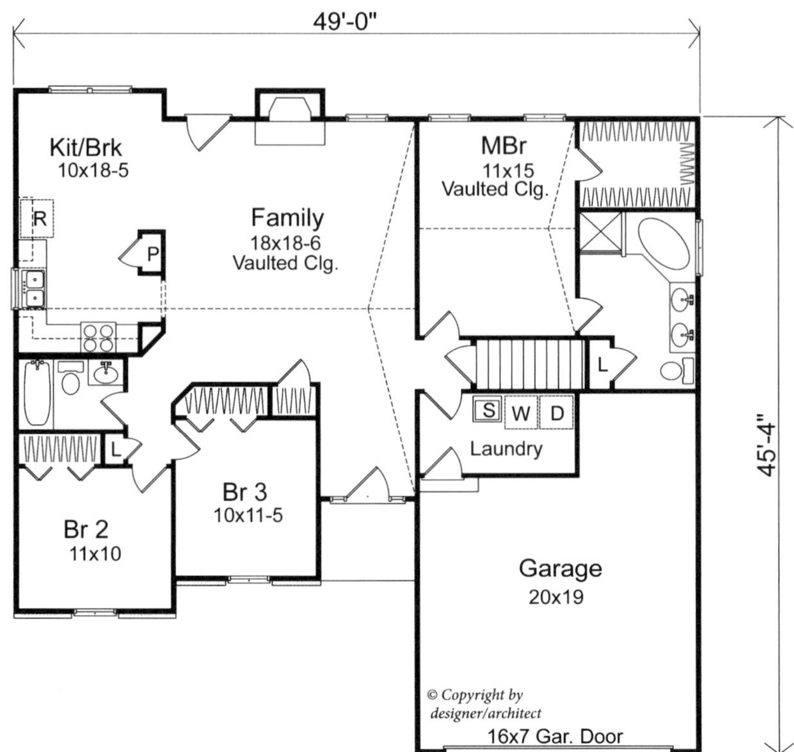

• To Order See Page 288 or Call Toll-Free 1-877-379-3420

Plan #541-087L-1671 • Price Code E

A Country Style Home With Character

- 1,542 total square feet of living area
- The large bayed dining room enjoys direct access to the outdoors and close proximity to the kitchen
- Two vaulted bedrooms and a full bath complete the second floor
- Both a separate shower and tub add great function to the master bath
- The future expansion on the second floor has an additional 226 square feet of living area
- 3 bedrooms, 2 1/2 baths, 2-car garage
- Slab foundation

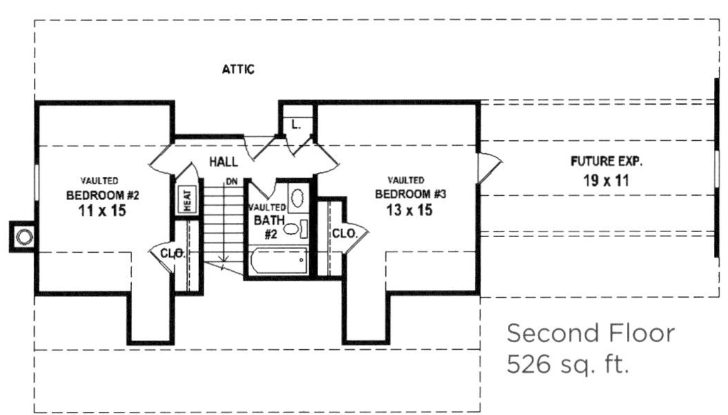

Second Floor
526 sq. ft.

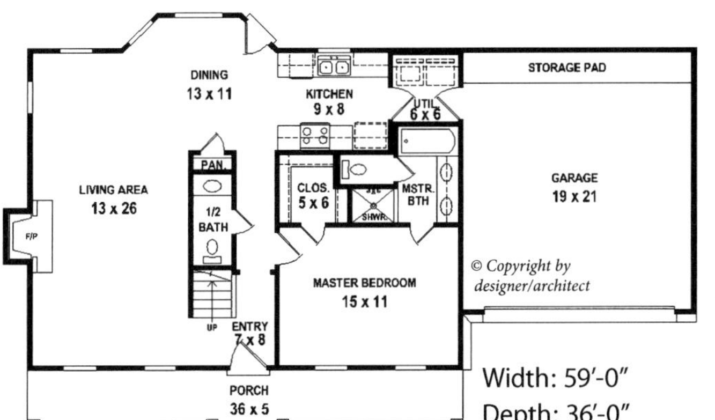

First Floor
1,016 sq. ft.

Plan #541-007D-0230 • Price Code D

Innovative Design With Sensational Looks

- 1,923 total square feet of living area
- A spacious entrance with double coat closets invites you into the grand-sized great room with fireplace, bar area open to the kitchen with glass sliding doors to the rear patio and adjacent dining room
- The large and smartly designed bay-shaped kitchen features cabinet and counter space galore with a 7' wide window above the sink for taking in the views
- A luxury bath with separate shower, double entry doors, a walk-in closet and 9' wide glass sliding doors to the rear patio are many special features of the master bedroom
- 3 bedrooms, 2 baths, 2-car side entry garage
- Slab foundation

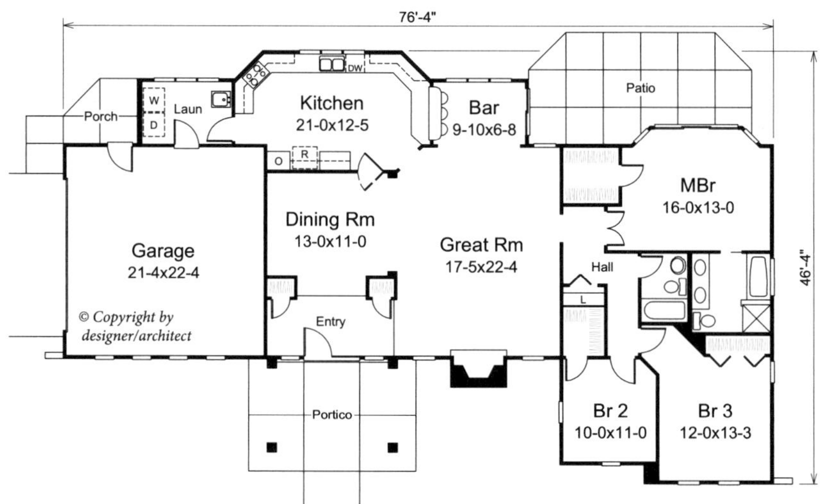

• To Order See Page 288 or Call Toll-Free 1-877-379-3420

Plan #541-121D-0015 • Price Code B

Welcoming Covered Front Porch

- 1,983 total square feet of living area
- The vaulted great room offers a fireplace and a wall of windows to brighten the space
- A separate toliet room, double-bowl vanity and large walk-in closet are features of the master bath
- Bedrooms #2 and #3 share a bath and each has a spacious closet perfect for storage
- The optional attic space above the garage has an additional 273 square feet of living area
- 3 bedrooms, 2 1/2 baths, 2-car side entry garage
- Basement foundation

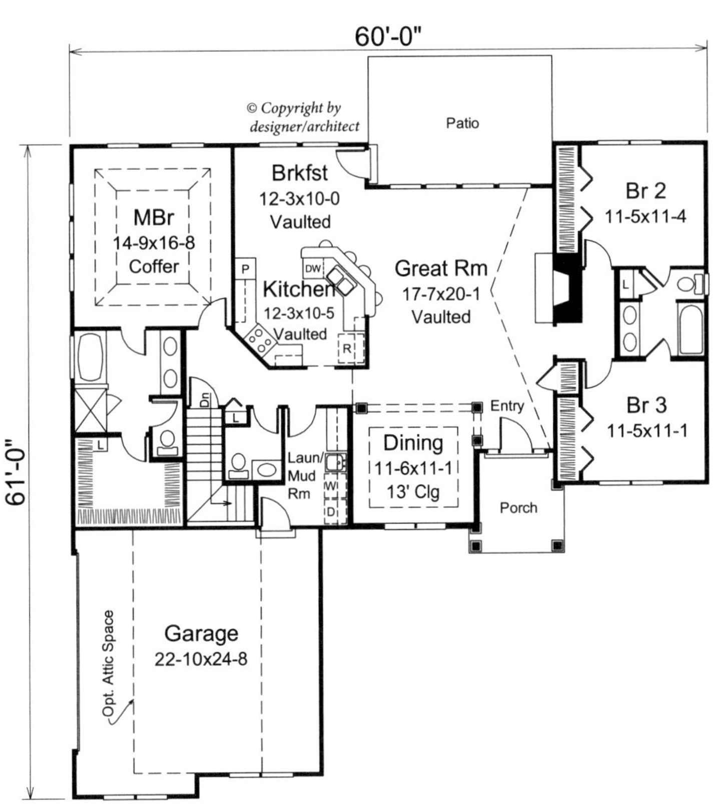

• To Order See Page 288 or Call Toll-Free 1-877-379-3420

Plan #541-014D-0013 • Price Code C

Handsome Facade, Compact Design

- 2,041 total square feet of living area
- Energy efficient home with 2" x 6" exterior walls
- Wonderful sunken family room features a fireplace and accesses the patio
- The kitchen with island cooktop and nook combines with the family room creating an open area
- Dining room is accessible from the kitchen and vaulted living room
- Bedroom #4 could easily convert to a study or den
- 4 bedrooms, 3 baths, 2-car side entry garage
- Partial basement/slab foundation

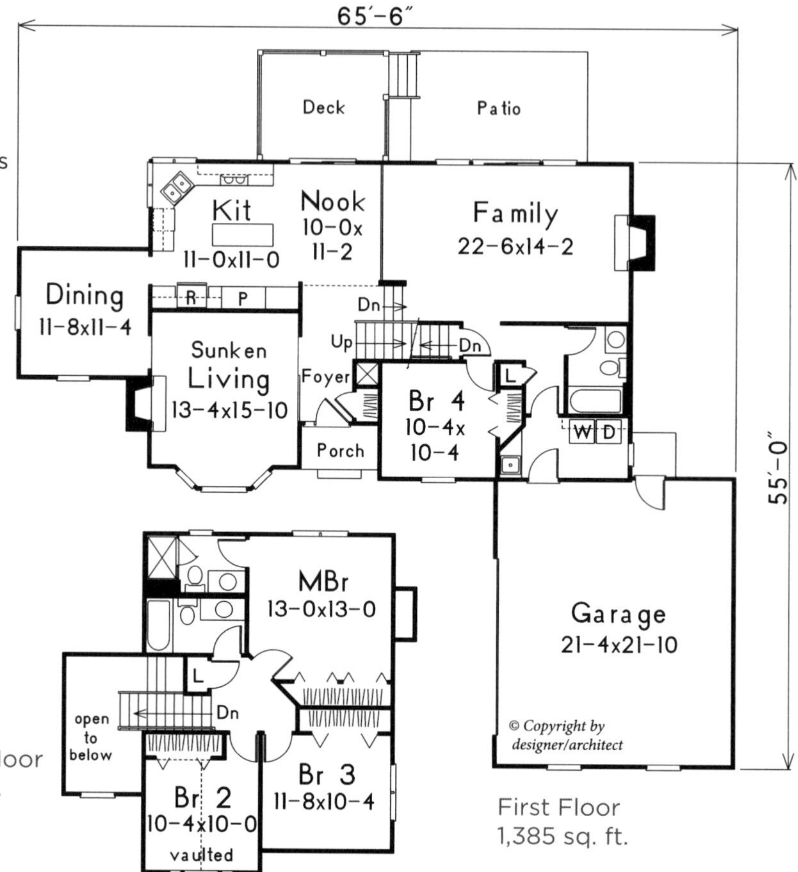

Second Floor
656 sq. ft.

First Floor
1,385 sq. ft.

• To Order See Page 288 or Call Toll-Free 1-877-379-3420

Plan #541-055L-0205 • Price Code D

Columns Define Dining Room

- 1,989 total square feet of living area
- The kitchen includes a counter with seating that opens to the charming breakfast room
- The guest bedroom is privately located and includes a bath and walk-in closet
- A tray ceiling, deluxe bath and massive walk-in closet enhance the master suite
- 4 bedrooms, 3 baths, 2-car side entry garage
- Slab, crawl space, basement or walk-out basement foundation, please specify when ordering

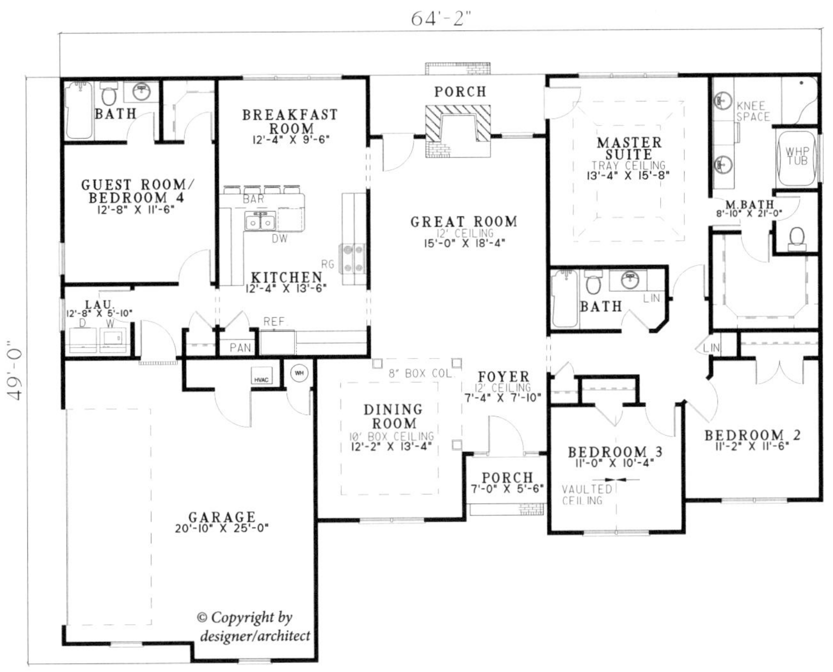

Plan #541-048D-0009 • Price Code C

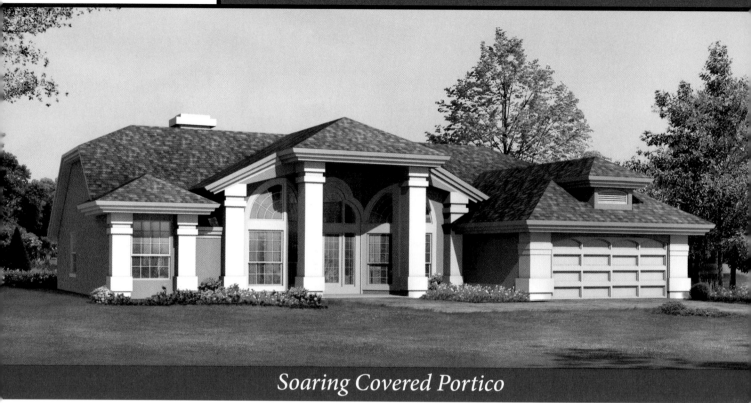

Soaring Covered Portico

- 2,056 total square feet of living area
- Columned foyer projects past the living and dining rooms into the family room
- Kitchen conveniently accesses the dining room and breakfast area
- Master bedroom features double-door access to the patio and a pocket door to the private bath with walk-in closet, double-bowl vanity and tub
- 4 bedrooms, 2 baths, 2-car garage
- Slab foundation, drawings also include crawl space foundation

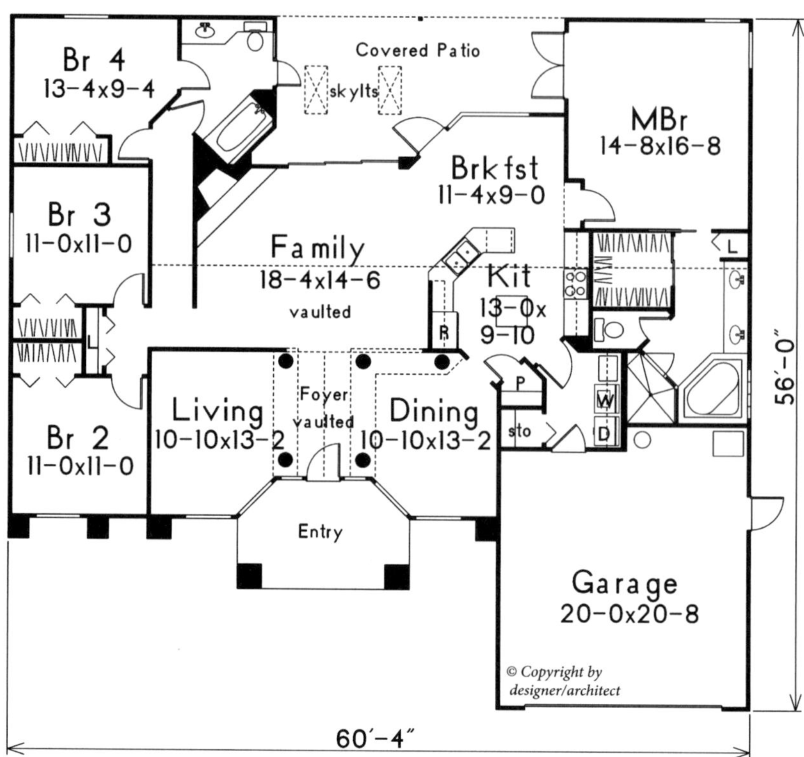

• To Order See Page 288 or Call Toll-Free 1-877-379-3420

Plan #541-007D-0216 • Price Code A

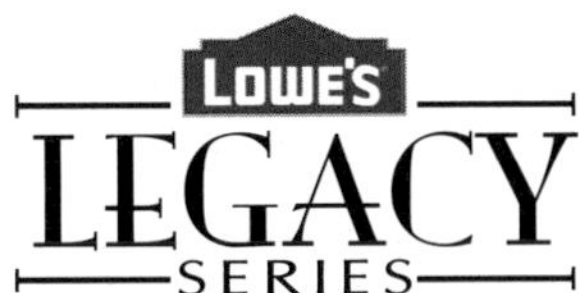

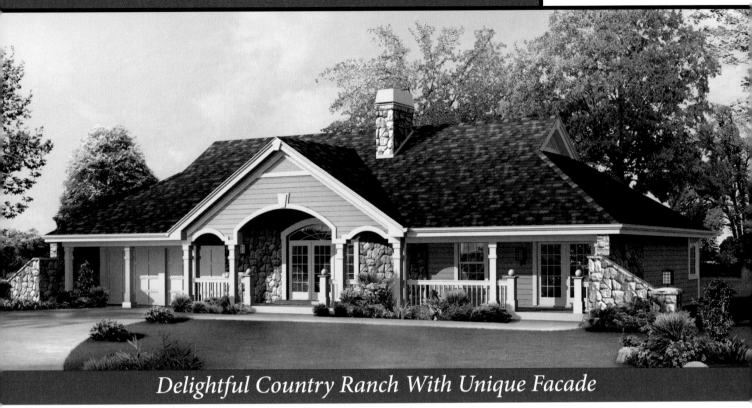

Delightful Country Ranch With Unique Facade

- 1,510 total square feet of living area
- Energy efficient home with 2" x 6" exterior walls
- The decorative porch arches, wood columns and stone walls combine to create an exterior that demands attention
- Open living and dining areas feature a vaulted ceiling, fireplace and French doors to rear patio
- The well-planned kitchen has a large built-in corner pantry and a snack counter, all open to the living areas
- Convenient to the kitchen is a nice sized laundry room with sink
- The garage comes complete with a very useful storage room
- 3 bedrooms, 2 baths, 2-car garage
- Slab foundation, drawings also include crawl space foundation

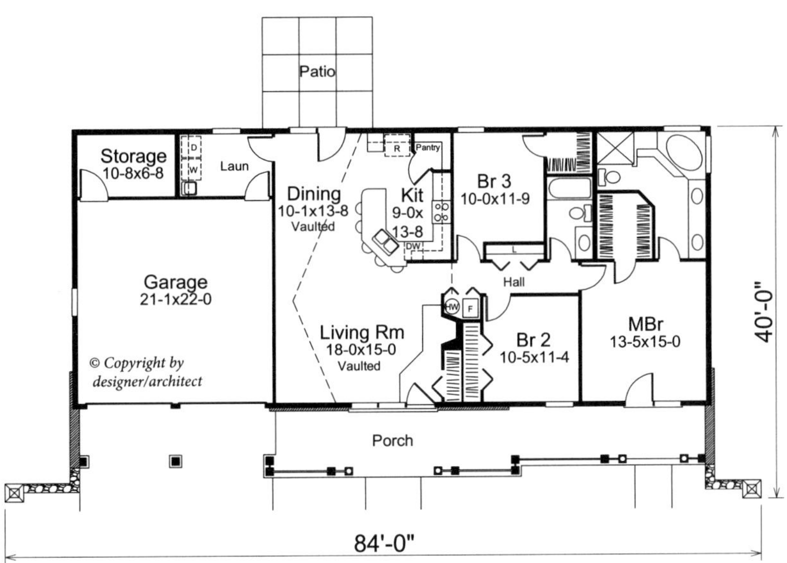

Plan #541-037D-0010 • Price Code B

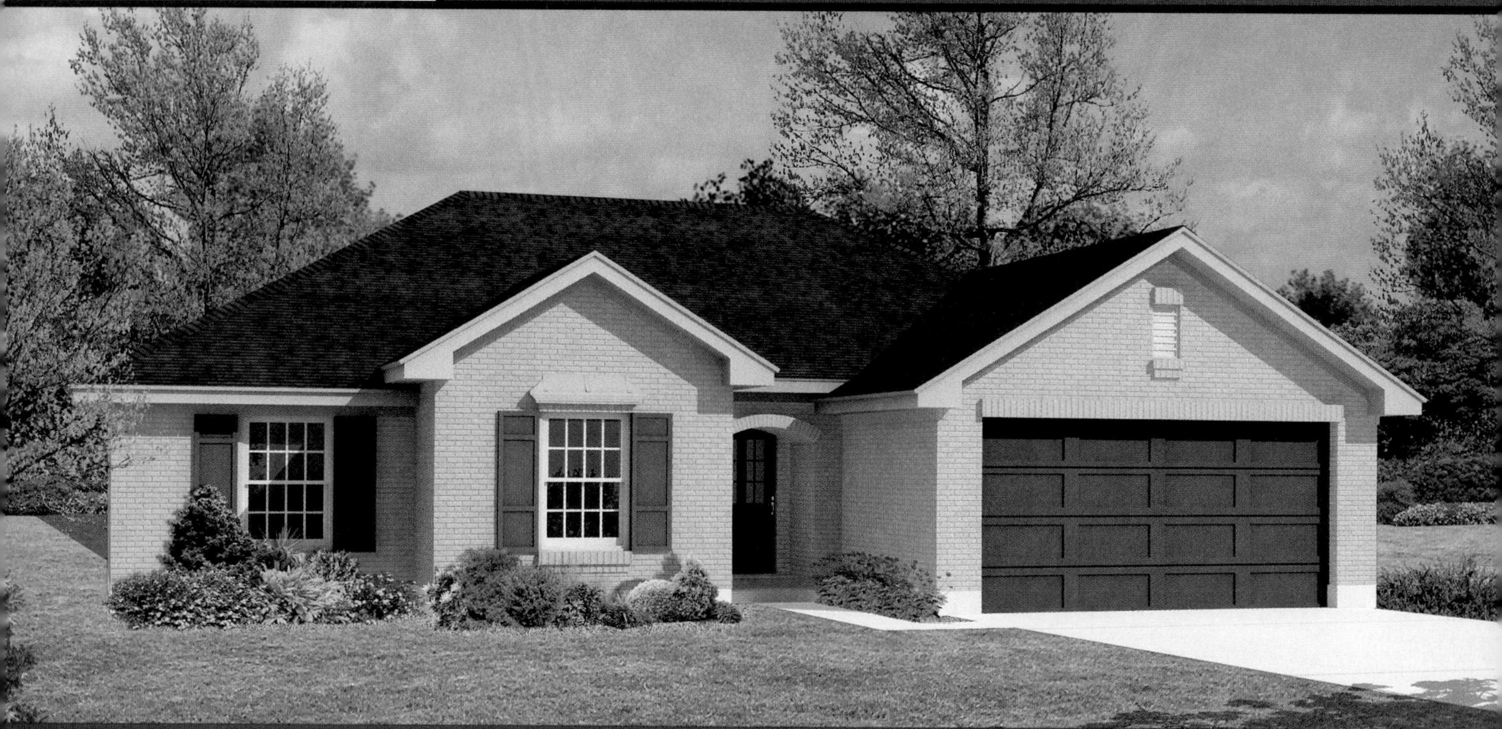

A Trim Arrangement Of Living Areas

- 1,770 total square feet of living area
- Distinctive covered entrance leads into spacious foyer
- Master bedroom, living and dining rooms feature large windows for plenty of light
- Oversized living room has a high ceiling and large windows that flank the fireplace
- Kitchen includes a pantry and large planning center
- Master bedroom has a high vaulted ceiling, deluxe bath, and private access outdoors
- 3 bedrooms, 2 baths, 2-car garage
- Slab foundation

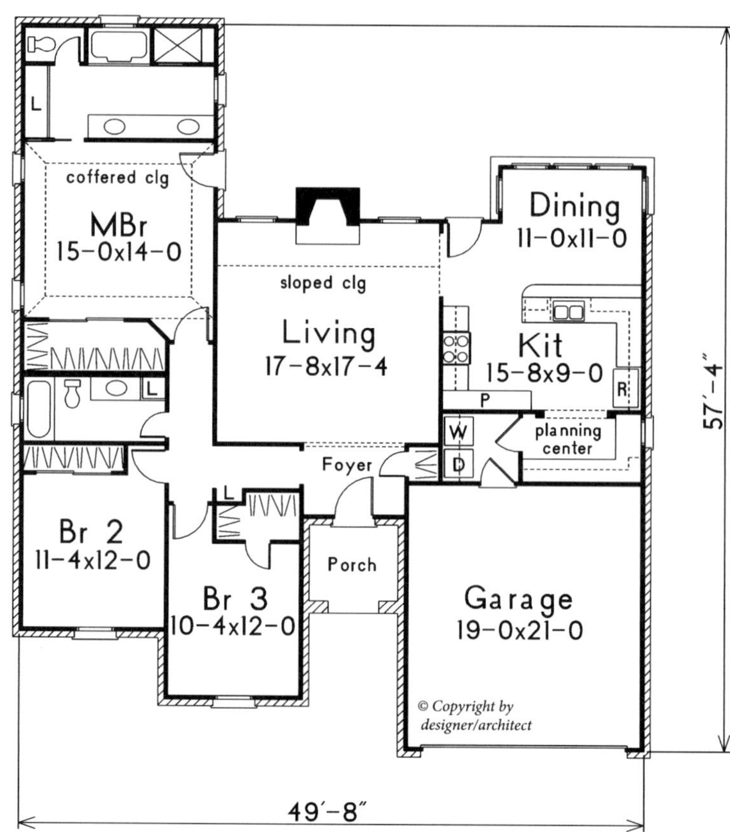

• To Order See Page 288 or Call Toll-Free 1-877-379-3420

Plan #541-013L-0149 • Price Code D

Luxurious Master Suite

- 2,058 total square feet of living area
- Designed for today's more narrow lots, this home adds style to any neighborhood
- All bedrooms are located on the second floor but are easily accessible thanks to a centrally located elevator
- The dramatic and spacious kitchen flows neatly from an angled pantry to the recipe desk and serving bar
- 3 bedrooms, 2 1/2 baths, 2-car garage
- Crawl space foundation

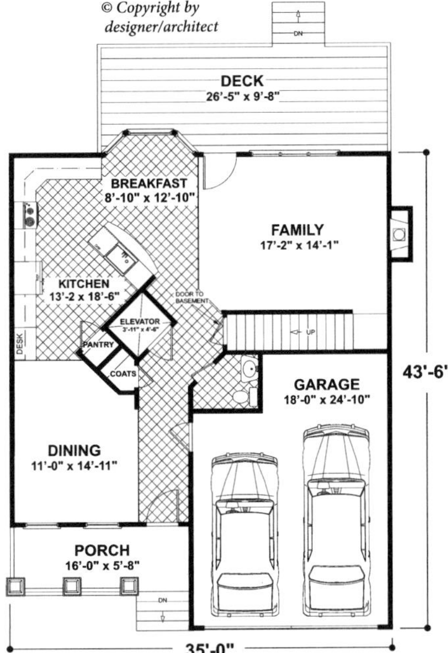

First Floor
1,135 sq. ft.

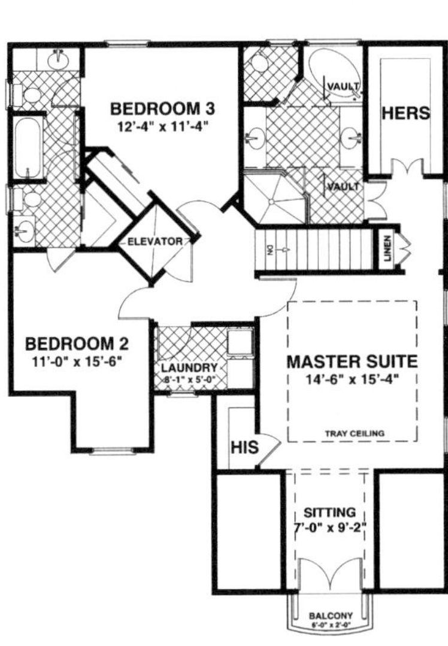

Second Floor
923 sq. ft.

Plan #541-040D-0004 • Price Code C

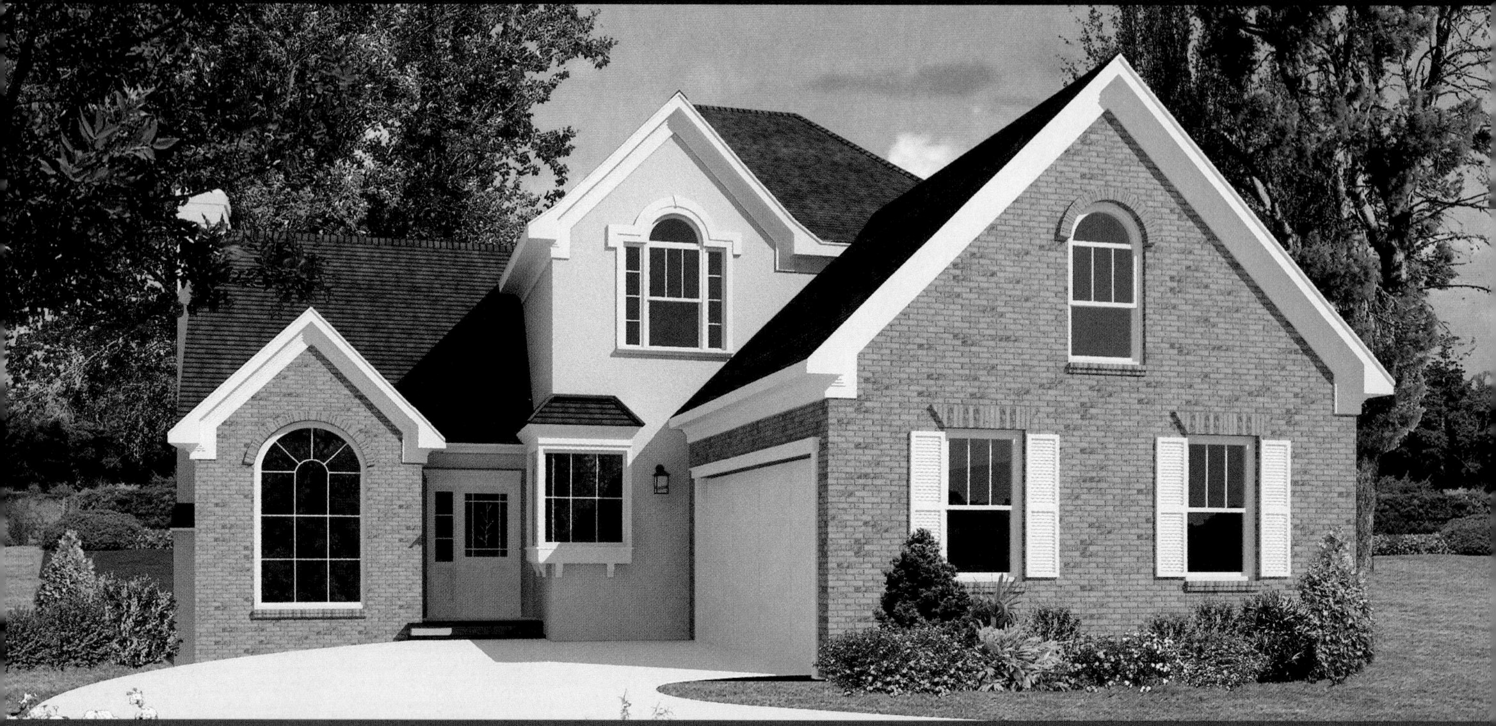

Charming With Many Gables

- 2,128 total square feet of living area
- Large bonus area over the garage, that is included in the square footage, converts to a fourth bedroom or activity center
- Family room fireplace and vaulted ceiling provide an attractive entry
- Master bedroom features a bath with windowed tub, walk-in closet, separate shower and plenty of storage space
- 3 bedrooms, 2 1/2 baths, 2-car side entry garage
- Basement foundation

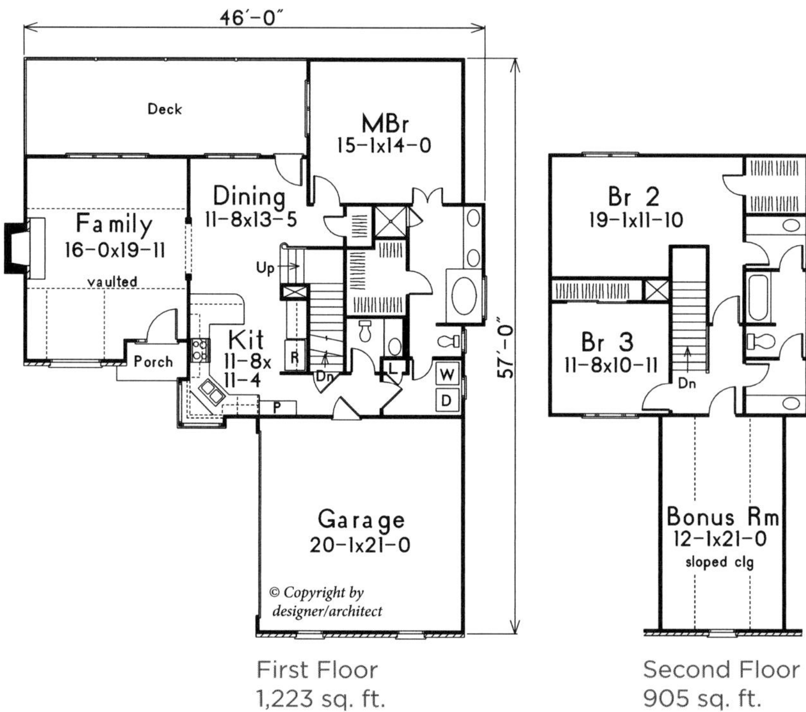

First Floor
1,223 sq. ft.

Second Floor
905 sq. ft.

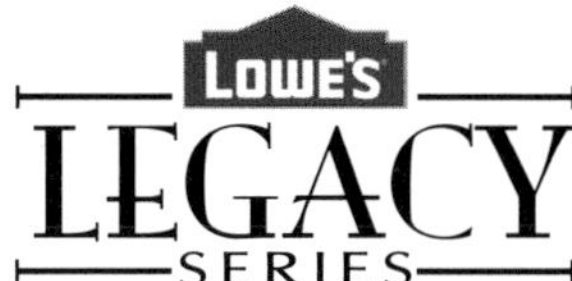

Plan #541-007D-0235 • Price Code E

Lowe's LEGACY SERIES

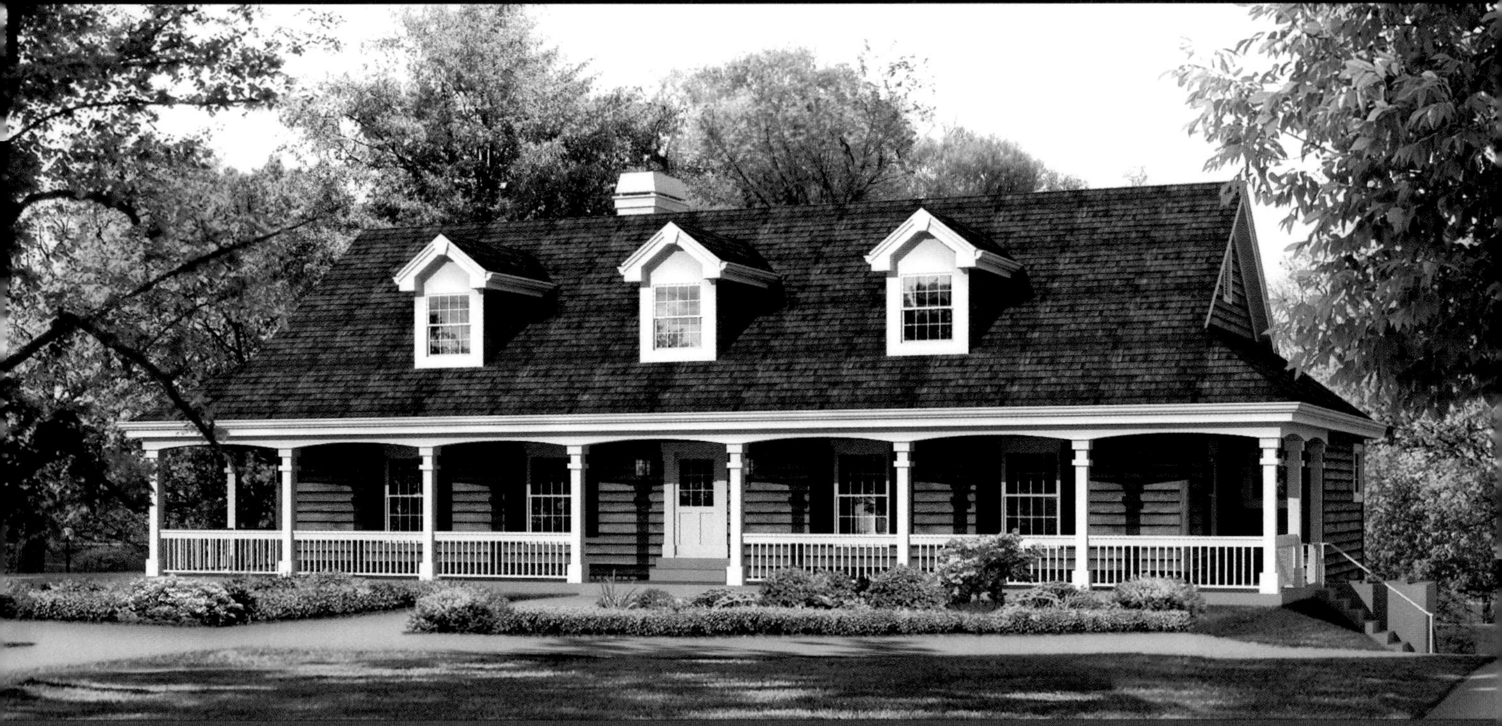

Unique Drive-Thru Basement Garage

- 2,213 total square feet of living area
- A wrap-around porch and roof dormers help to create great country charm
- The spacious great room features a fireplace, wide glass sliding doors to rear sundeck and a square colonade that defines the foyer
- A huge walk-in pantry, large island and generous cabinet space are among the many amenities of the smartly-designed kitchen and adjacent breakfast area
- The walk-out basement garage offers a convenient drive-through design, abundant storage area or parking for up to 8 cars, extra wide garage doors and two 9′ glass sliding doors for natural light
- 3 bedrooms, 2 baths, 8-car drive under side entry garage
- Walk-out basement foundation

First Floor
2,213 sq. ft.

Lower Level

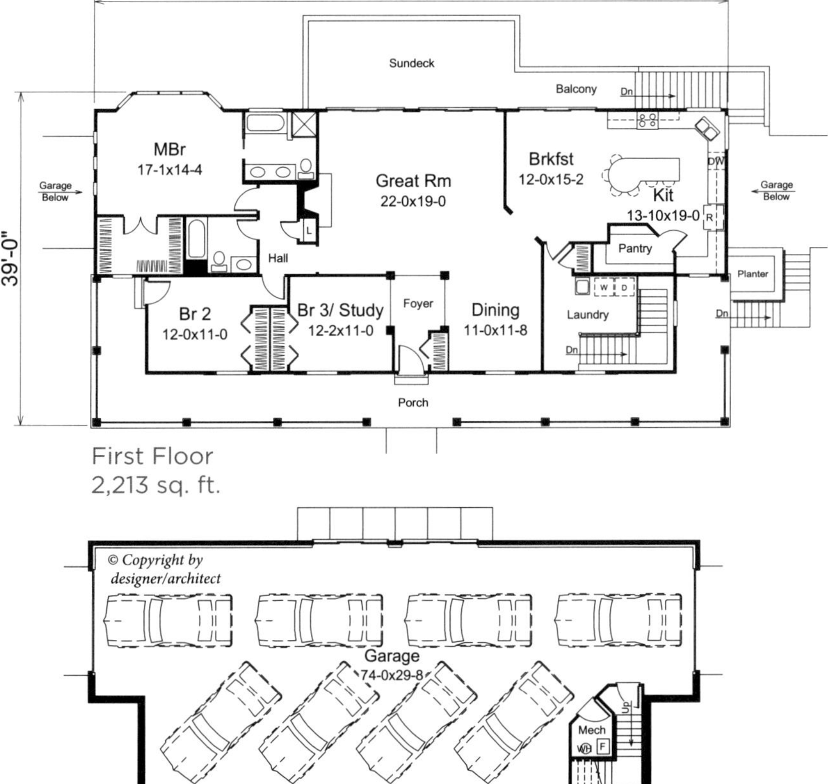

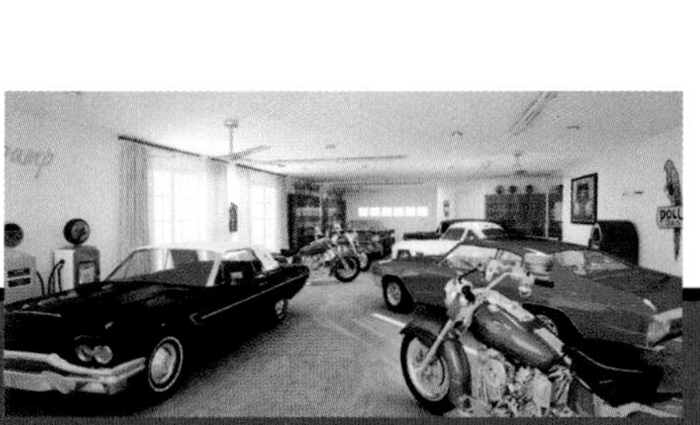

Plan #541-014D-0001 • Price Code C

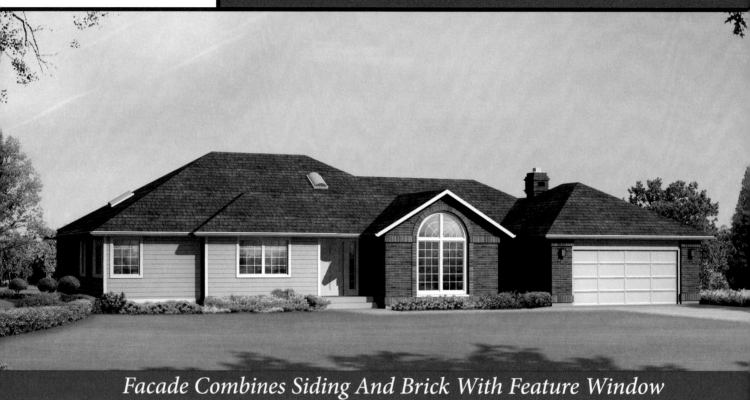

Facade Combines Siding And Brick With Feature Window

- 2,159 total square feet of living area
- Energy efficient home with 2" x 6" exterior walls
- Covered entry opens into the large foyer with a skylight and coat closet
- Master bedroom includes a private bath with angled vanity, separate spa and shower and walk-in closet
- Family and living rooms feature vaulted ceilings and sunken floors for added openness
- Kitchen features an island counter and convenient pantry
- 3 bedrooms, 2 baths, 2-car garage
- Basement foundation, drawings also include crawl space and slab foundations

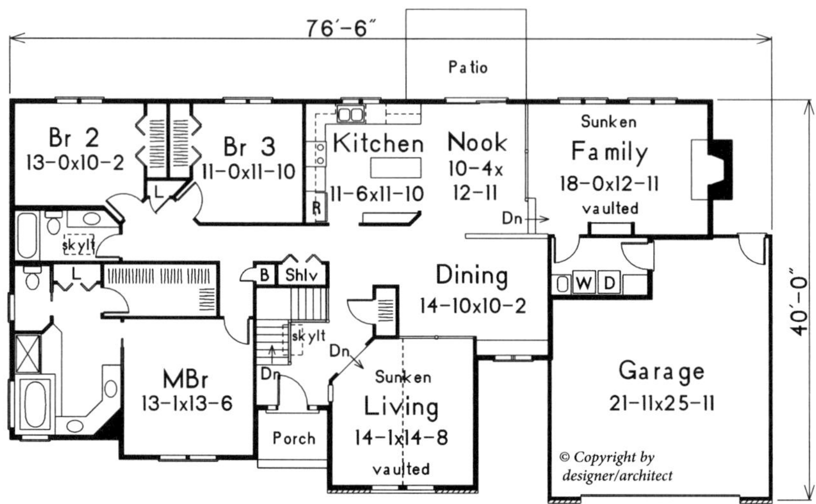

• To Order See Page 288 or Call Toll-Free 1-877-379-3420

Plan #541-048D-0001 • Price Code D

LOWE'S LEGACY SERIES

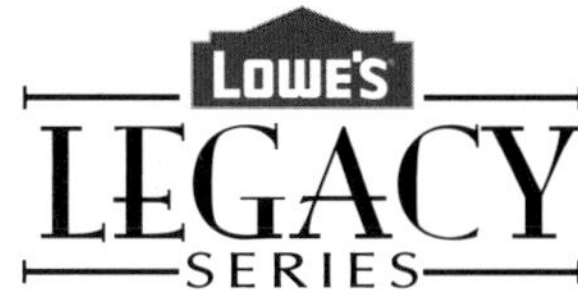

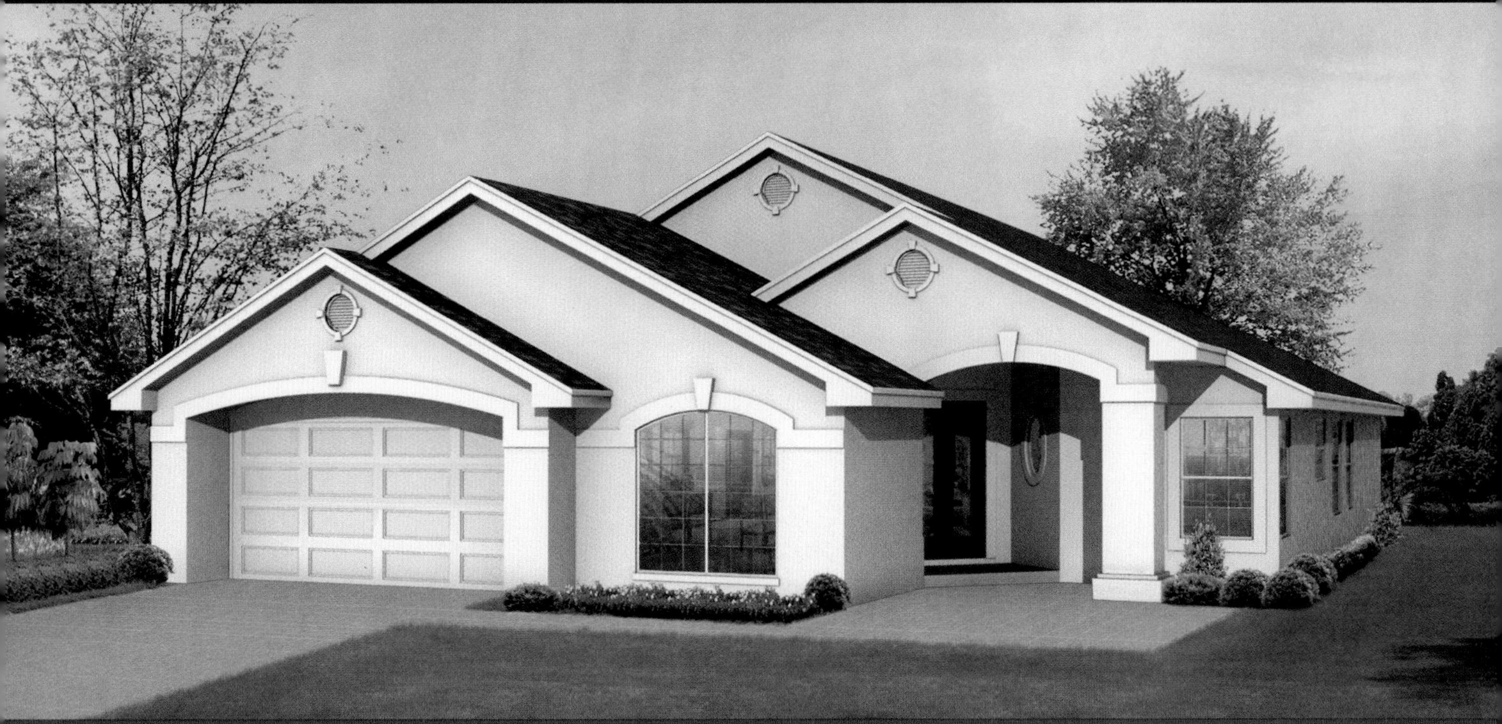

Wonderful Great Room

- 1,865 total square feet of living area
- The large foyer opens into an expansive dining area and great room
- Home features vaulted ceilings throughout
- Master bedroom features an angled entry, vaulted ceiling, plant shelf and bath with double vanity, tub and shower
- 4 bedrooms, 2 baths, 2-car garage
- Slab foundation, drawings also include crawl space foundation

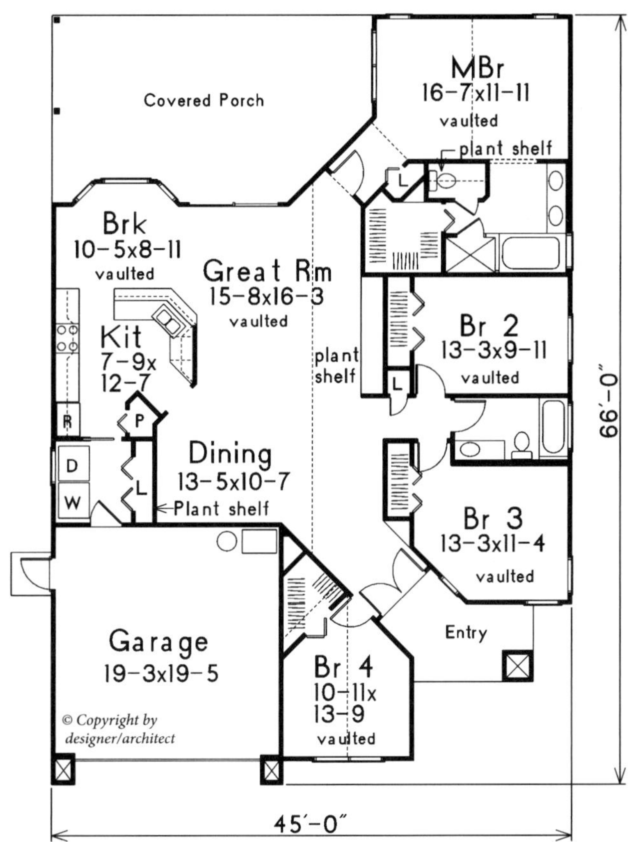

Plan #541-077L-0140 • Price Code D

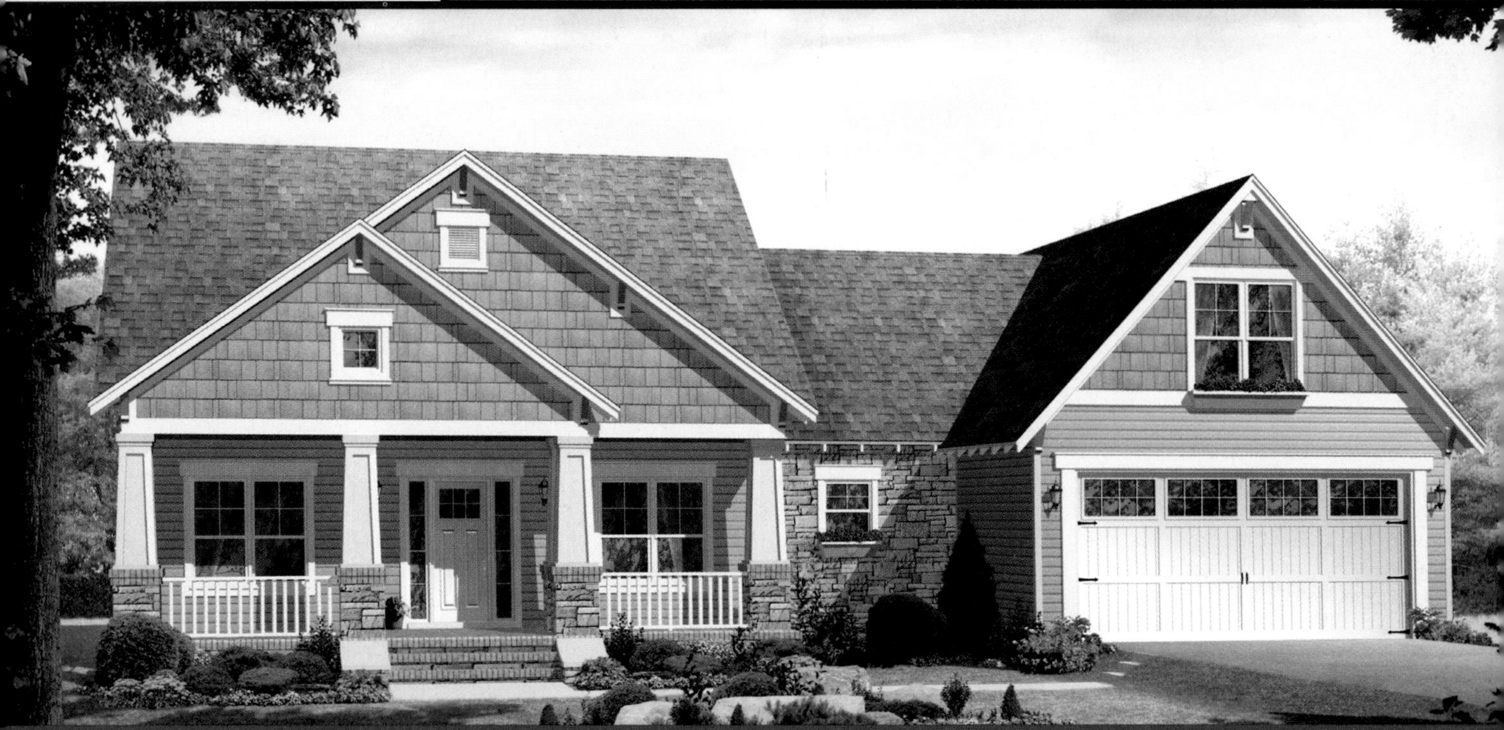

Stylish Craftsman Home

- 1,800 total square feet of living area
- A large flex space can easily convert to a home office or formal dining room depending on the owner's needs
- A large and spacious kitchen has a center island with eating bar and an attached breakfast room with bay window
- The corner jet tub in the master bath pampers the homeowners in their private retreat
- The unfinished bonus room has an additional 326 square feet of living area
- 3 bedrooms, 2 baths, 2-car garage
- Slab foundation, drawings also include crawl space foundation

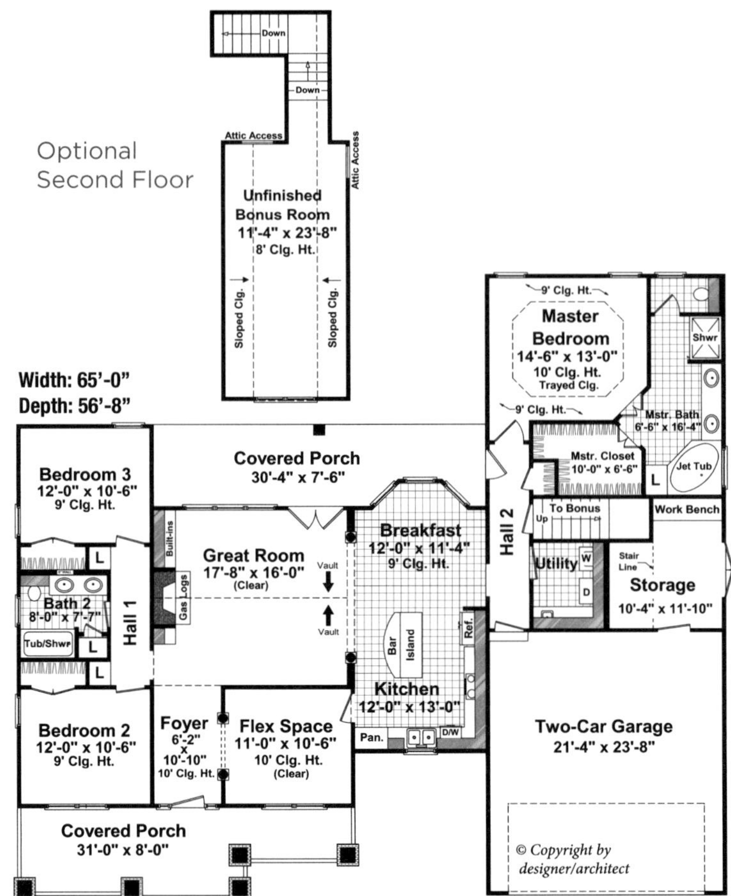

First Floor
1,800 sq. ft.

• To Order See Page 288 or Call Toll-Free 1-877-379-3420

Plan #541-013L-0132 • Price Code F

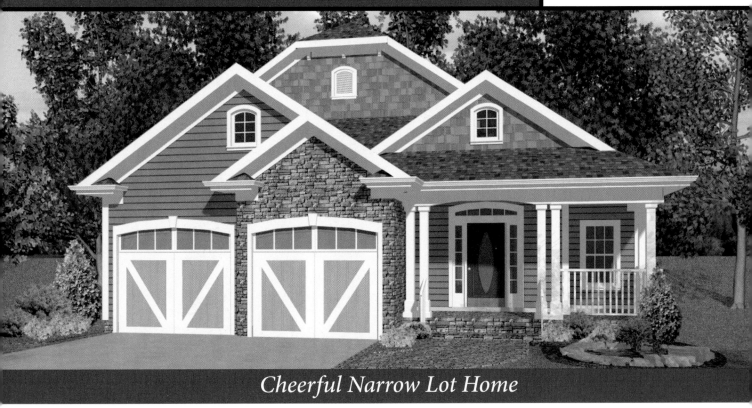

Cheerful Narrow Lot Home

- 2,296 total square feet of living area
- The highly functional kitchen offers double snack bars, a pantry and an adjacent breakfast nook
- Located off of the breakfast nook is an oversized laundry room with plenty of space for a washer and dryer as well as a laundry sink and upright freezer
- The spacious master bedroom, with its bowed window, tray ceiling, sitting area, luxurious bath and abundant closet, is truly an owner's retreat
- The second floor features two secondary bedroom suites, each featuring a walk-in closet and private bath
- 3 bedrooms, 3 1/2 baths, 2-car garage
- Crawl space foundation

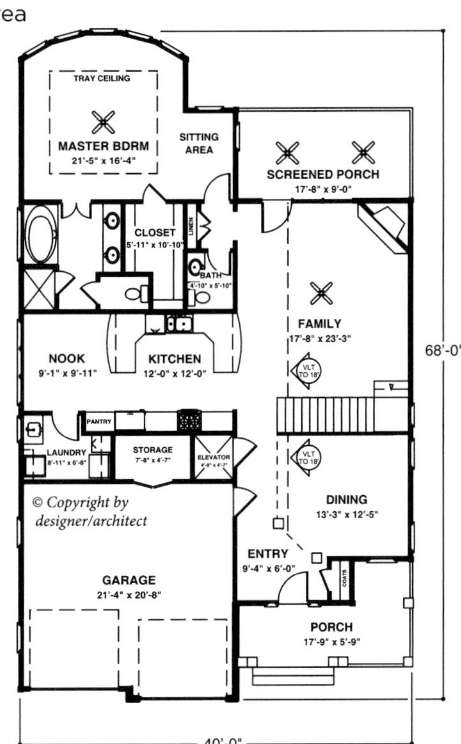

First Floor
1,636 sq. ft.

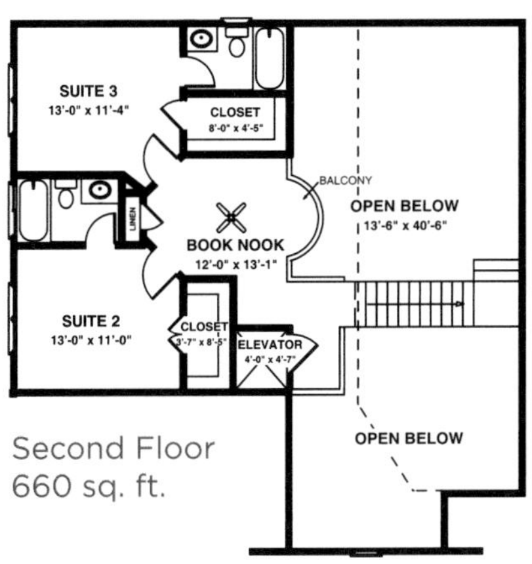

Second Floor
660 sq. ft.

Plan #541-007D-0014 • Price Code C

Great Room's Symmetry Steals The Show

- 1,985 total square feet of living area
- Charming design for a narrow lot
- Dramatic sunken great room features a vaulted ceiling, large double-hung windows and transomed patio doors
- Grand master bedroom includes a double-door entry, large closet, elegant bath and patio access
- 4 bedrooms, 3 1/2 baths, 2-car garage
- Basement foundation, drawings also include crawl space and slab foundations

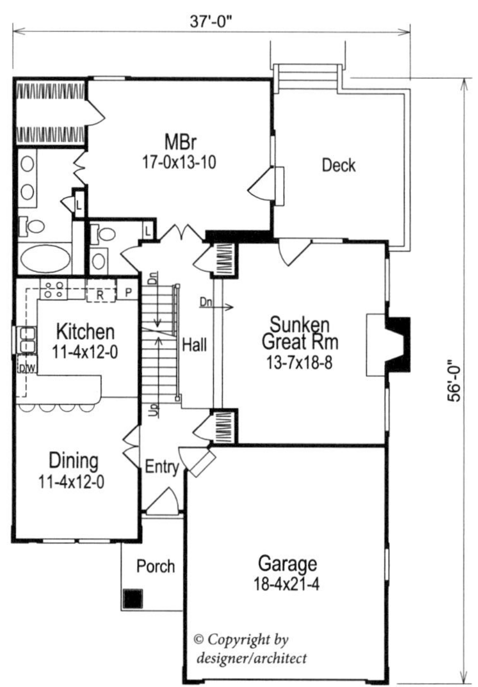

First Floor
1,114 sq. ft.

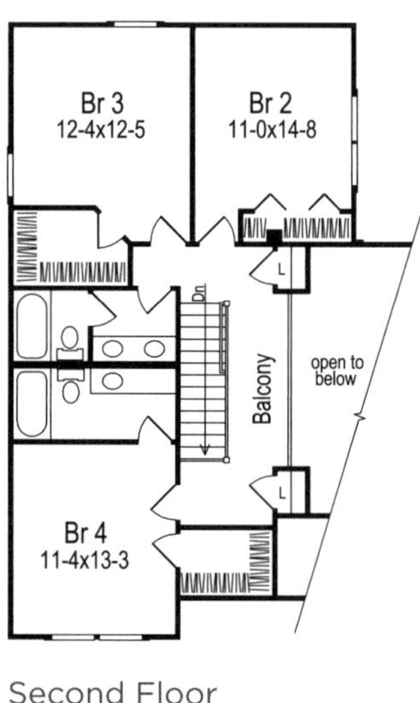

Second Floor
871 sq. ft.

• To Order See Page 288 or Call Toll-Free 1-877-379-3420

Plan #541-001D-0031 • Price Code B

Country-Style Home With Large Front Porch

- 1,501 total square feet of living area
- Spacious kitchen with dining area is open to the outdoors
- Convenient utility room is adjacent to the garage
- Master bedroom features a private bath, dressing area and access to the large covered porch
- Large family room creates openness
- Plan also available with energy efficient R-Control® SIPs (Structural Insulated Panels), please call 1-877-379-3420 for more information
- 3 bedrooms, 2 baths, 2-car side entry garage
- Basement foundation, drawings also include crawl space and slab foundations

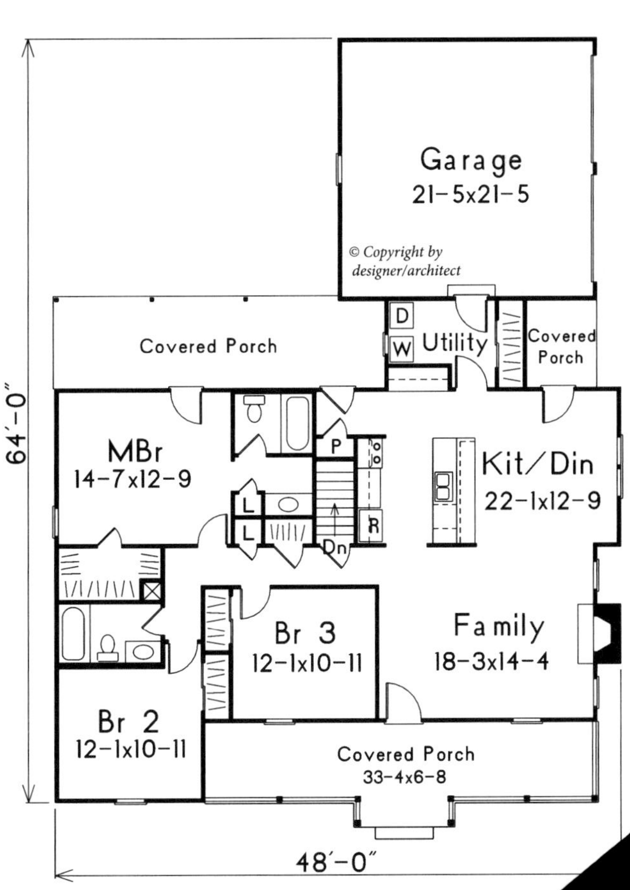

• To Order See Page 288 or Call Toll-Free 1-

Plan #541-077L-0138 • Price Code D

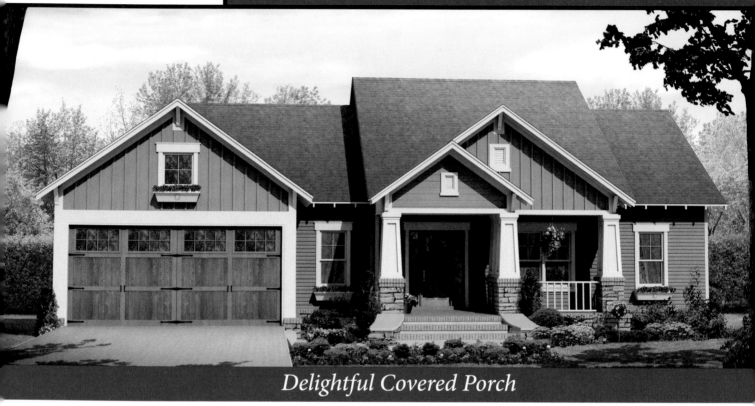

Delightful Covered Porch

- 1,509 total square feet of living area
- A large eating area has covered porch access and is near the kitchen and vaulted great room
- Double walk-in closets and a luxury bath complete the master bedroom
- Cabinets flank the fireplace in the vaulted great room
- 3 bedrooms, 2 baths, 2-car garage
- Basement foundation, drawings also include crawl space and slab foundations

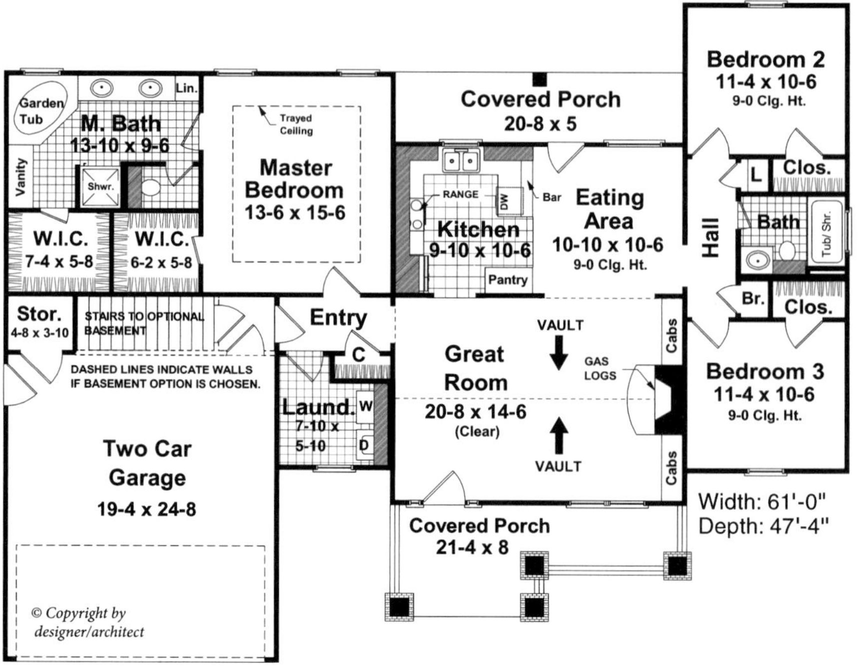

Plan #541-007D-0177 • Price Code AA

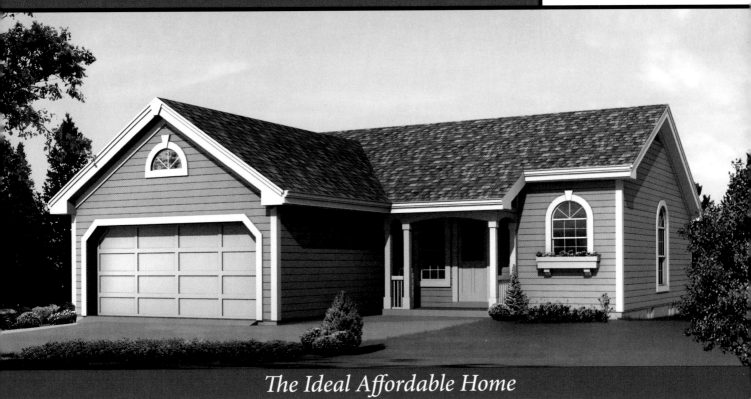

The Ideal Affordable Home

- 1,102 total square feet of living area
- Attractive exterior features a cozy porch, palladian windows and a decorative planter box
- The vaulted great room has a fireplace, view to rear patio and dining area with feature window
- Open to the great room is a U-shaped kitchen that includes all the necessities and a breakfast bar
- The master bedroom offers a vaulted ceiling, private bath, walk-in closet and sliding doors to the rear patio
- 3 bedrooms, 2 baths, 2-car garage
- Basement foundation, drawings also include slab and crawl space foundations

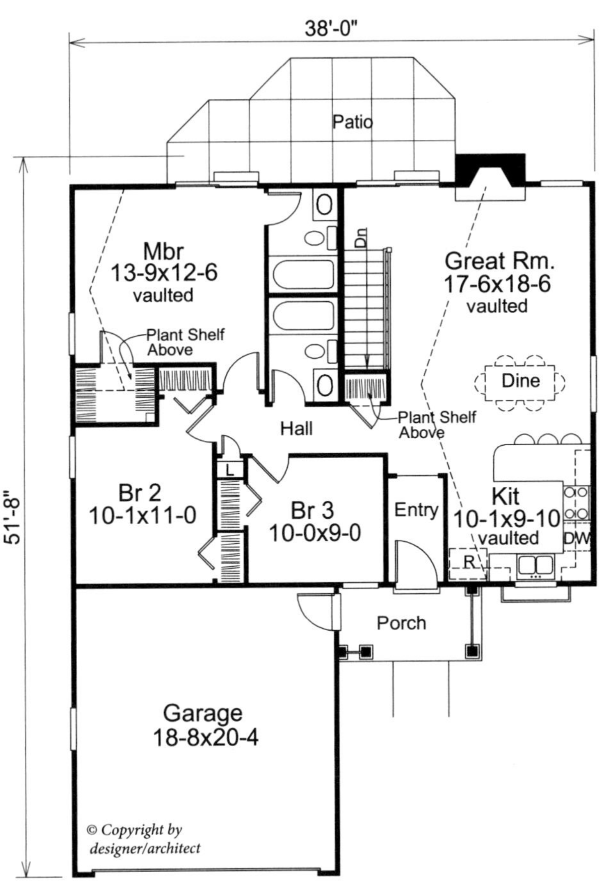

Plan #541-057D-0044 • Price Code B

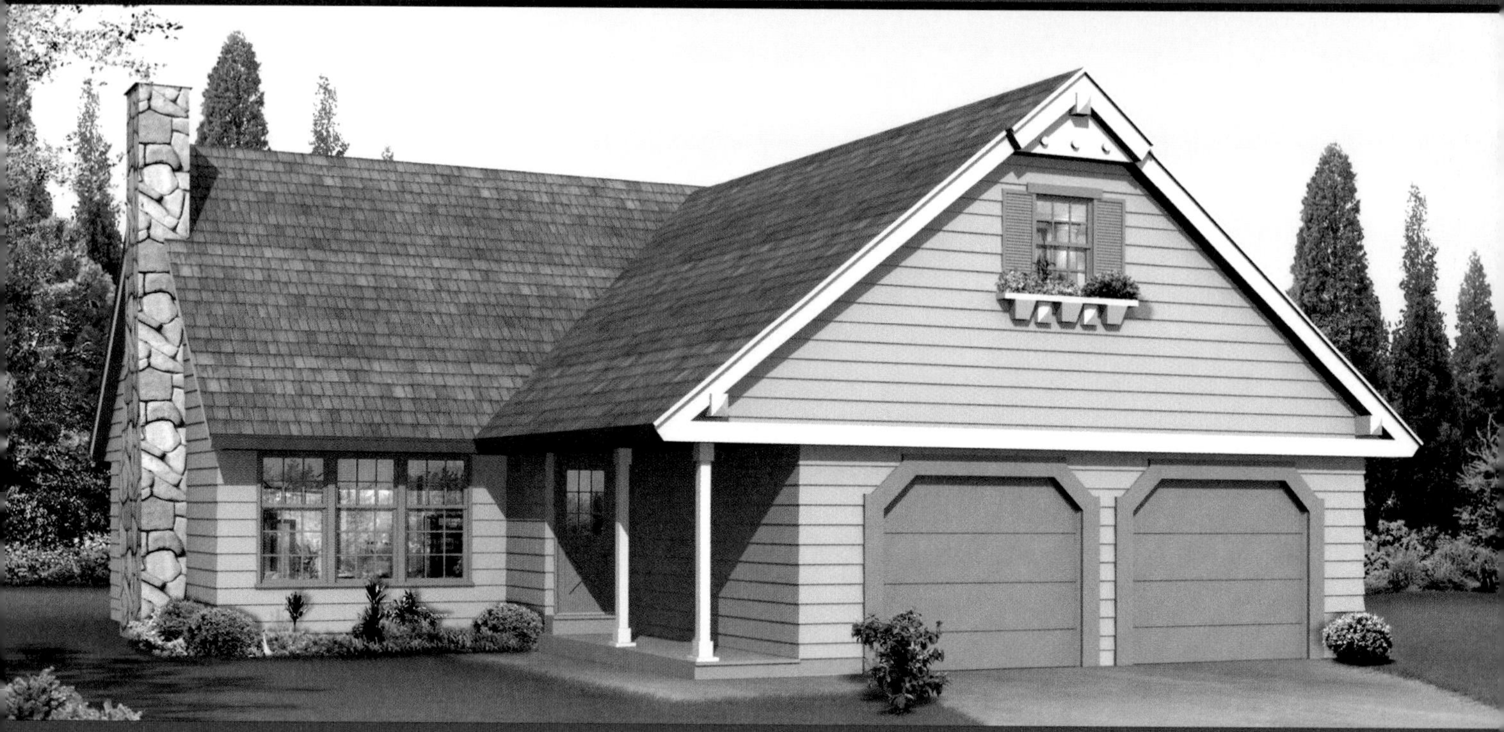

Charming Country Home

- 1,935 total square feet of living area
- The living and dining areas combine for an open atmosphere perfect for entertaining
- One first floor bedroom offers an abundance of closets, a dressing area and private bath access
- The second floor is comprised of a family relaxing area and a large bedroom with private bath access and plenty of storage
- 3 bedrooms, 2 baths, 2-car garage
- Basement foundation

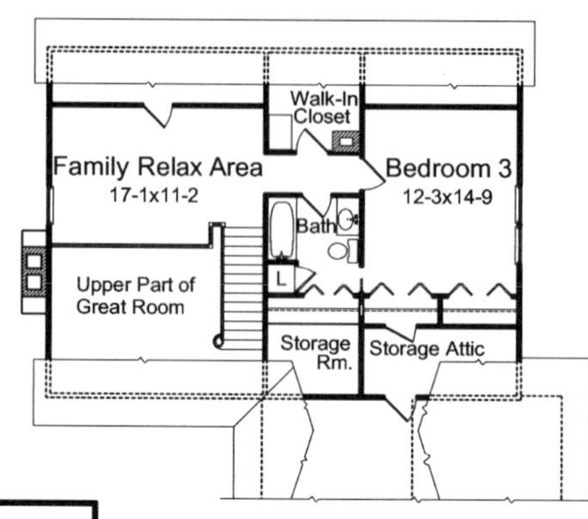

Second Floor
848 sq. ft.

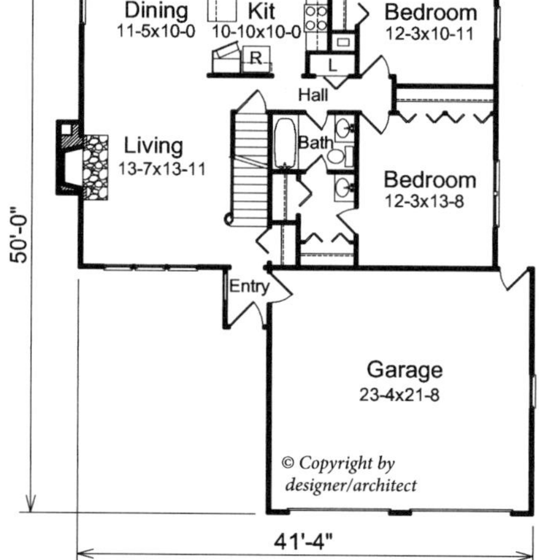

First Floor
1,087 sq. ft.

Plan #541-077L-0098 • Price Code E

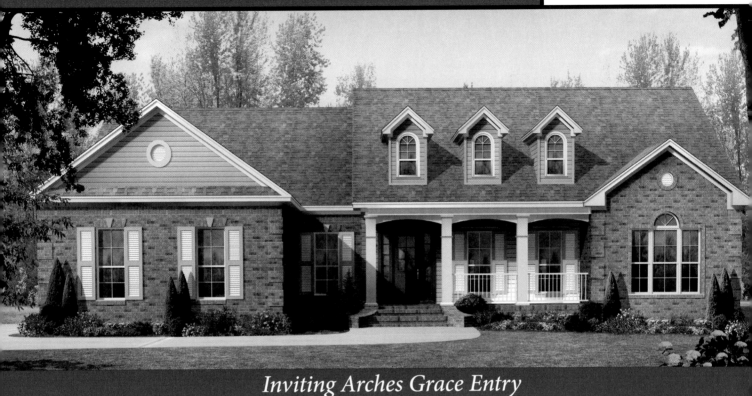

Inviting Arches Grace Entry

- 2,000 total square feet of living area
- Triple dormers above a covered porch offer country-style curb appeal
- The open great room, kitchen and eating area include a gas fireplace and curved island bar as focal points
- Entertain in style with your outdoor kitchen located on the rear covered porch
- 3 bedrooms, 2 1/2 baths, 2-car side entry garage
- Basement foundation, drawings also include slab and crawl space foundations

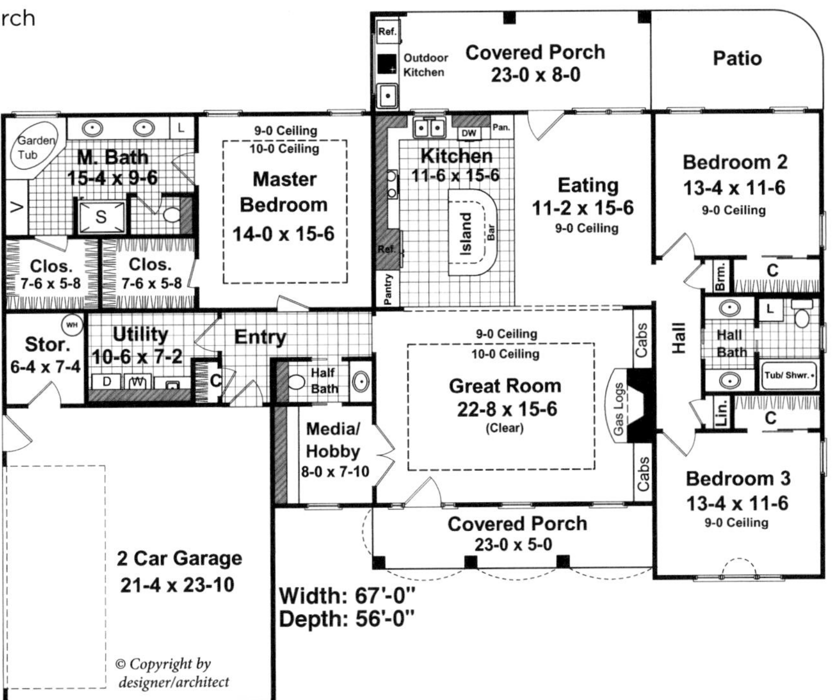

Plan #541-001D-0112 • Price Code C

Dramatic Layout Created By Victorian Turret

- 2,050 total square feet of living area
- Energy efficient home with 2" x 6" exterior walls
- Large kitchen and dining area has access to the garage and porch
- Master bedroom features unique turret design, private bath and large walk-in closet
- 3 bedrooms, 2 1/2 baths, 2-car side entry garage
- Basement foundation, drawings also include crawl space and slab foundations

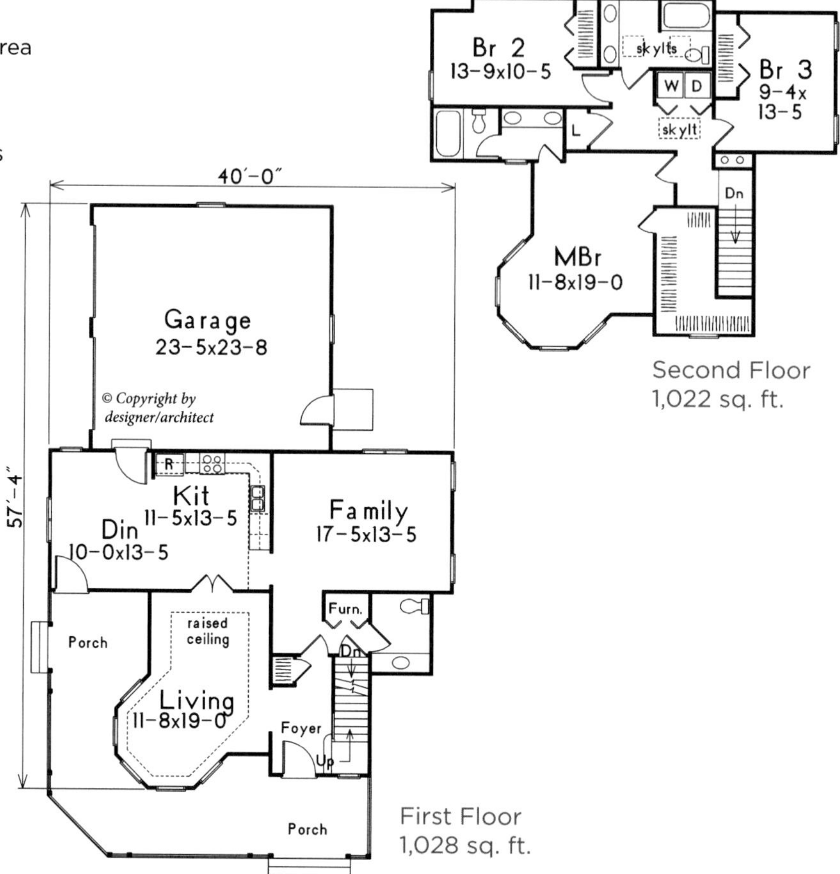

Second Floor
1,022 sq. ft.

First Floor
1,028 sq. ft.

• To Order See Page 288 or Call Toll-Free 1-877-379-3420

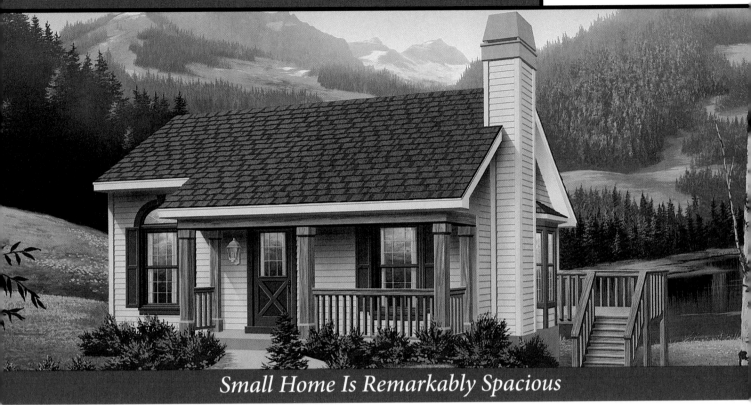

Small Home Is Remarkably Spacious

- 914 total square feet of living area
- Large porch for leisure evenings
- Dining area with bay window, open stairs and a pass-through kitchen create openness
- Basement includes generous garage space, a storage area, finished laundry and mechanical room
- 2 bedrooms, 1 bath, 2-car drive under rear entry garage
- Basement foundation

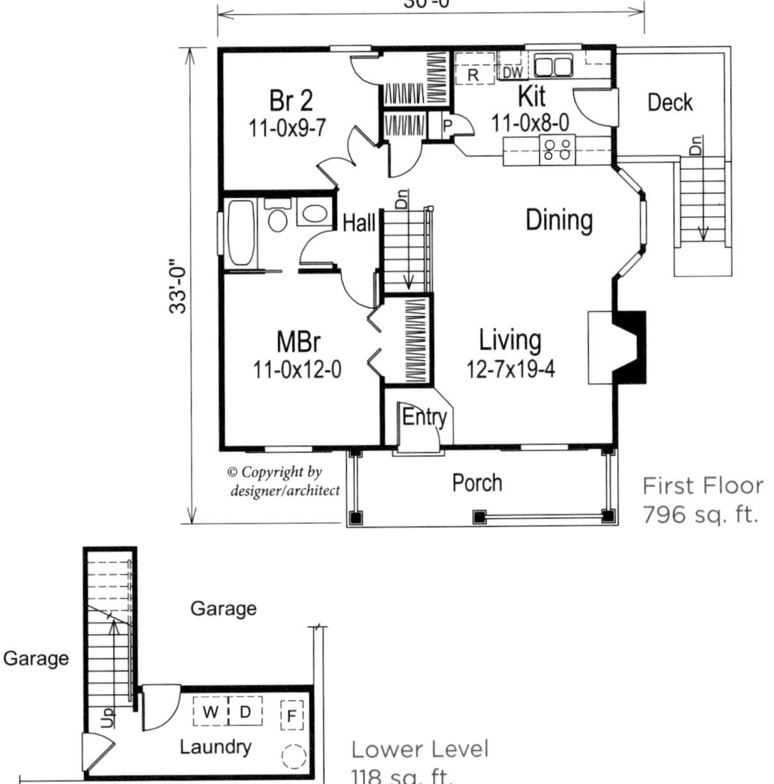

First Floor
796 sq. ft.

Lower Level
118 sq. ft.

Plan #541-023D-0006 • Price Code D

Attractive Entry Created By Full-Length Porch

- 2,357 total square feet of living area
- 9′ ceilings on the first floor
- Secluded master bedroom includes a private bath with double walk-in closets and vanity
- Balcony overlooks living room with large fireplace
- The future game room on the second floor has an additional 303 square feet of living area
- 4 bedrooms, 3 1/2 baths, 2-car side entry garage
- Slab foundation, drawings also include crawl space foundation

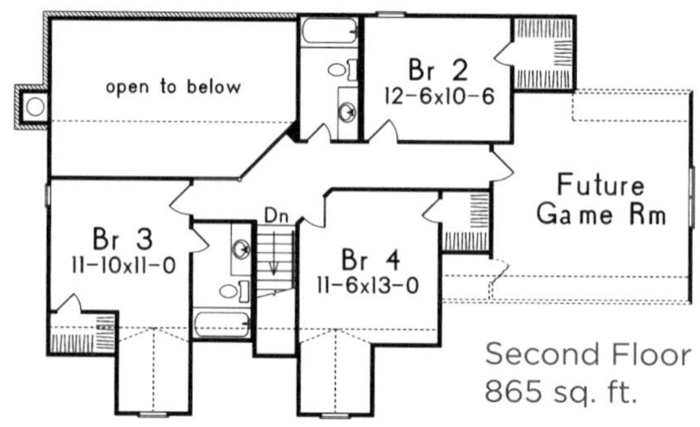

Second Floor
865 sq. ft.

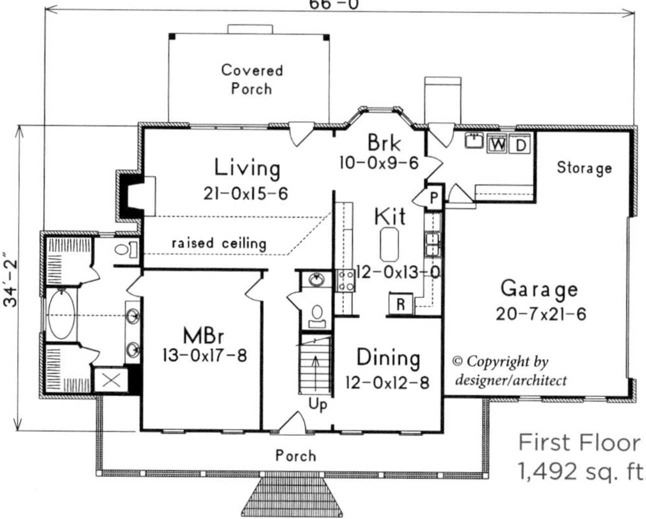

First Floor
1,492 sq. ft.

• To Order See Page 288 or Call Toll-Free 1-877-379-3420

Plan #541-057D-0037 • Price Code A

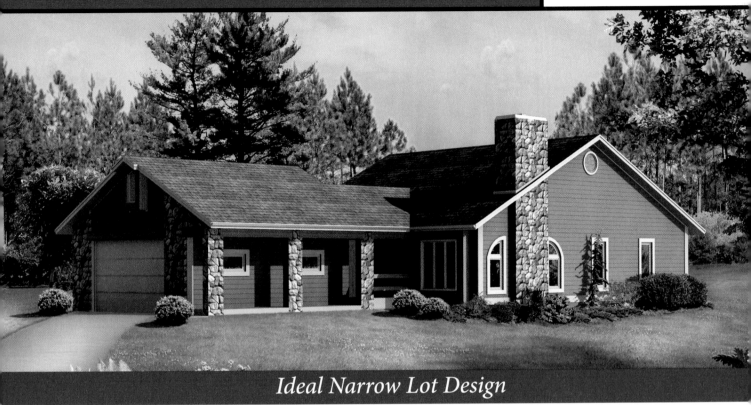

Ideal Narrow Lot Design

- 1,608 total square feet of living area
- Easily relax in this spacious living room that features a unique soffit ceiling and a handsome fireplace
- The kitchen is designed for efficiency with a nearby pantry for storage and opens to the dining room
- A walk-in closet and deluxe private bath enhance the master bedroom suite
- 2 bedrooms, 2 baths, 2-car side entry garage
- Basement foundation

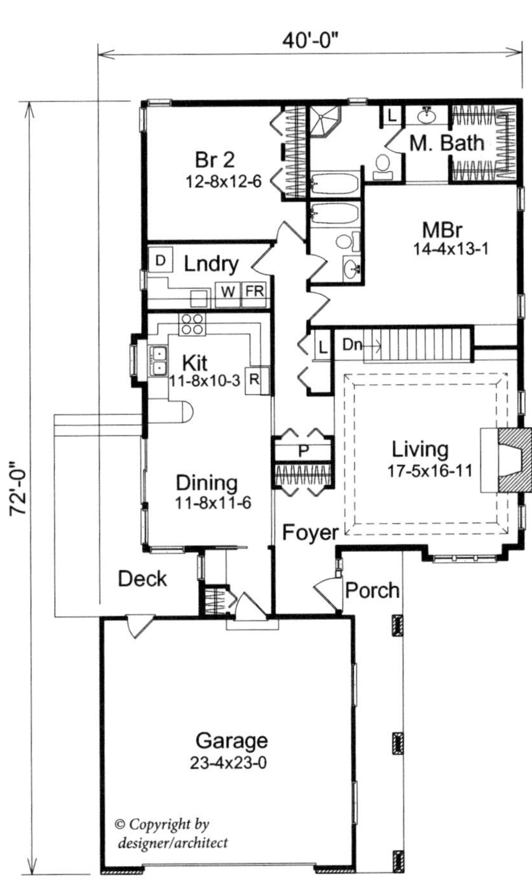

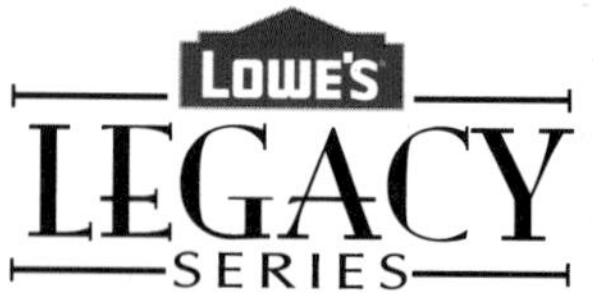

Plan #541-013L-0047 • Price Code C

Beautiful Bayed Bedrooms

- 1,897 total square feet of living area
- No doors between the main rooms on the first floor allows easy flow between spaces
- Family room has large windows and a fireplace, perfect for summer or winter living
- Master bedroom has a generous walk-in closet
- Distinctive bayed bedrooms are flooded with warm, natural light
- The optional playroom/media room provides an additional 263 square feet of living area
- 4 bedrooms, 3 baths, 3-car side entry garage
- Basement foundation

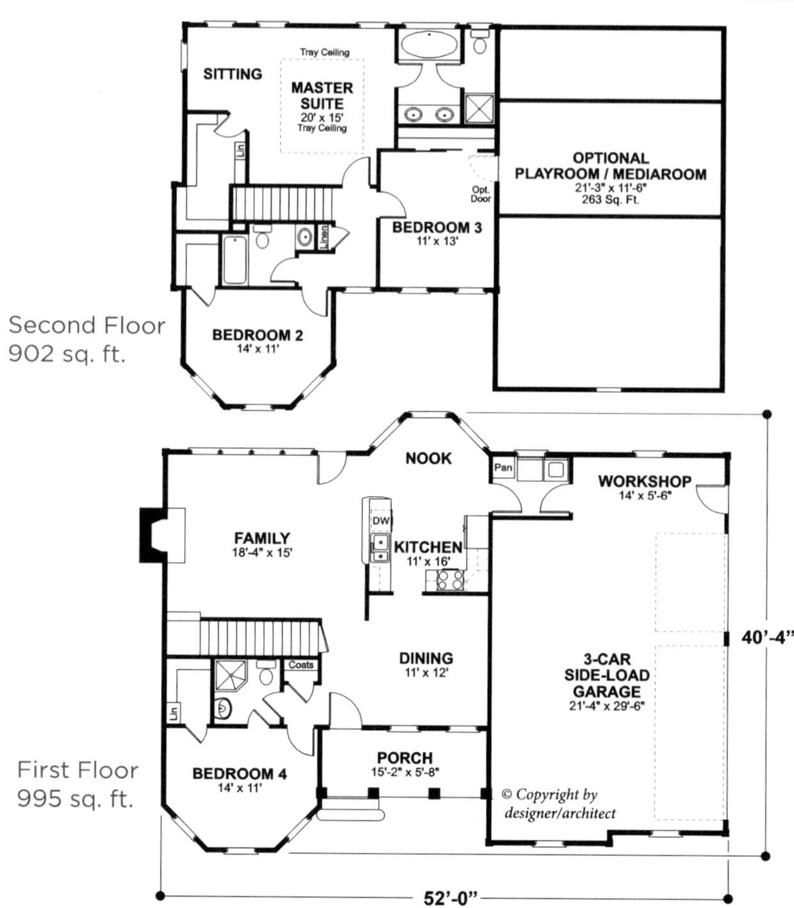

Second Floor
902 sq. ft.

First Floor
995 sq. ft.

• To Order See Page 288 or Call Toll-Free 1-877-379-3420

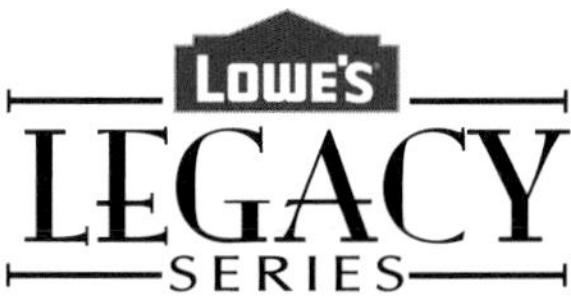

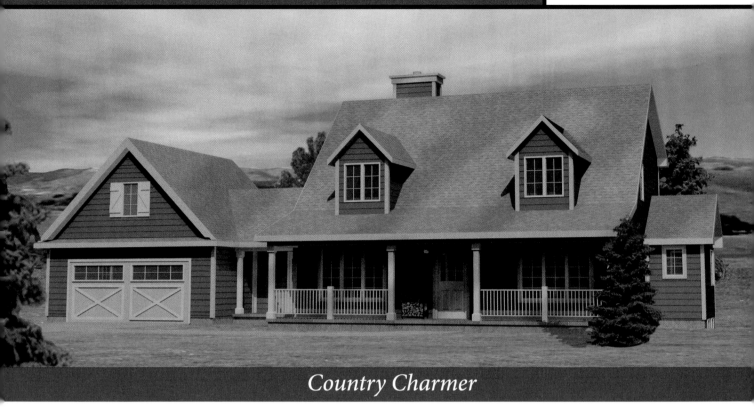

Country Charmer

- 1,897 total square feet of living area
- The kitchen/breakfast room is spacious enough for plenty of family to relax and dine without feeling crowded
- A corner whirlpool tub and large walk-in closet are great additions to the master bedroom
- A large open loft area on the second floor offers a casual gathering space perfect for a children's playroom
- The bonus room above the garage has an additional 264 square feet of living area
- 2″ x 6″ exterior walls available, please order plan #541-058D-0125
- 3 bedrooms, 2 1/2 baths, 2-car garage
- Basement foundation

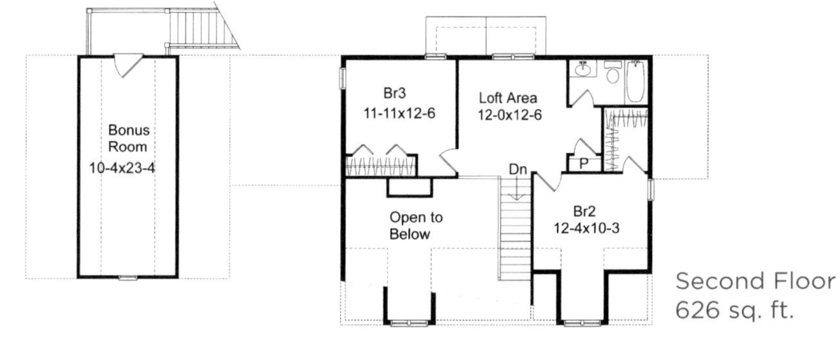

Second Floor
626 sq. ft.

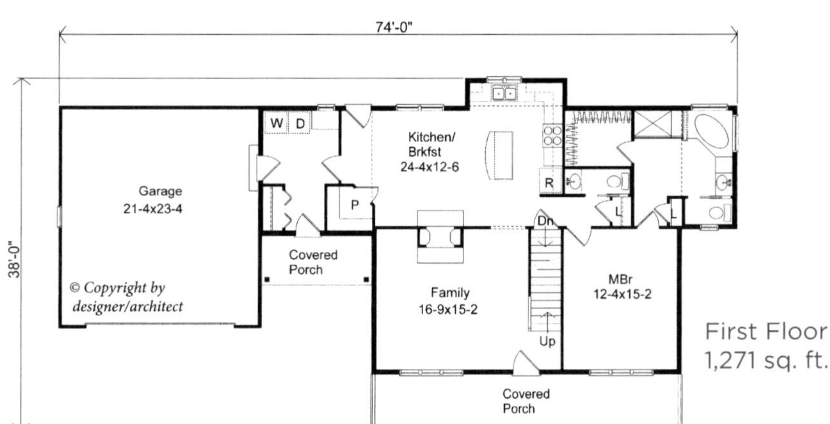

First Floor
1,271 sq. ft.

Plan #541-007D-0168 • Price Code C

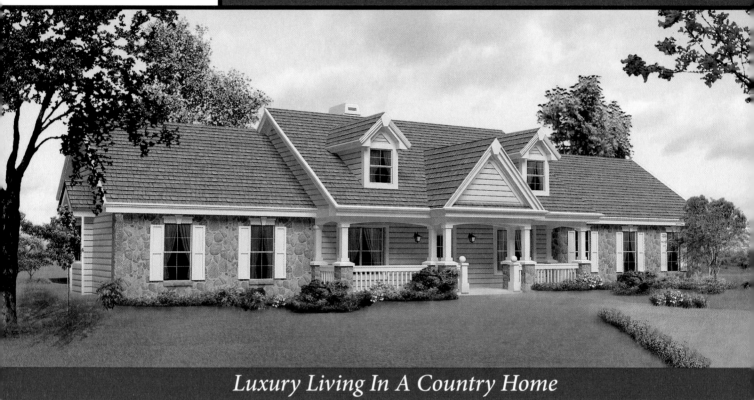

Luxury Living In A Country Home

- 1,814 total square feet of living area
- This home enjoys a large country porch for a perfect leisure living area
- The vaulted great room, sunny breakfast room and kitchen with snack bar are all open to one another to create a very open sense of spaciousness
- A sensational lavish bath is the highlight of the master bedroom suite that features double vanities with a makeup counter, a 5' x 5' shower with seat, separate toilet and a step-up whirlpool-in-a-sunroom
- 3 bedrooms, 2 baths, 3-car side entry garage
- Basement foundation

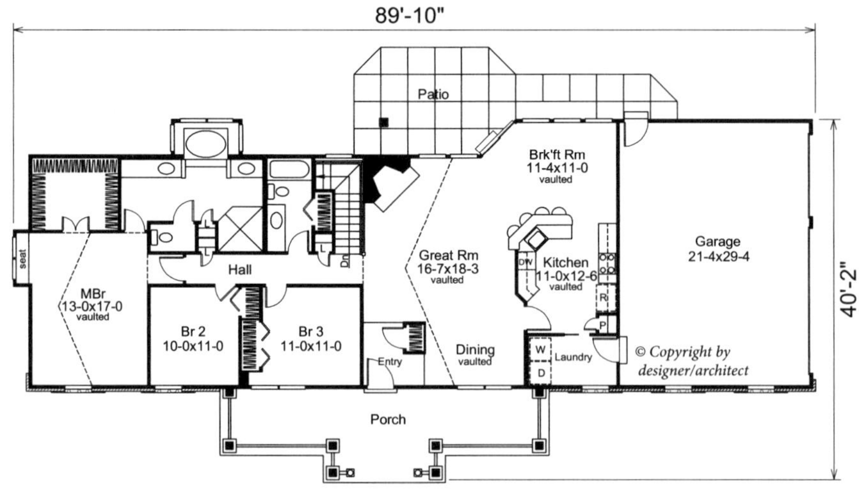

• To Order See Page 288 or Call Toll-Free 1-877-379-3420

Plan #541-058D-0030 • Price Code AA

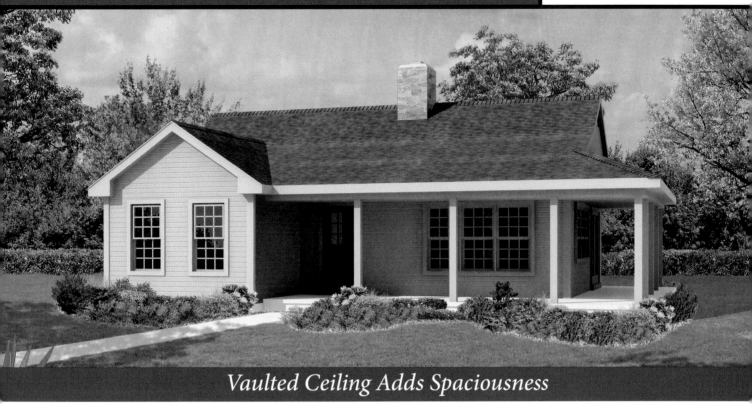

Vaulted Ceiling Adds Spaciousness

- 990 total square feet of living area
- Wrap-around porch creates a relaxing retreat
- Combined family and dining rooms boast a vaulted ceiling
- Space for an efficiency washer and dryer unit offers convenience
- 2" x 6" exterior walls available, please order plan #541-058D-0086
- 2 bedrooms, 1 bath
- Crawl space foundation

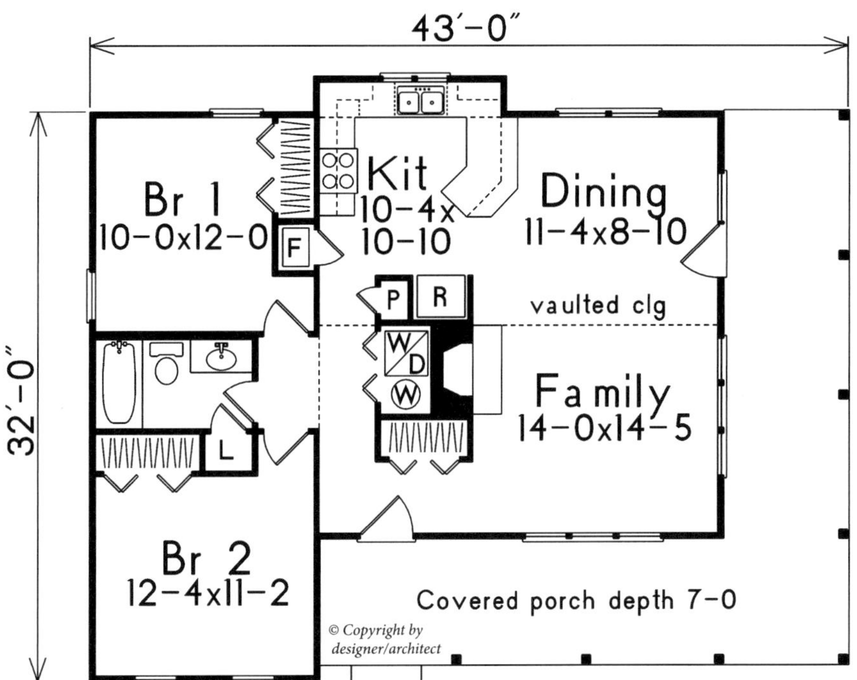

Plan #541-007D-0125 • Price Code A

Cozy Ranch With Spacious Features

- 1,302 total square feet of living area
- Triple gables, decorative porch and brickwork create a handsome exterior
- The U-shaped kitchen features a snack bar, built-in pantry, open woodcrafted stairs to the basement and adjacent laundry/mud room
- Sliding doors to the patio and a fireplace with flanking windows adorn the large vaulted family room
- The master bedroom accesses the patio through glass sliding doors and includes a private bath and walk-in closet
- 3 bedrooms, 2 baths, 2-car garage
- Basement foundation

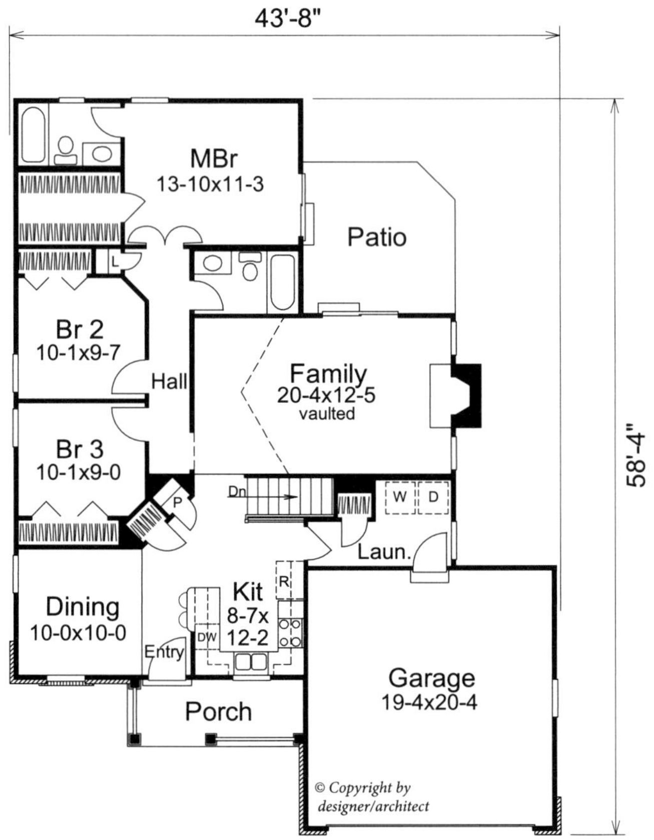

• To Order See Page 288 or Call Toll-Free 1-877-379-3420

Plan #541-013L-0044 • Price Code B

Abundance of Closet Space

- 1,420 total square feet of living area
- Windowed wall in the master suite lets in plenty of light and creates an open atmosphere
- High ceiling connects the family room and dining area into a large, airy room
- Large corner counter in kitchen provides an easy place for quick meals
- 3 bedrooms, 2 baths
- Crawl space foundation, drawings also include slab foundation

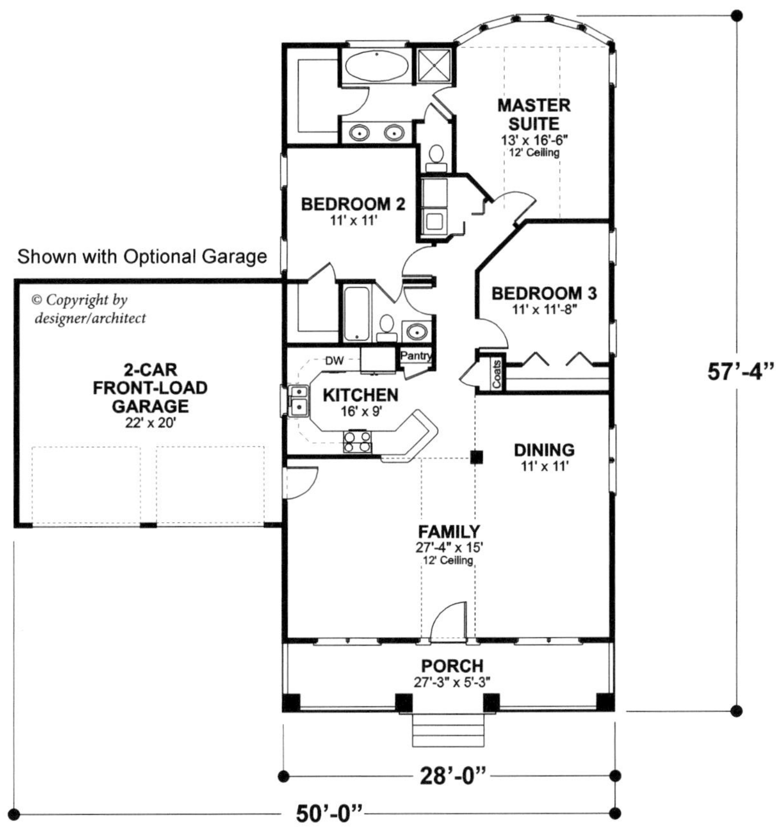

Plan #541-121D-0017 • Price Code AA

Handsome Two Bedroom Ranch

- 1,379 total square feet of living area
- The kitchen shares the center island and eating bar with the open great room for easy meals
- Both bedrooms have ample closet space and enjoy bay windows
- The vaulted breakfast area boasts a bay window with access to the rear patio
- 2 bedrooms, 1 bath, 2-car garage
- Basement foundation

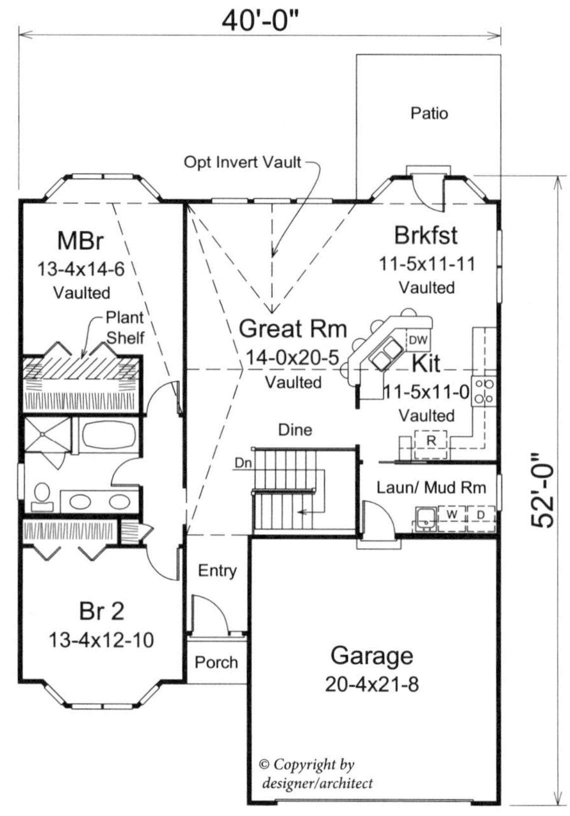

• To Order See Page 288 or Call Toll-Free 1-877-379-3420

Plan #541-007D-0236 • Price Code B

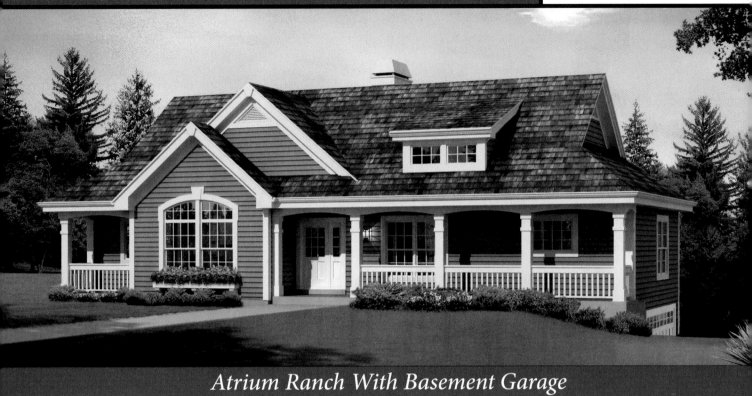

Atrium Ranch With Basement Garage

- 1,676 total square feet of living area
- Pleasant country home has a second porch private to master bedroom
- The great room features a fireplace, vaulted ceiling, vaulted atrium stair with arched window wall and convenient access to the rear patio and bedroom 3/study
- A walk-in pantry, handy laundry room and breakfast area are the many amenities of the large kitchen with center island
- The master bedroom has a vaulted ceiling, arched windows with planter box, two walk-in closets, a luxury bath with separate shower and access to a covered porch
- The lower level atrium has 85 square feet of living area which is included in the total square footage
- 3 bedrooms, 2 baths, 2-car drive under side entry garage
- Basement foundation

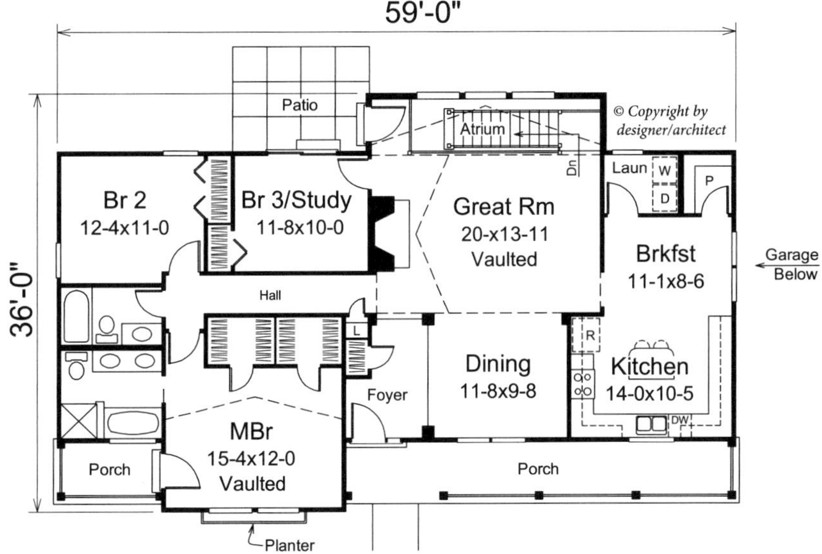

Plan #541-013L-0159 • Price Code B

Great Porch Opportunities

- 1,992 total square feet of living area
- Enter double doors off the foyer and discover a secluded living room that could also be converted to a home office
- The spacious master suite enjoys its own sunny sitting area, pampering bath and walk-in closet
- The kitchen is positioned perfectly between the bayed breakfast area and the formal dining room with tray ceiling
- 3 bedrooms, 2 1/2 baths, 3-car side entry garage
- Slab foundation

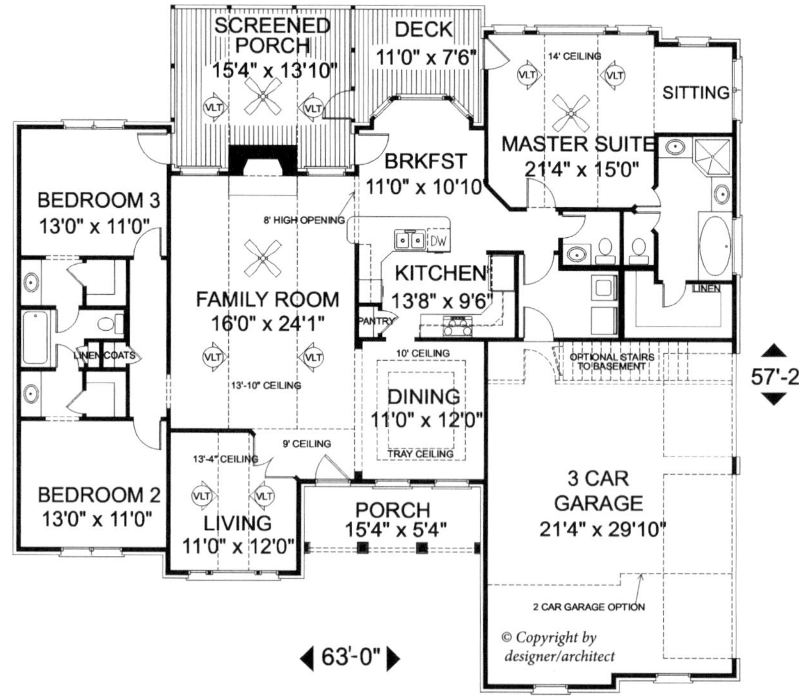

• To Order See Page 288 or Call Toll-Free 1-877-379-3420

Plan #541-058D-0065 • Price Code B

Delightful Family Home

- 1,512 total square feet of living area
- The spacious family room is warmed by a grand fireplace
- The kitchen/breakfast area features a pantry and access to the outdoors
- The laundry area includes space for an optional sink
- All bedrooms are located on the second floor for privacy
- 3 bedrooms, 2 1/2 baths, 2-car garage
- Basement foundation

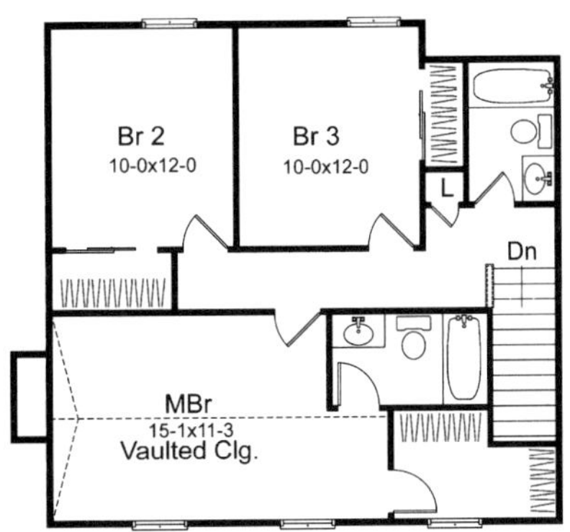

Second Floor
777 sq. ft.

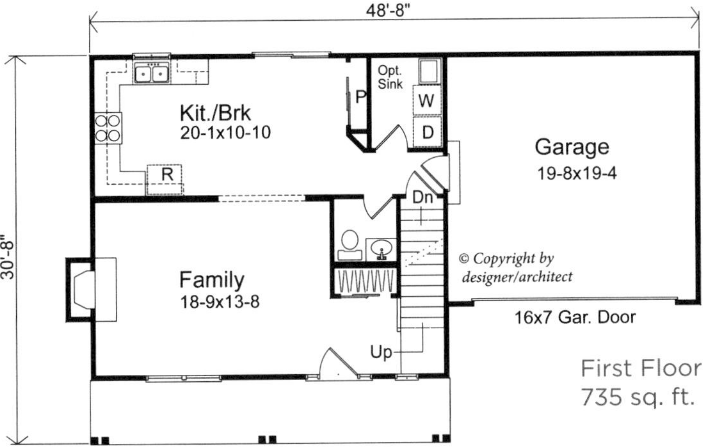

First Floor
735 sq. ft.

Plan #541-013L-0045 • Price Code C

Efficiently Designed Two-Story

- 1,695 total square feet of living area
- Large family room with fireplace makes a spacious, yet cozy gathering place
- Garage has convenient workshop space in back
- Screened back porch offers protection from sun and insects and connects to the open deck
- 3 bedrooms, 3 baths, 2-car garage
- Basement foundation

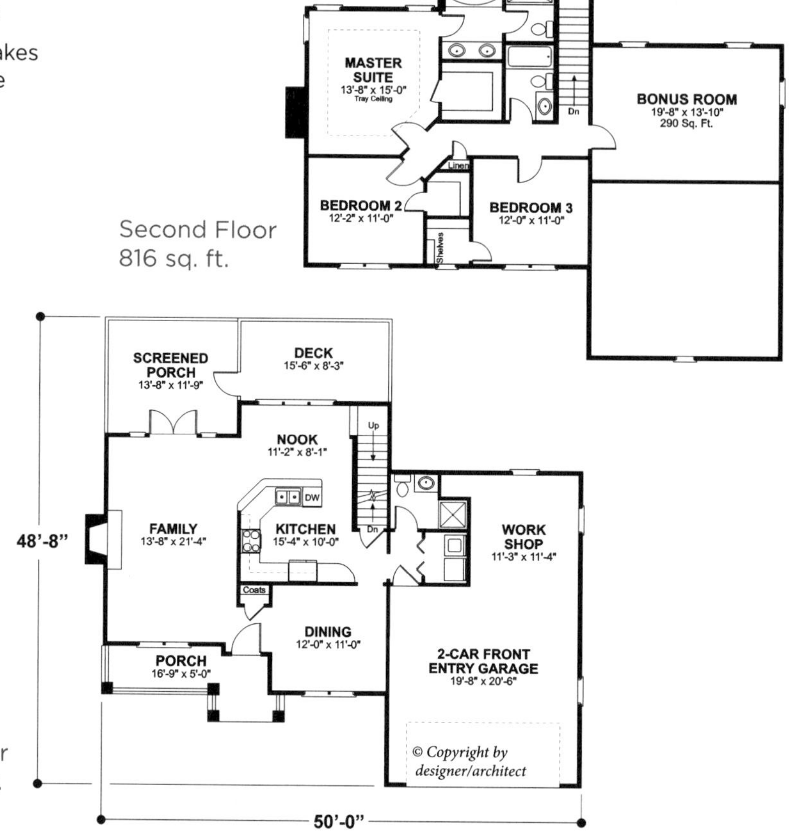

Second Floor
816 sq. ft.

First Floor
879 sq. ft.

• To Order See Page 288 or Call Toll-Free 1-877-379-3420

Plan #541-008D-0178 • Price Code C

LOWE'S LEGACY SERIES

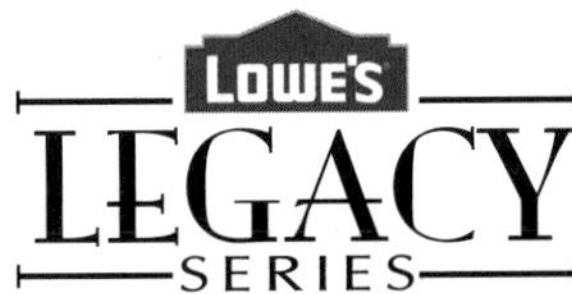

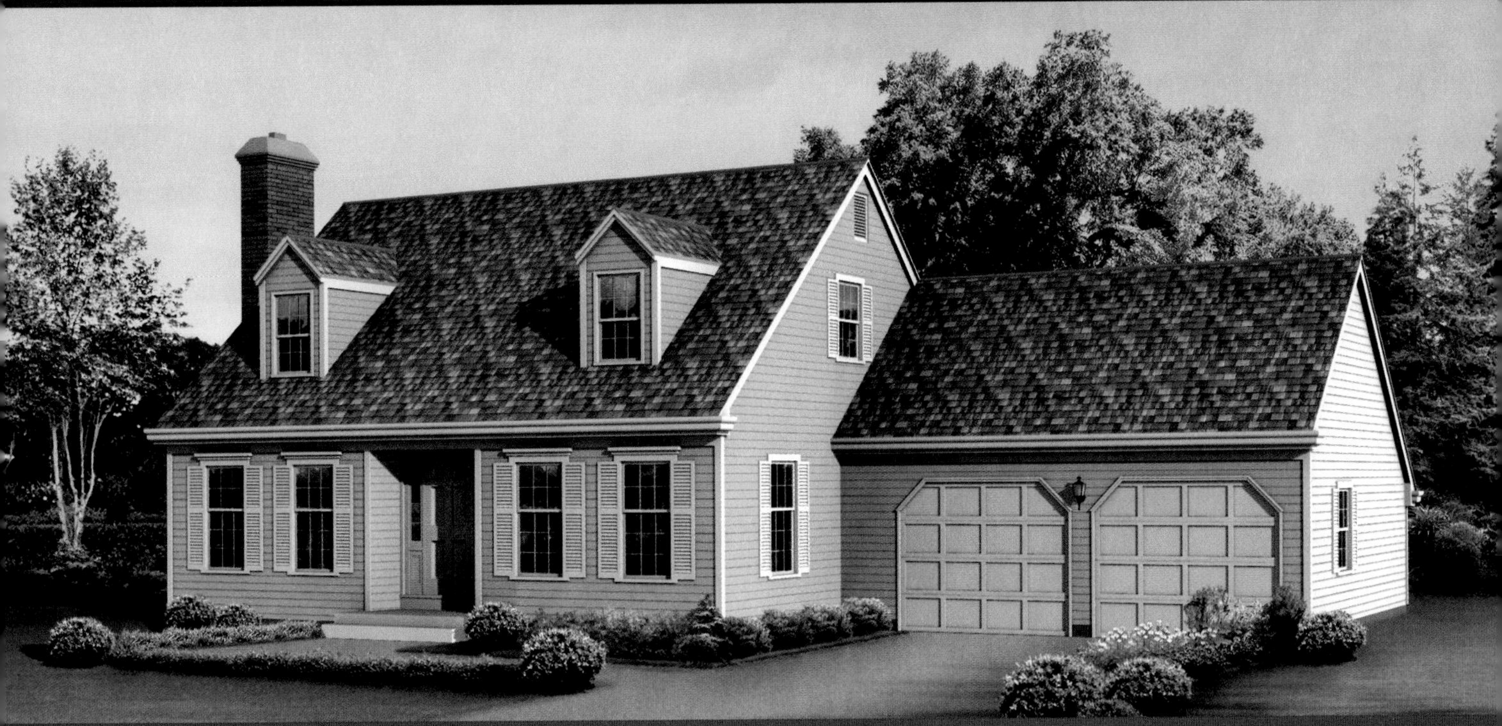

Design Has Traditional Elegance

- 1,872 total square feet of living area
- Recessed porch has entry door with sidelights and roof dormers adding charm
- Foyer with handcrafted stair adjoins living room with fireplace
- First floor bedroom has access to the bath and laundry room making it perfect for the master bedroom or a live-in parent
- Largest of three second floor bedrooms enjoys double closets and private access to the hall bath
- 4 bedrooms, 2 baths, 2-car garage
- Basement foundation, drawings also include crawl space and slab foundations

Second Floor
804 sq. ft.

First Floor
1,068 sq. ft.

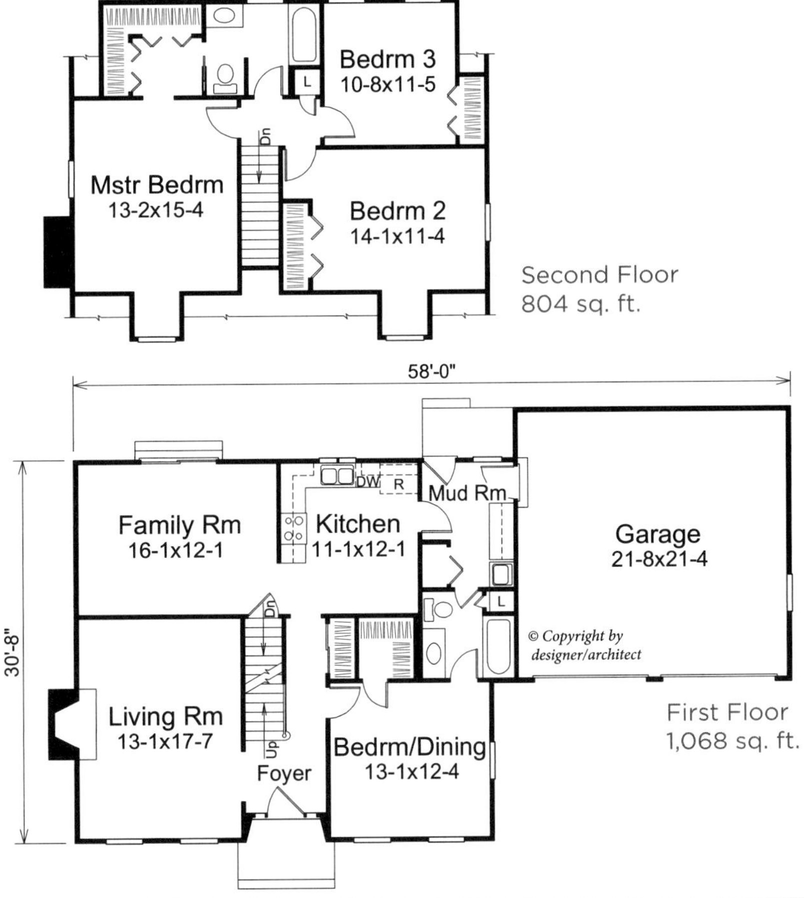

Plan #541-121D-0009 • Price Code C

Vaulted Two-Story Great Room

- 2,205 total square feet of living area
- The master bedroom enjoys a private first floor location along with a private bath and walk-in closet
- A flexible loft space can be found on the second floor perfect for a home office or children's play area
- The functional kitchen offers an eating bar and a corner walk-in pantry for added storage space
- 3 bedrooms, 2 1/2 baths, 2-car side entry garage
- Basement foundation

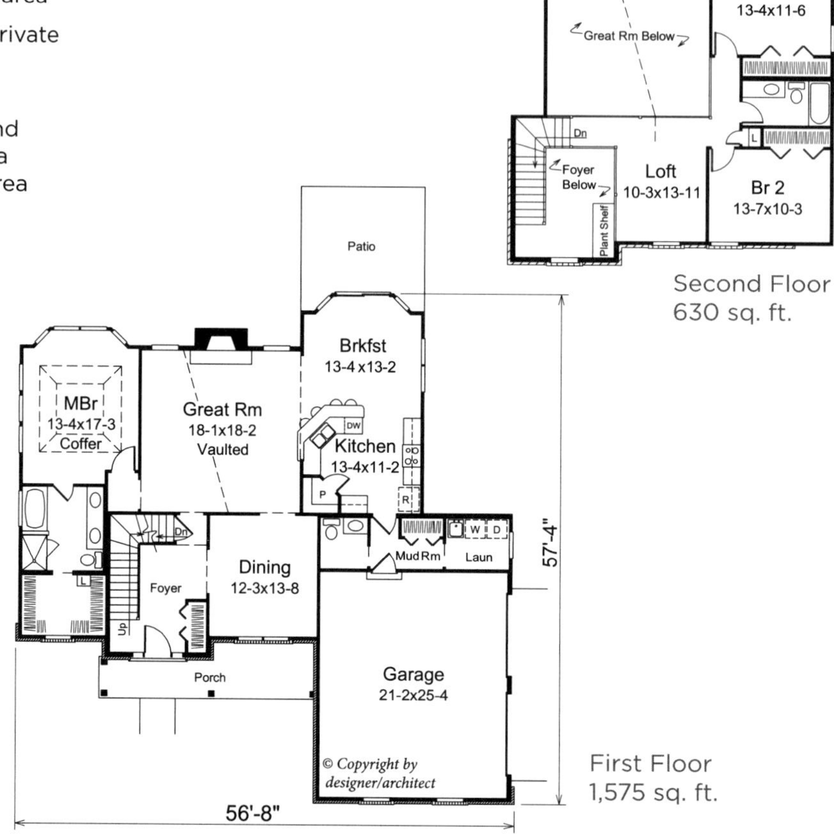

Second Floor
630 sq. ft.

First Floor
1,575 sq. ft.

To Order See Page 288 or Call Toll-Free 1-877-379-3420

Plan #541-013L-0160 • Price Code B

Stylish One-Level Living

- 1,898 total square feet of living area
- A large and open family room has a corner fireplace and screen porch access
- A stunning corner whirlpool tub provides the ultimate escape in the master suite
- A cozy and comforting breakfast area is perfect for intimate meals anytime of the day
- Bonus room above the garage has an additional 474 square feet of living space
- 3 bedrooms, 3 baths, 3-car side entry garage
- Basement foundation

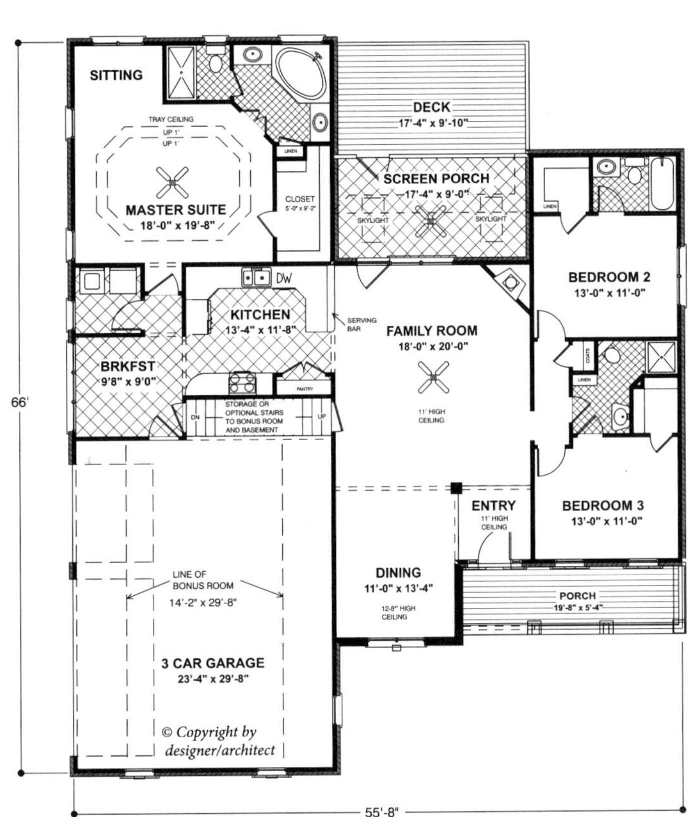

Plan #541-058D-0143 • Price Code AAA

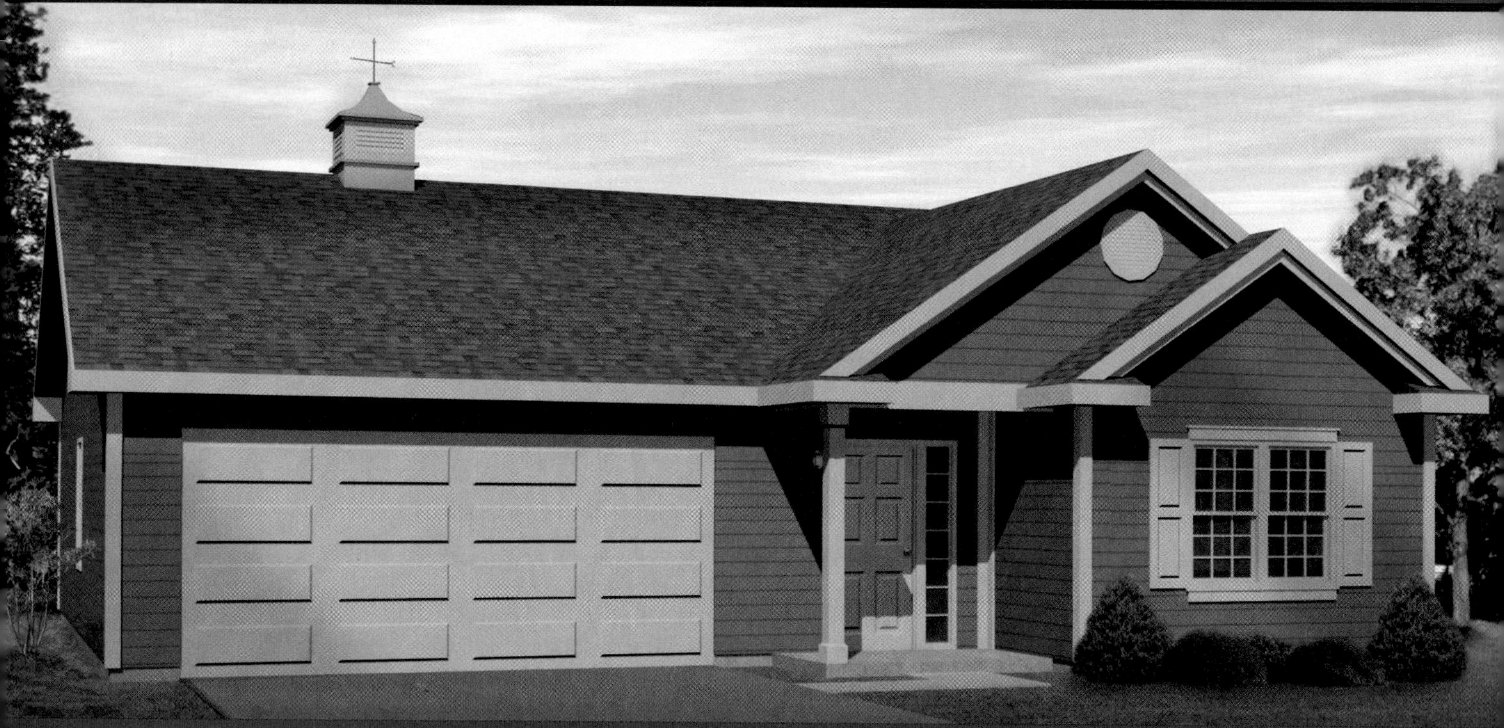

Cheerful Cottage

- 665 total square feet of living area
- Spacious breakfast/sitting area flows into kitchen area
- A stacked washer and dryer adds convenience to this cottage home
- A coat closet at the entry and a pantry in the kitchen provide essential storage space
- 1 bedroom, 1 bath, 1-car garage
- Slab foundation

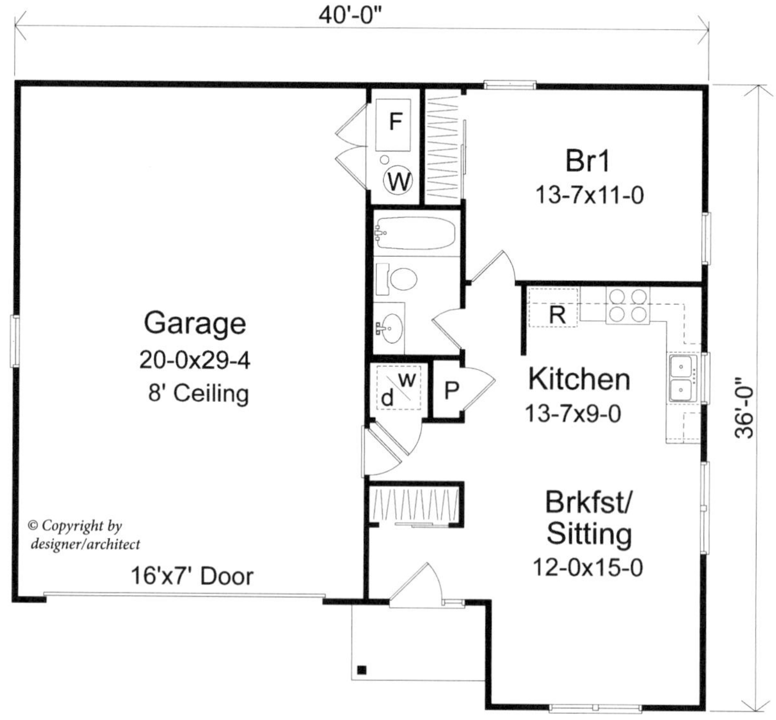

Plan #541-077L-0056 • Price Code E

Appealing Brick Exterior

- 2,000 total square feet of living area
- The vaulted ceiling and handsome gas fireplace draw guests to the great room
- The screened porch is great for year-round weather and opens to the covered porch for relaxing in warmer weather
- The hobby/office area near the great room is the perfect working space
- 4 bedrooms, 2 1/2 baths, 2-car side entry garage
- Basement foundation, drawings also include crawl space and slab foundations

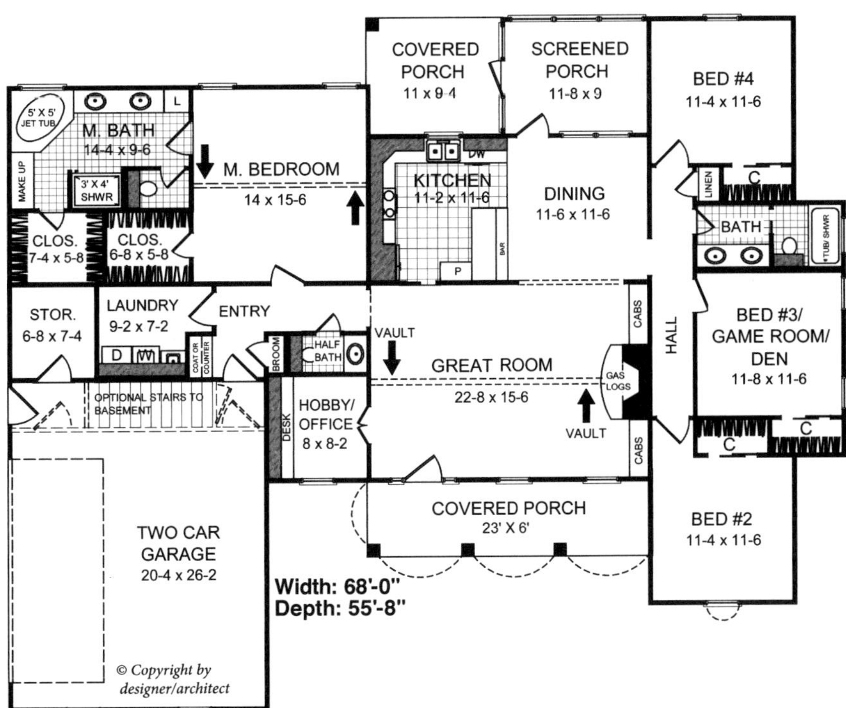

Plan #541-014D-0009 • Price Code A

Vaulted Ceilings Throughout Create Dramatic Interior

- 1,428 total square feet of living area
- Energy efficient home with 2" x 6" exterior walls
- 10' ceilings in the entry and hallway
- Vaulted secondary bedrooms
- Kitchen is loaded with amenities including an island with salad sink and pantry
- Master bedroom with vaulted ceiling includes a large walk-in closet and private master bath
- 3 bedrooms, 2 baths, 2-car garage
- Basement foundation, drawings also include crawl space foundation

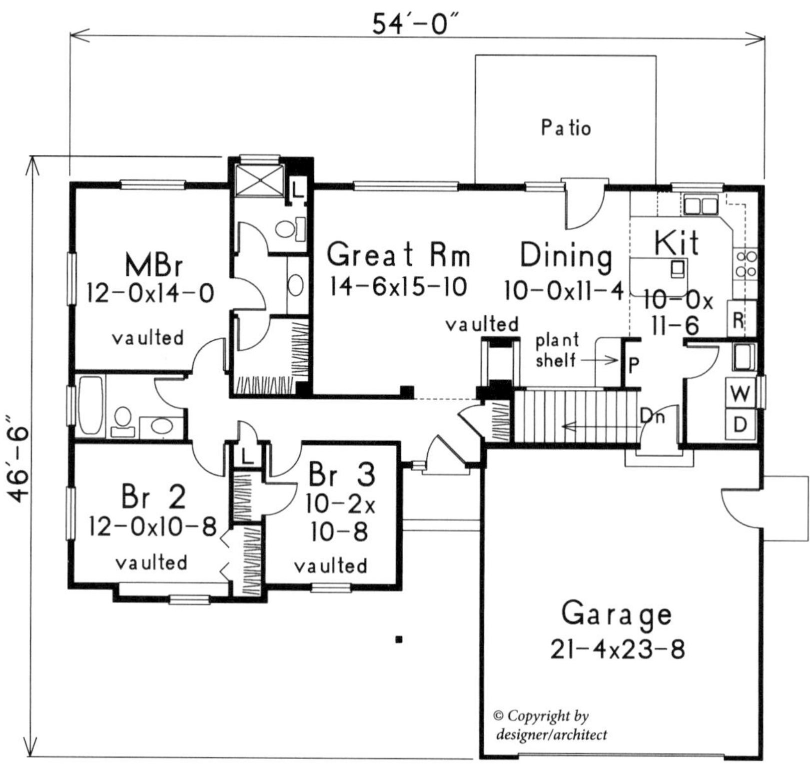

To Order See Page 288 or Call Toll-Free 1-877-379-3420

Plan #541-053D-0043 • Price Code A

LOWE'S LEGACY SERIES

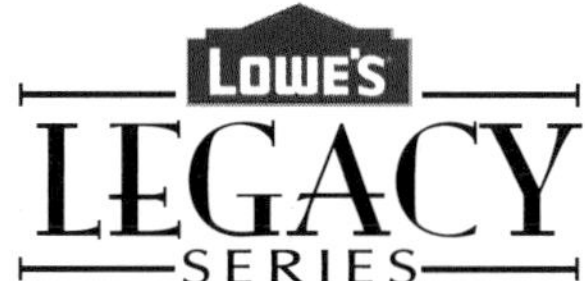

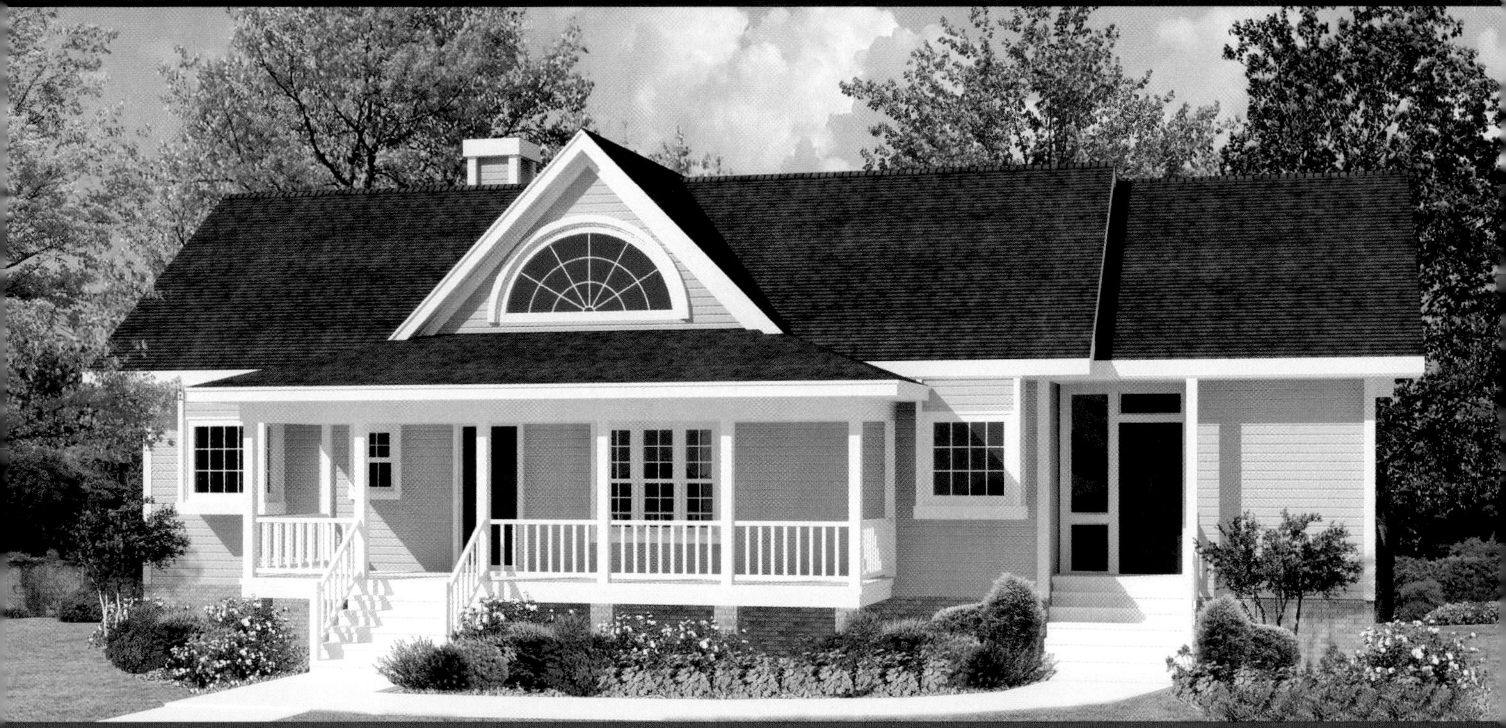

Large Sundeck Creates Outdoor Living Area

- 1,732 total square feet of living area
- Spacious great room has a vaulted ceiling and fireplace that overlooks the large sundeck
- Dramatic dining room boasts extensive windows and angled walls
- Vaulted master bedroom includes a private bath with laundry area and accesses the sundeck
- Convenient second entrance leads to the screen porch and dining area
- 3 bedrooms, 2 1/2 baths, 2-car side entry drive under garage
- Walk-out basement foundation

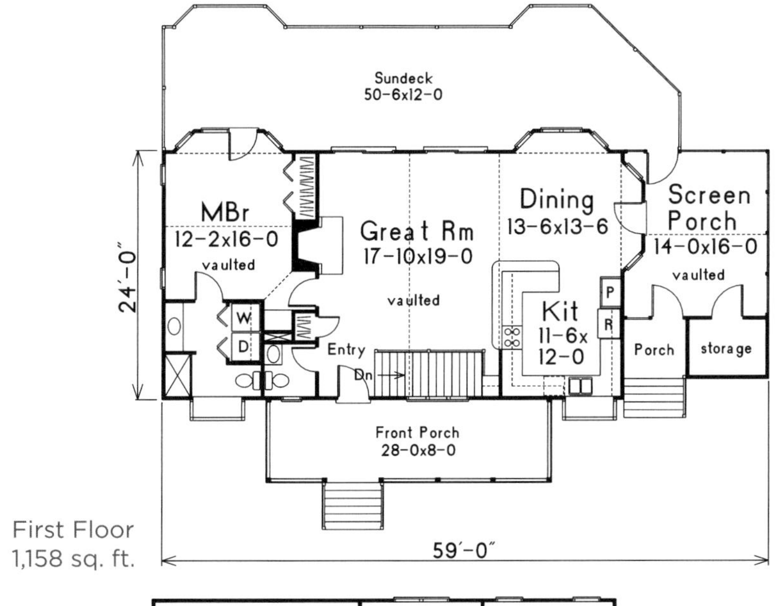

First Floor
1,158 sq. ft.

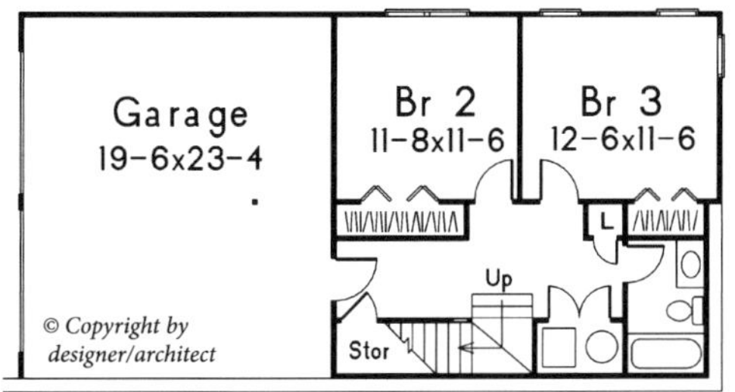

Lower Level
574 sq. ft.

Plan #541-008D-0004 • Price Code B

Charming Country Facade

- 1,643 total square feet of living area
- An attractive front entry porch gives this ranch a country accent
- Spacious family room is the focal point of this design
- The kitchen and hobby/laundry room are conveniently located near the gathering areas
- Formal living room in the front of the home provides area for quiet and privacy
- Master bedroom has view to the rear of the home and a generous walk-in closet
- 3 bedrooms, 2 baths, 2-car garage
- Basement foundation, drawings also include crawl space and slab foundations

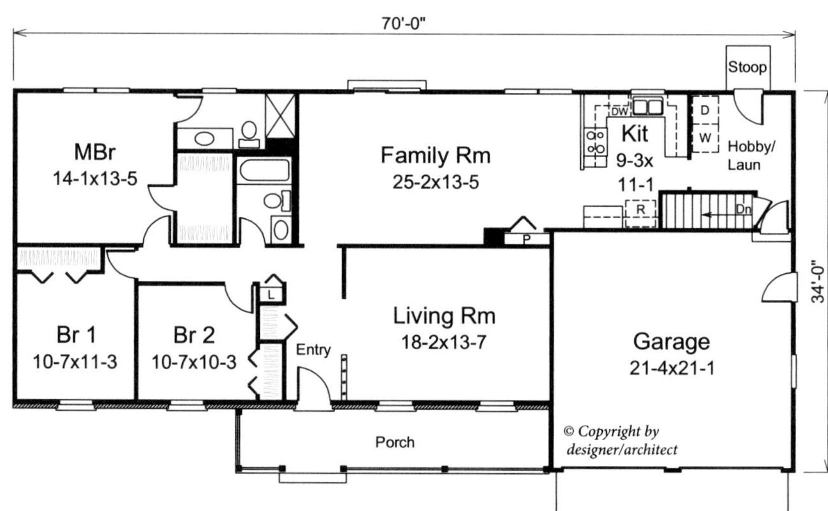

• To Order See Page 288 or Call Toll-Free 1-877-379-3420

Plan #541-037D-0022 • Price Code B

The Fireplace Is The Focal Point In The Living Room

- 1,539 total square feet of living area
- Standard 9' ceilings
- Master bedroom features a 10' tray ceiling, access to the porch, ample closet space and a full bath
- Serving counter separates kitchen and dining room
- Foyer with handy coat closet opens to living area with fireplace
- Handy utility room near kitchen
- 3 bedrooms, 2 baths, 2-car garage
- Slab foundation

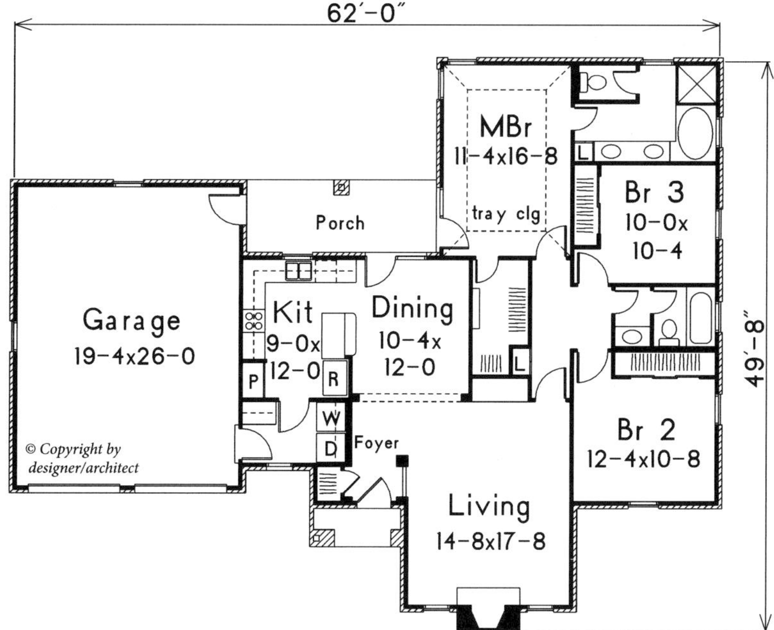

Plan #541-007D-0107 • Price Code AA

Three Bedroom Luxury In A Small Home

- 1,161 total square feet of living area
- Brickwork and feature window add elegance to this home for a narrow lot
- Living room enjoys a vaulted ceiling, fireplace and opens to the kitchen
- U-shaped kitchen offers a breakfast area with bay window, snack bar and built-in pantry
- 3 bedrooms, 2 baths
- Basement foundation

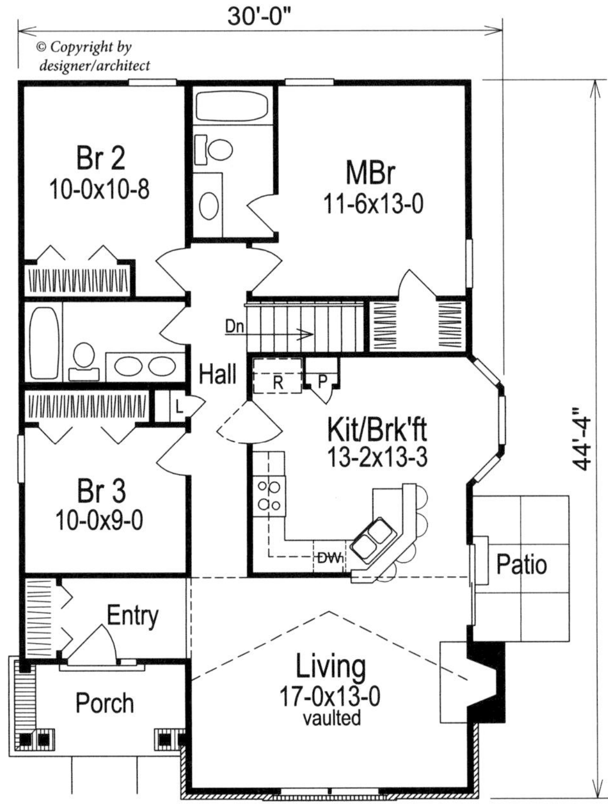

• To Order See Page 288 or Call Toll-Free 1-877-379-3420

Plan #541-053D-0002 • Price Code A

Bay Window Graces Luxury Master Bedroom

- 1,668 total square feet of living area
- Large bay windows grace the breakfast area, master bedroom and dining room
- Extensive walk-in closets and storage spaces are located throughout the home
- Handy covered entry porch
- Large living room has a fireplace, built-in bookshelves and a sloped ceiling
- 3 bedrooms, 2 baths, 2-car side entry drive under garage
- Walk-out basement foundation

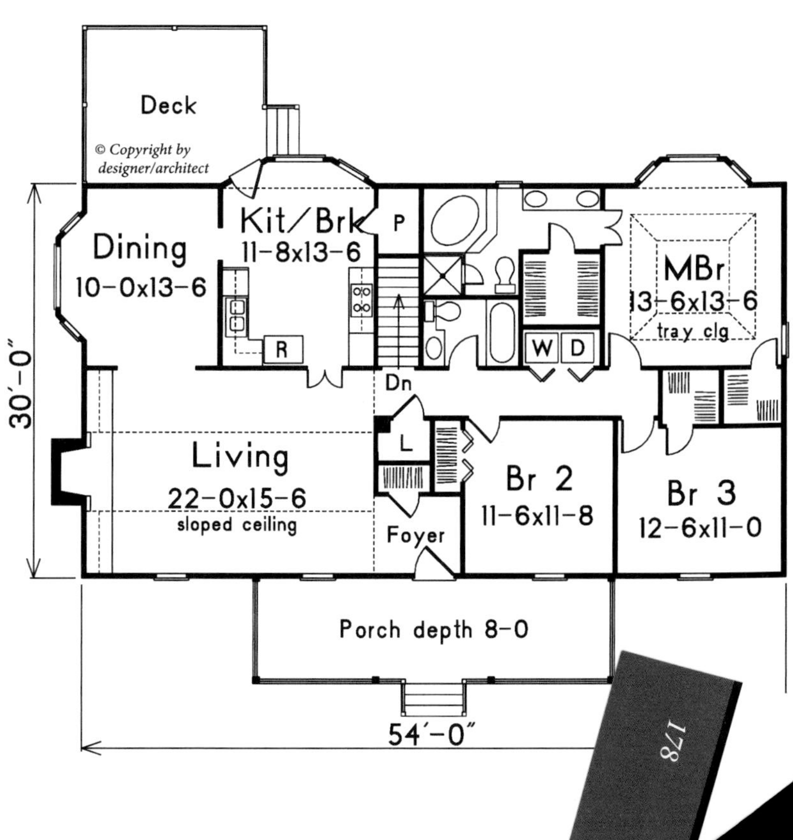

• To Order See Page 288 or Call Toll-Free 1-

LOWE'S LEGACY SERIES

Plan #541-017D-0002 • Price Code D

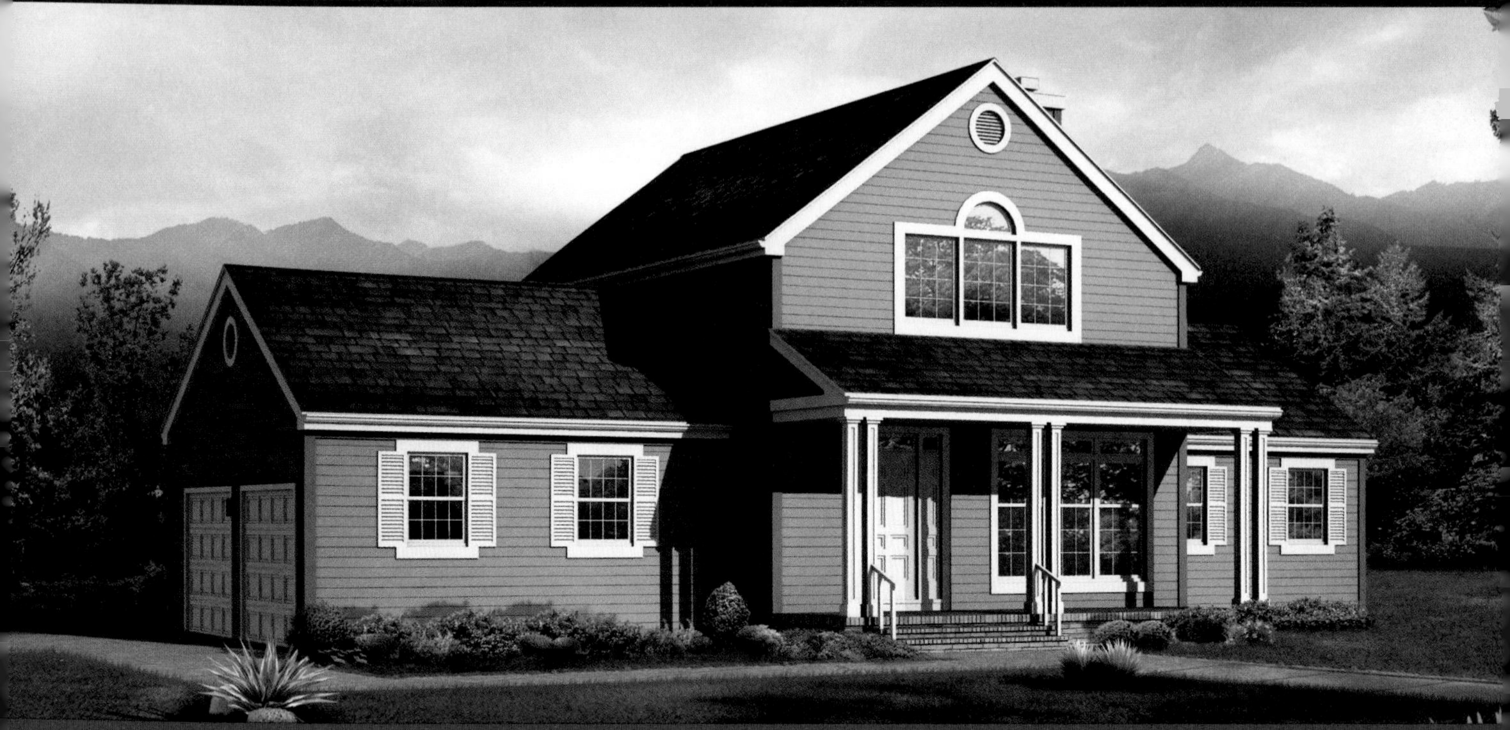

Modern Living

- 1,805 total square feet of living area
- Energy efficient home with 2" x 6" exterior walls
- Master bedroom forms its own wing
- Second floor bedrooms share a hall bath
- Large great room with fireplace blends into the formal dining room
- 3 bedrooms, 2 1/2 baths, 2-car side entry garage
- Basement foundation, drawings also include slab foundation

Second Floor
560 sq. ft.

First Floor
1,245 sq. ft.

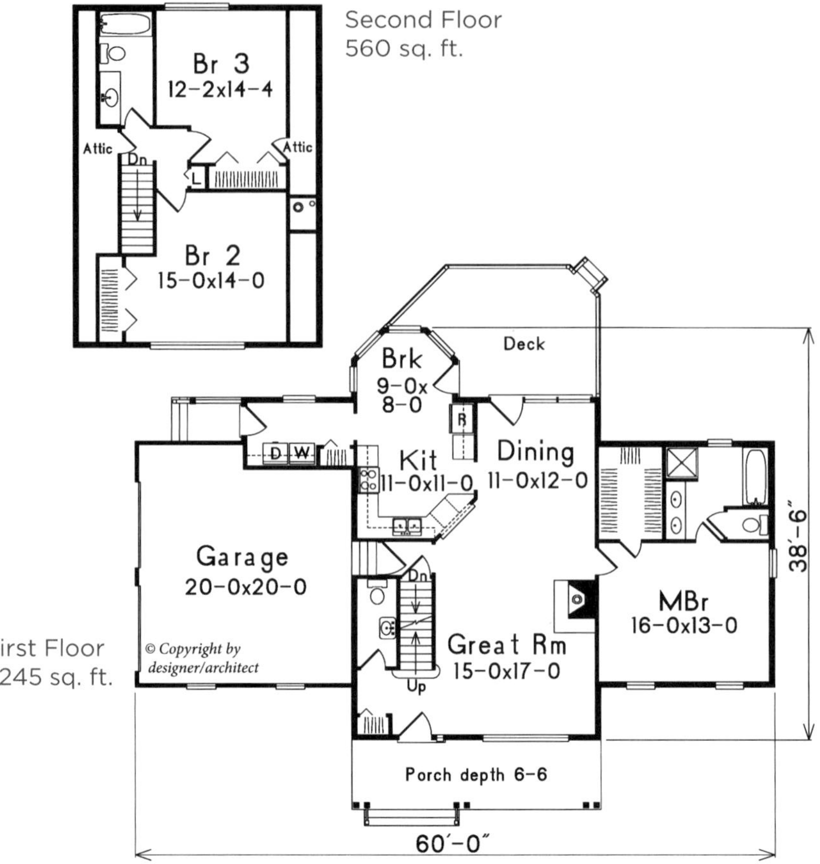

• To Order See Page 288 or Call Toll-Free 1-877-379-3420

Plan #541-061D-0001 • Price Code B

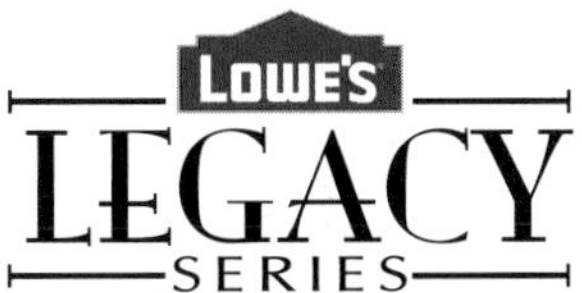

Contemporary Design With Large Family Room

- 1,747 total square feet of living area
- Entry opens into a large family room with coat closet, angled fireplace and attractive plant shelf
- Kitchen and master bedroom access the covered patio
- Functional kitchen includes ample workspace
- 4 bedrooms, 2 baths, 2-car garage
- Slab foundation

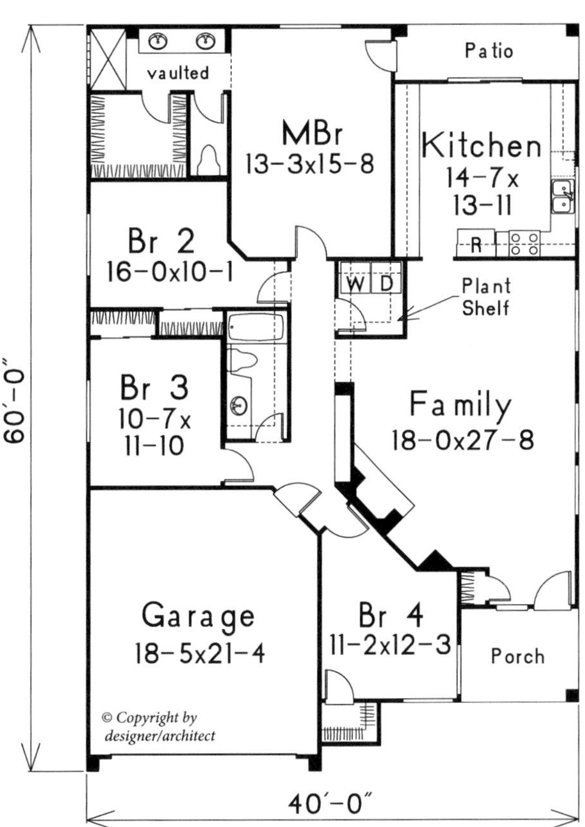

Plan #541-007D-0121 • Price Code B

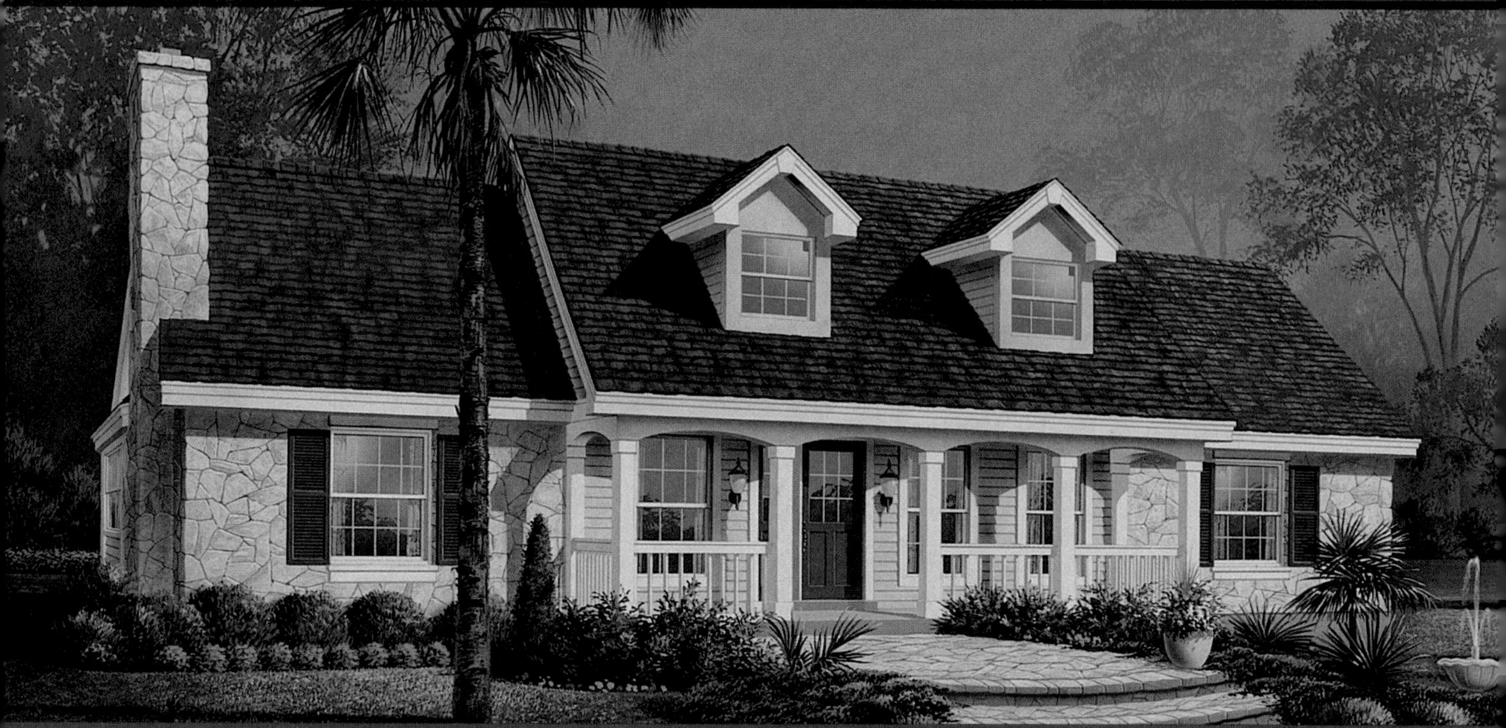

Ranch Of Enchantment

- 1,559 total square feet of living area
- A cozy country appeal is provided by a spacious porch, masonry fireplace, roof dormers and a perfect balance of stonework and siding
- Large living room enjoys a fireplace, bayed dining area and separate entry
- A U-shaped kitchen is adjoined by a breakfast room with bay window and large pantry
- 3 bedrooms, 2 1/2 baths, 2-car drive under side entry garage
- Basement foundation

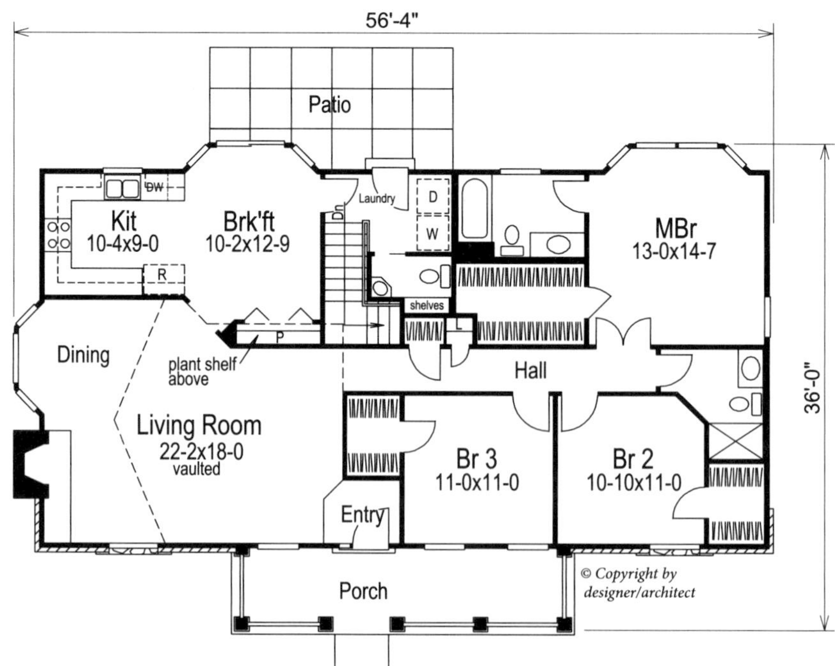

LOWE'S LEGACY SERIES

Plan #541-077L-0135 • Price Code E

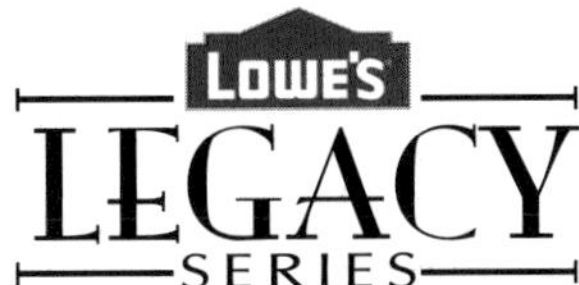

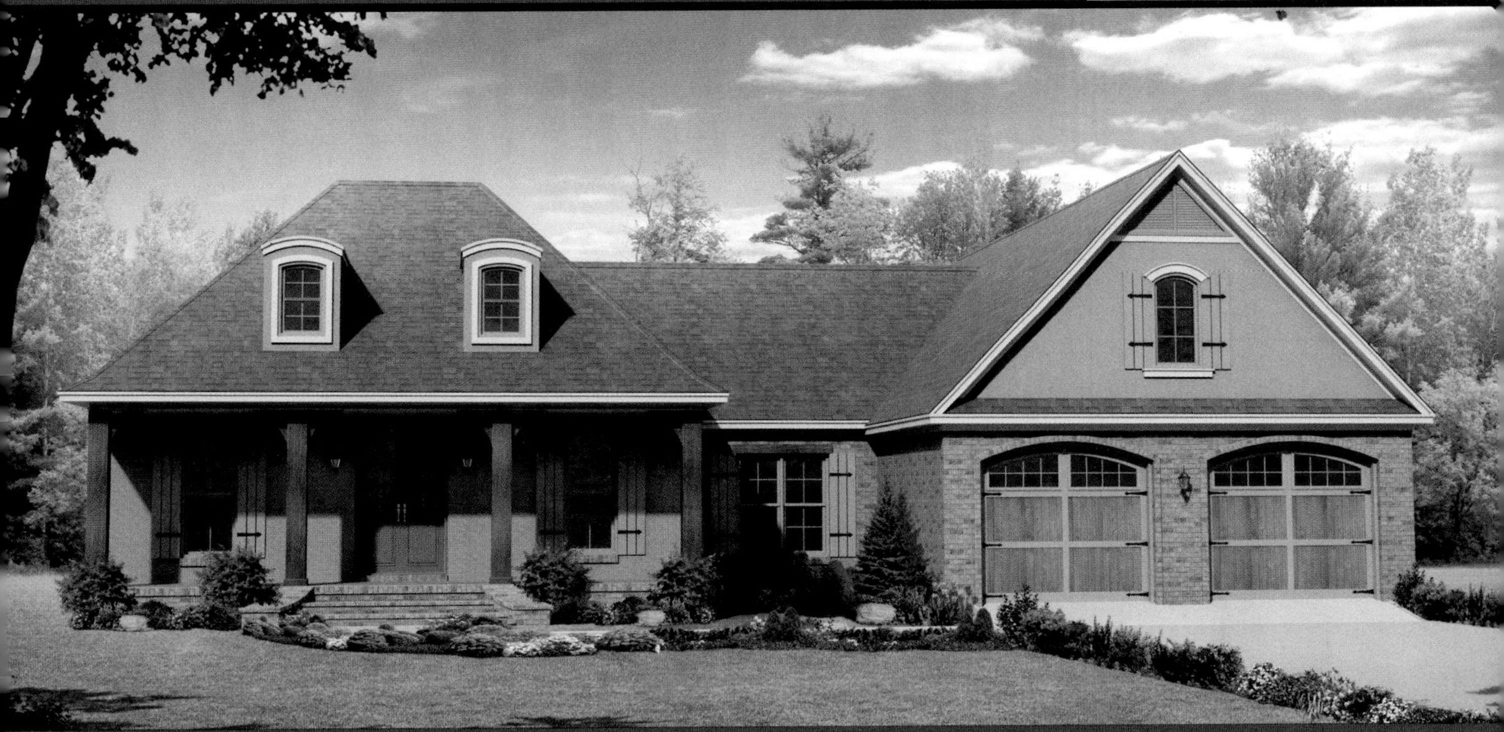

Quaint Acadian Style Home

- 2,060 total square feet of living area
- The large flex space off the kitchen and foyer provides an ideal location for a formal dining room or home office
- The decorative tray ceiling tops the distinctive great room adding a formal feel to the interior of this room
- Extra storage in the garage really helps keep lawn equipment organized
- The unfinished bonus room has an additional 350 square feet of living area
- 3 bedrooms, 2 1/2 baths, 2-car garage
- Basement foundation, drawings also include crawl space and slab foundations

Optional Second Floor

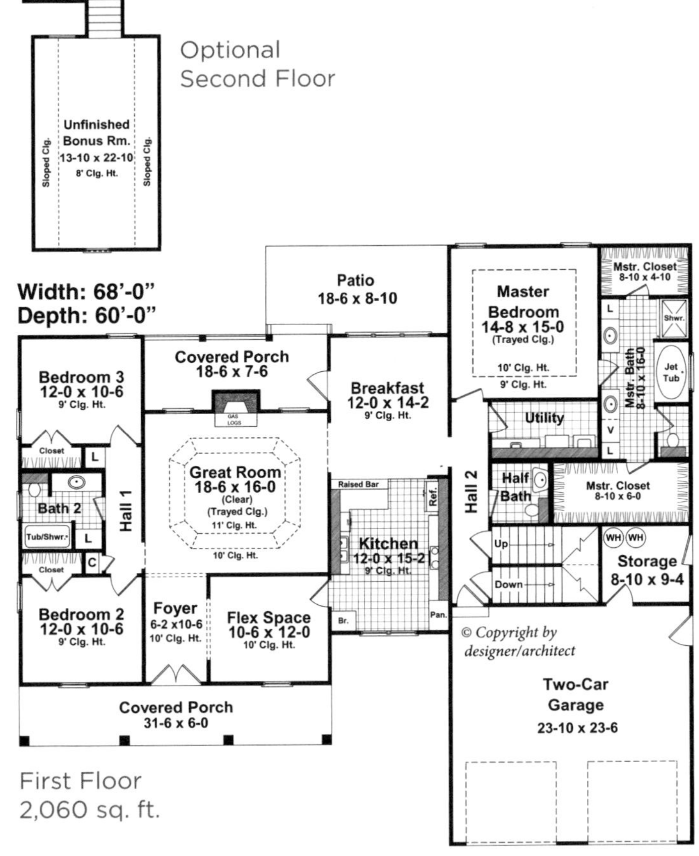

First Floor
2,060 sq. ft.

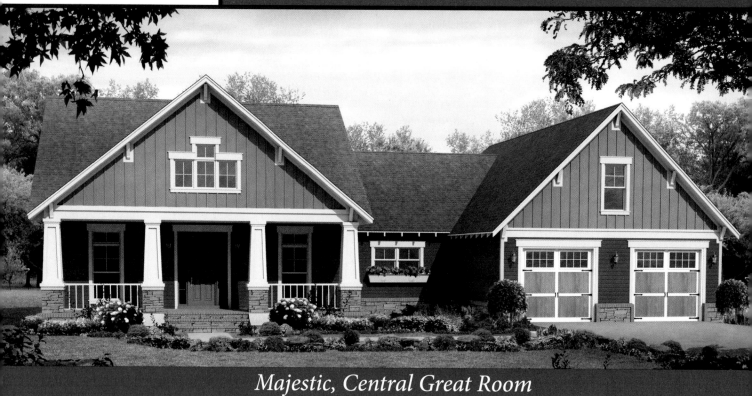

Majestic, Central Great Room

- 2,067 total square feet of living area
- An enormous master bath has separate vanities, a whirlpool tub and a walk-in closet on each end
- The flex space would make an excellent formal dining room or home office space
- The rear covered porch is a fantastic outdoor retreat and leads onto the open patio
- The unfinished bonus room has an additional 379 square feet of living area
- 3 bedrooms, 2 1/2 baths, 2-car garage
- Slab foundation, drawings also include crawl space foundation

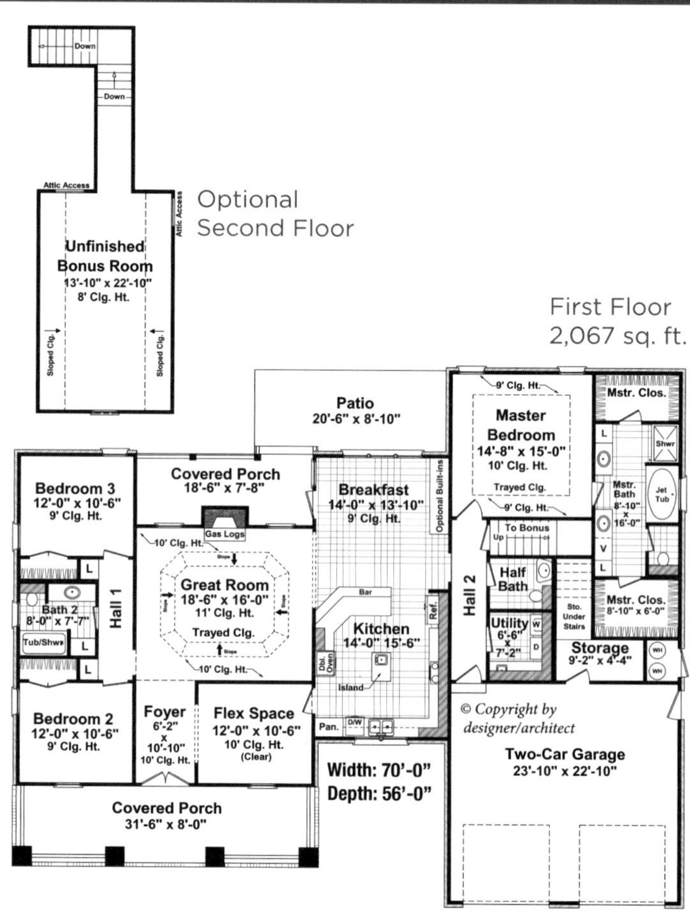

• To Order See Page 288 or Call Toll-Free 1-877-379-3420

Plan #541-058D-0136 • Price Code AAA

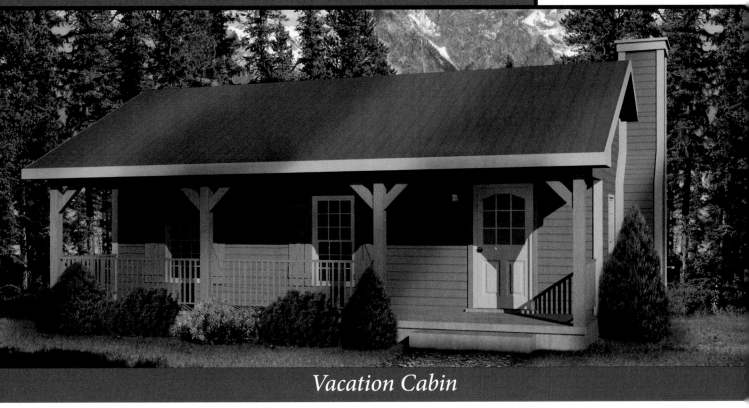

Vacation Cabin

- 480 total square feet of living area
- A wide, covered porch greets guests and offers a grand outdoor living space
- A fireplace warms the cozy sitting area that is adjacent to the dining room
- The bedroom enjoys a walk-in closet for easy organization
- 2″ x 6″ exterior walls available, please order plan #541-058D-0149
- 1 bedroom, 1 bath
- Basement foundation

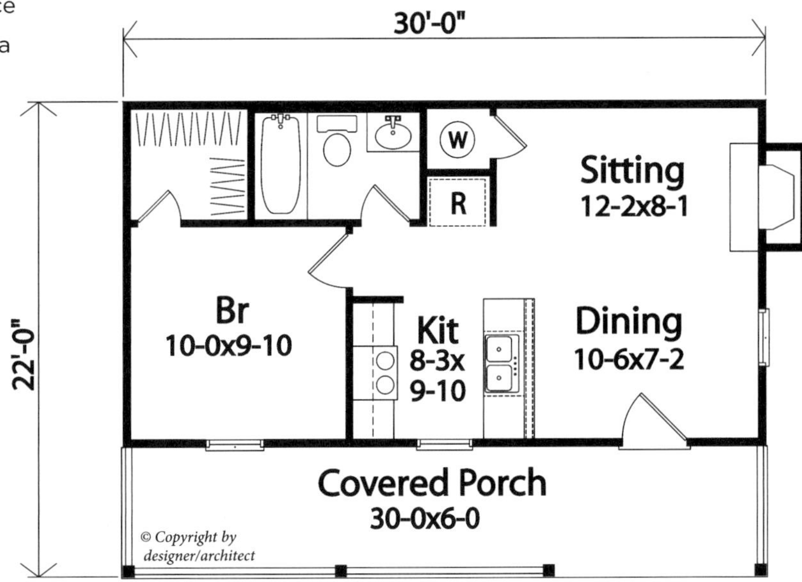

Plan #541-058D-0123 • Price Code AA

Open Sitting Area With Fireplace

- 1,144 total square feet of living area
- Energy efficient home with 2" x 6" exterior walls
- A large laundry room connects the home to the garage and contains a sink for ease with household chores
- Vaulted spaces including the kitchen, dining and sitting rooms provide an open atmosphere offering the spaciousness homeowners crave
- Two bedrooms share a centrally located full bath
- 2 bedrooms, 1 bath, 2-car garage
- Crawl space foundation

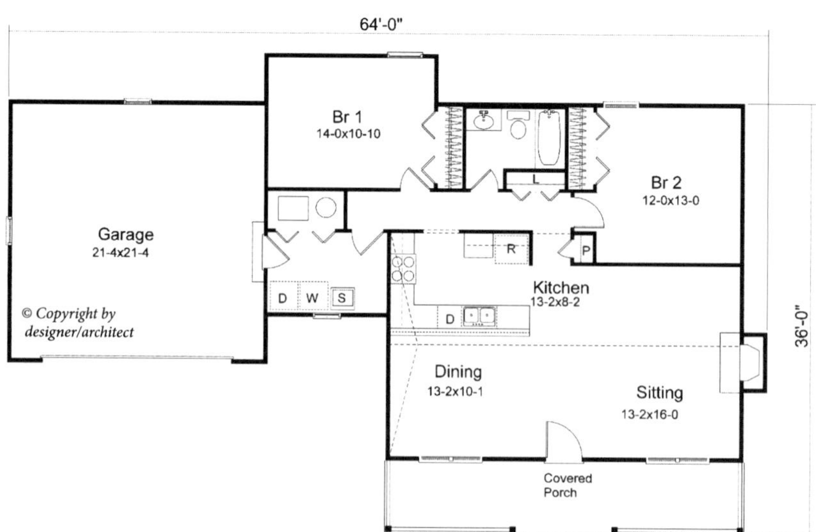

• To Order See Page 288 or Call Toll-Free 1-877-379-3420

Plan #541-121D-0011 • Price Code C

See-Through Fireplace Is A Beautiful Focal Point

- 2,241 total square feet of living area
- 11' ceilings can be found in the entry, great room, kitchen and dining room
- The large kitchen island with breakfast bar also includes a table extension providing enough dining space for up to seven people
- The elegant master bedroom is topped with a coffered ceiling and enjoys amenities such as two walk-in closets and a private bath
- 4 bedrooms, 2 1/2 baths, 2-car side entry garage
- Basement foundation

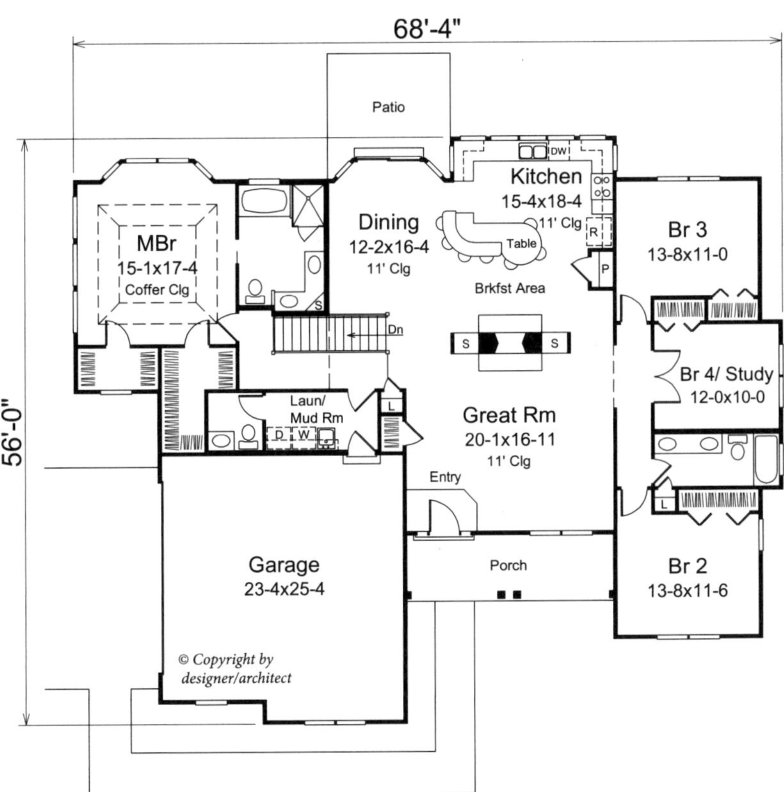

LOWE'S LEGACY SERIES

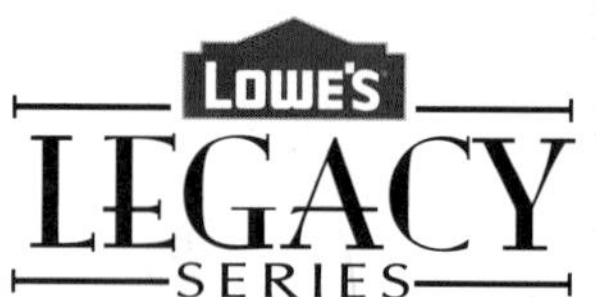

Plan #541-040D-0006 • Price Code B

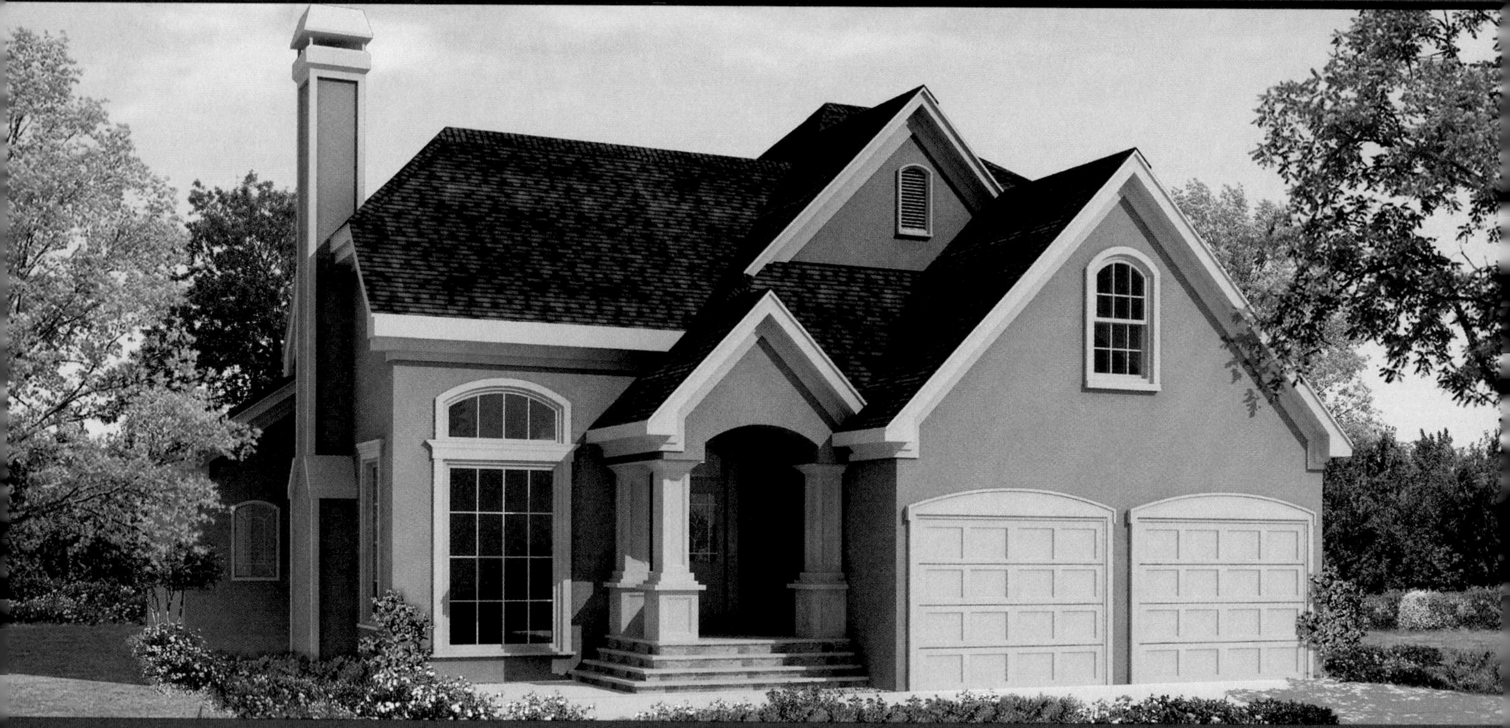

Well-Sculptured Design, Inside And Out

- 1,759 total square feet of living area
- The striking entry is created by a unique stair layout, an open high ceiling and a fireplace
- Bonus area over garage, which is included in the square footage, could easily convert to a fourth bedroom or activity center
- Second floor bedrooms share a private dressing area and bath
- 3 bedrooms, 2 1/2 baths, 2-car garage
- Basement foundation

First Floor
1,128 sq. ft.

Second Floor
631 sq. ft.

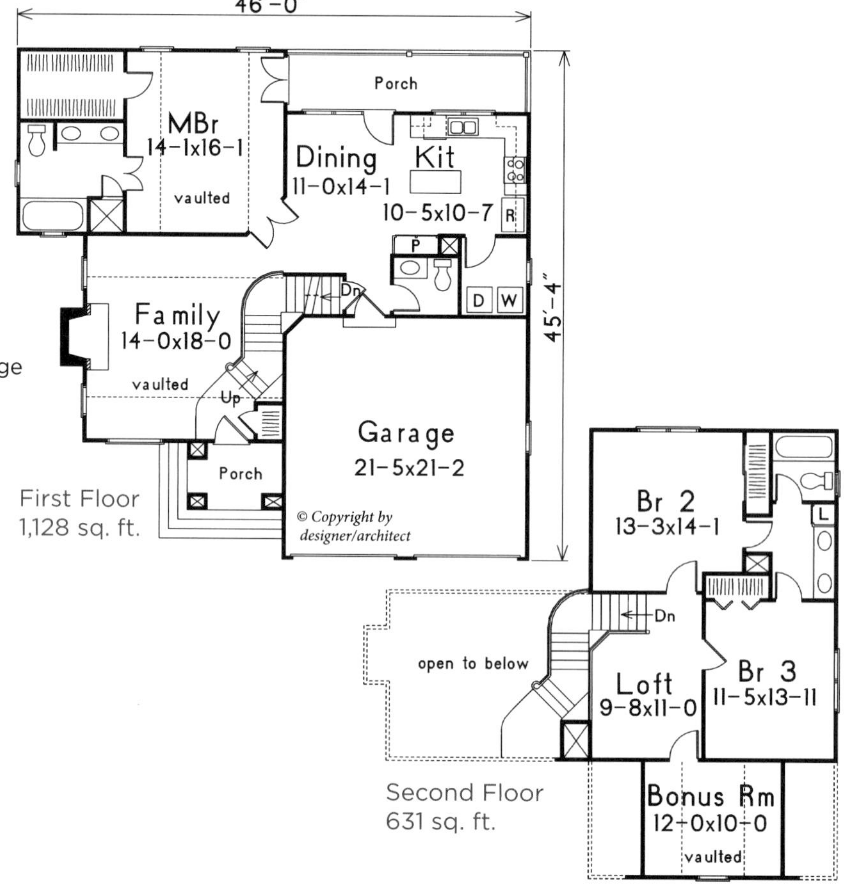

• To Order See Page 288 or Call Toll-Free 1-877-379-3420

Plan #541-077L-0025 • Price Code D

Lovely Arched Entryway

- 1,500 total square feet of living area
- Energy efficient home with 2″ x 6″ exterior walls
- The elegant great room has a vaulted ceiling and a curved hearth at the fireplace
- The garage opens discreetly on the side
- The master bedroom has two closets, one attached to the bedroom, one attached to the bath
- 3 bedrooms, 2 baths, 2-car side entry garage
- Slab foundation, drawings also include crawl space and basement foundations

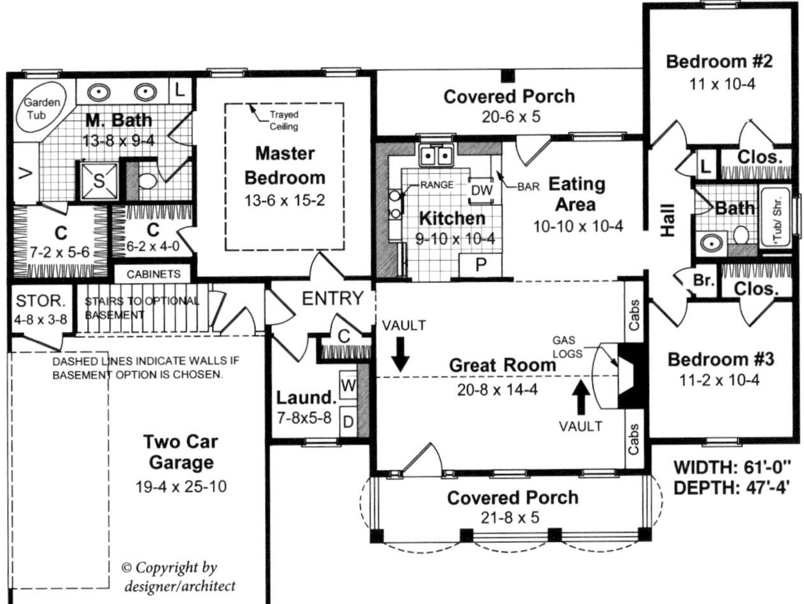

Plan #541-007D-0161 • Price Code A

Earth Berm Home With Style

- 1,480 total square feet of living area
- Energy efficient home with 2" x 6" exterior walls
- Home has great looks and lots of space
- Nestled in a hillside with only one exposed exterior wall, this home offers efficiency, protection and affordability
- Triple patio doors with an arched transom bathe the living room with sunlight
- The kitchen features a snack bar open to the living room, large built-in pantry and adjoins a spacious dining area
- 2 bedrooms, 2 baths, 2-car garage
- Slab foundation

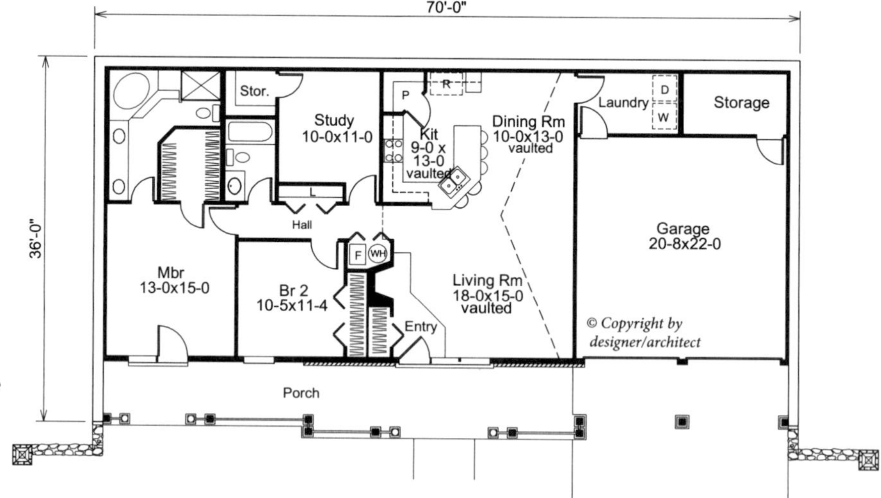

• To Order See Page 288 or Call Toll-Free 1-877-379-3420

Plan #541-058D-0083 • Price Code C

Home Features Generous Room Sizes

- 2,164 total square feet of living area
- Energy efficient home with 2" x 6" exterior walls
- Great design for entertaining with a wet bar and see-through fireplace in the great room
- Plenty of closet space
- Vaulted ceilings enlarge the master bedroom, great room and kitchen/breakfast area
- Great room features great view to the rear of the home
- 3 bedrooms, 2 1/2 baths, 2-car side entry garage
- Basement foundation

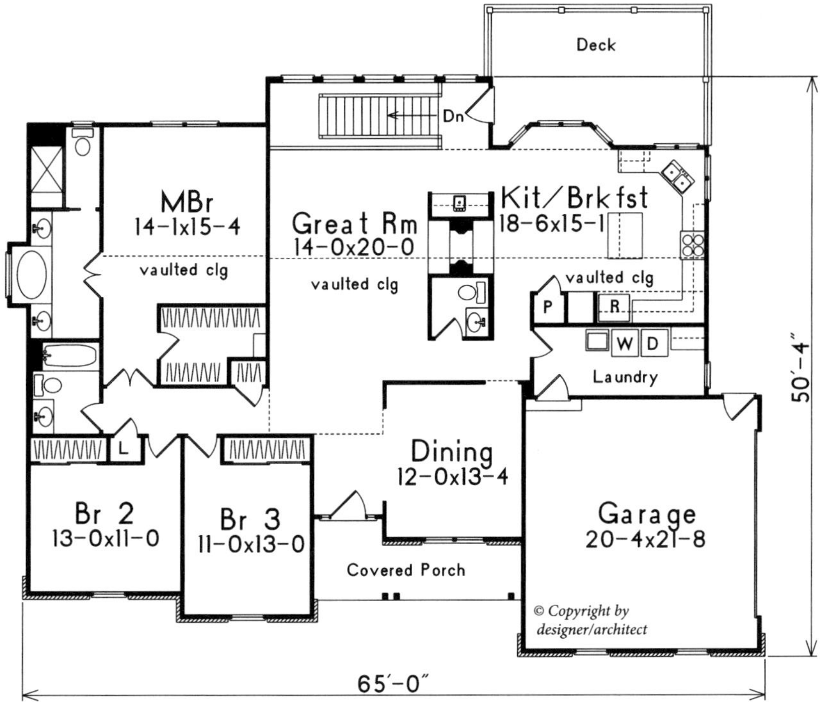

Plan #541-007D-0222 • Price Code A

Two Patio Home With Courtyard

- 1,522 total square feet of living area
- This open floor plan design has very spacious rooms, 9' ceilings and is perfect for a narrow lot
- A cozy covered porch leads to an entry that's open to a large U-shaped kitchen with snack bar, built-in pantry, abundant cabinets and 26 linear feet of counter space
- The huge great room offers two locations for an optional fireplace and enjoys an adjacent rear covered patio
- A large walk-in closet, double-entry doors and luxury bath are the many features of the master bedroom
- Both nice-sized secondary bedrooms share a private patio with rear orientation
- 3 bedrooms, 2 baths, 2-car garage
- Crawl space foundation, drawings also include slab foundation

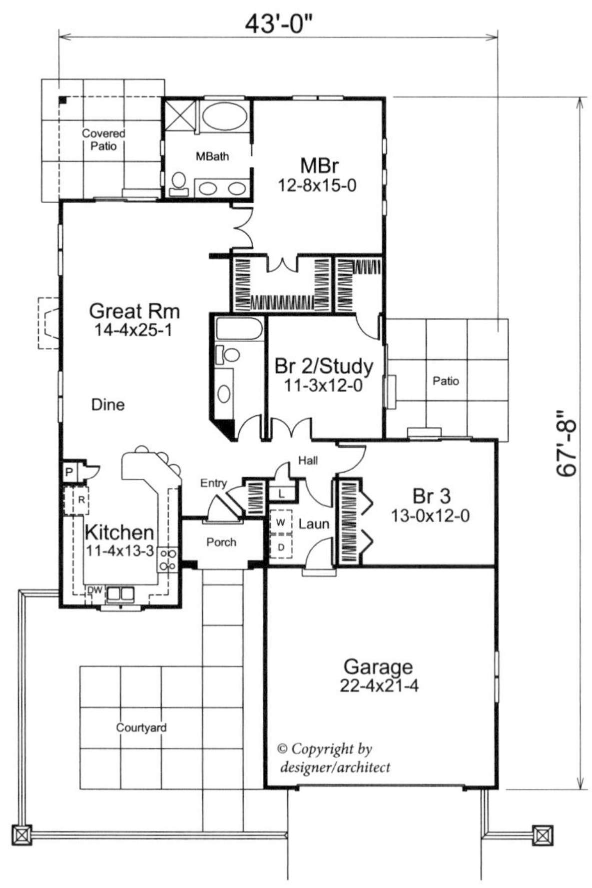

• To Order See Page 288 or Call Toll-Free 1-877-379-3420

Plan #541-045D-0014 • Price Code AA

Compact Home Maximizes Space

- 987 total square feet of living area
- Galley kitchen opens into the cozy breakfast room
- Convenient coat closets are located by both entrances
- Dining/living room offers an expansive open area
- Breakfast room has access to the outdoors
- Front porch is great for enjoying outdoor living
- 3 bedrooms, 1 bath
- Basement foundation

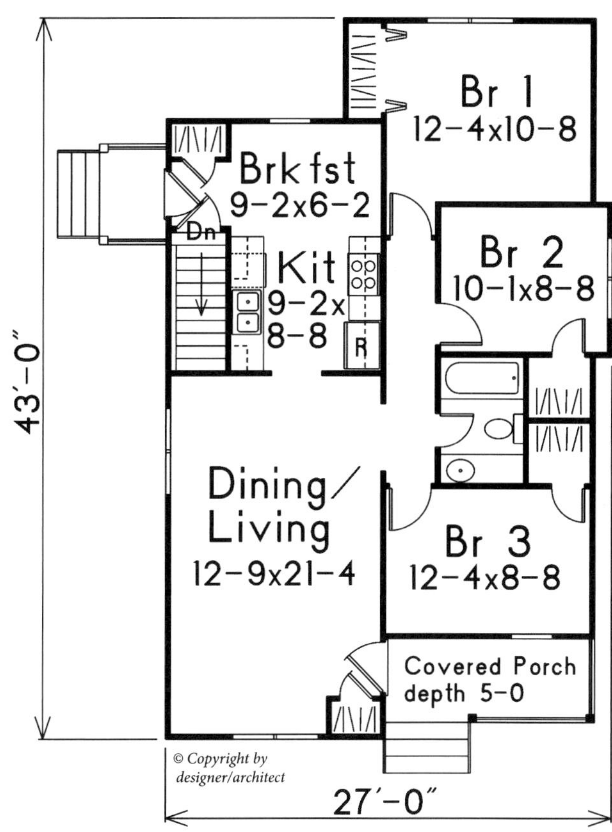

Plan #541-077L-0074 • Price Code D

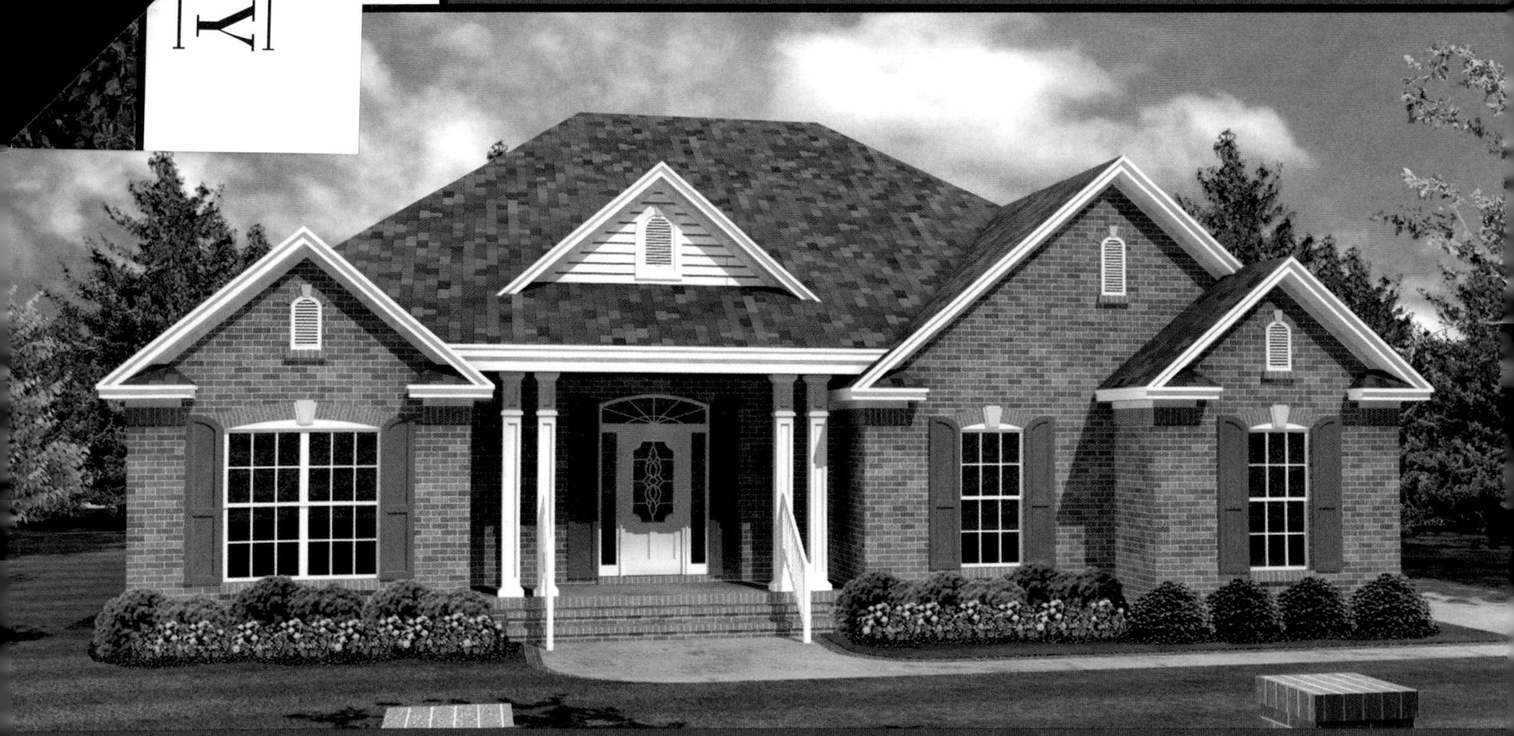

Shutters Add Style To The Exterior

- 1,502 total square feet of living area
- The dining area or sunroom is open and airy with windows all around and includes a 9' ceiling and patio access
- The kitchen features raised bars facing the dining and living rooms
- The gas fireplace makes the living room a warm, friendly place to gather
- 3 bedrooms, 2 baths, 2-car side entry garage
- Crawl space foundation, drawings also include slab foundation

To Order See Page 288 or Call Toll-Free 1-877-379-3420

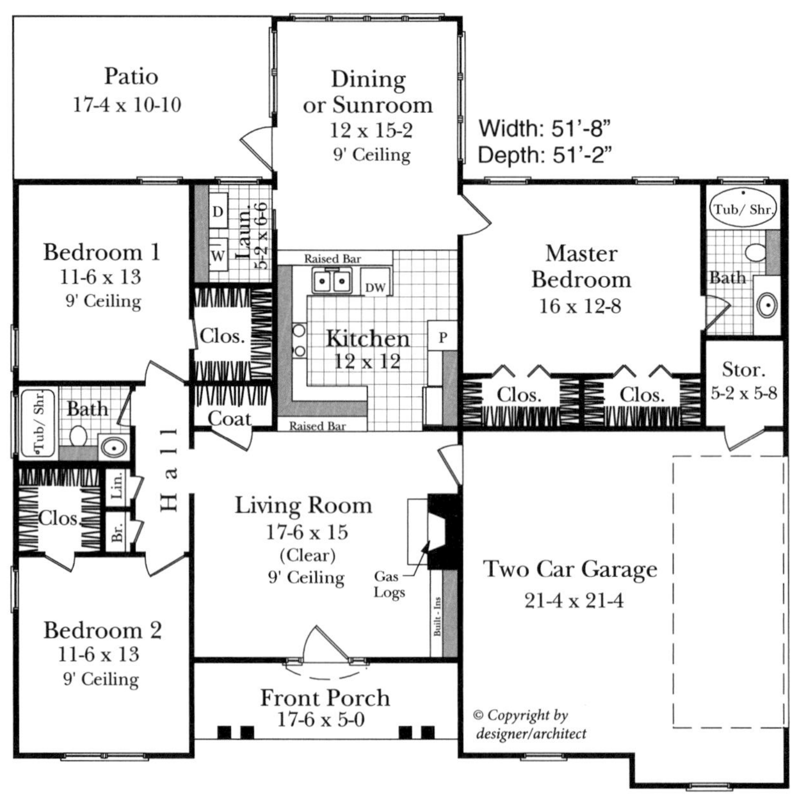

Plan #541-058D-0094 • Price Code B

Vaulted Great Room

- 1,895 total square feet of living area
- Energy efficient home with 2" x 6" exterior walls
- The foyer opens into the airy great room that features a grand fireplace
- The kitchen/breakfast area enjoys a work island, built-in desk, walk-in pantry and access to the outdoors
- Both baths include a double vanity for convenience
- 3 bedrooms, 2 baths, 2-car garage
- Basement foundation

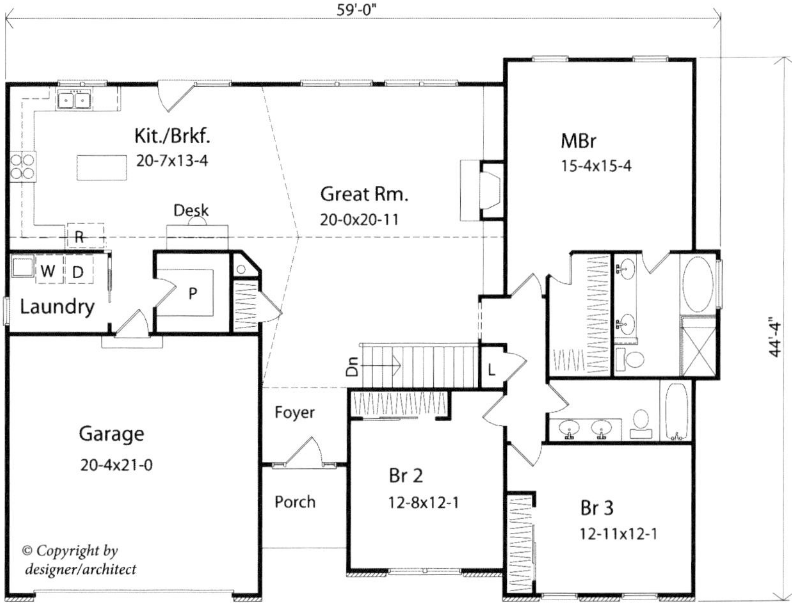

• To Order See Page 288 or Call Toll-Free 1-877

Plan #541-121D-0003 • Price Code C

Dormers And Porch Add Great Striking Curb Appeal

- 2,215 total square feet of living area
- The stunning great room is topped with an inverted vaulted ceiling and shares a see-through stone surround fireplace with the cheerful vaulted hearth room
- The pampering master bedroom features a coffered ceiling for an elegant feel along with a large private bath and walk-in closet
- The open and spacious kitchen is outfitted with a large wrap-around counter with enough casual dining space for five people
- 3 bedrooms, 2 1/2 baths, 2-car garage
- Basement foundation

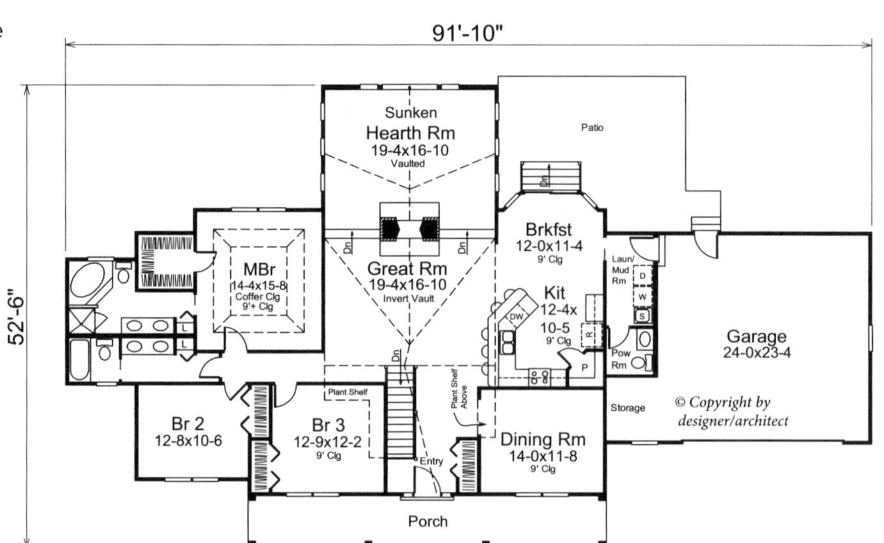

• To Order See Page 288 or Call Toll-Free 1-877-379-3420

Plan #541-001D-0036 • Price Code A

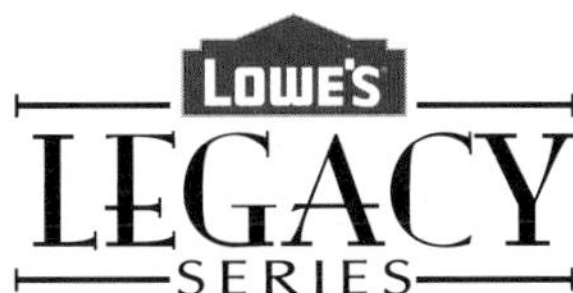

Gabled, Covered Front Porch

- 1,320 total square feet of living area
- Functional U-shaped kitchen features a pantry
- Large living and dining areas join to create an open atmosphere
- Secluded master bedroom includes a private full bath
- Covered front porch opens into a large living area with a convenient coat closet
- Utility/laundry room is located near the kitchen
- 3 bedrooms, 2 baths
- Crawl space foundation

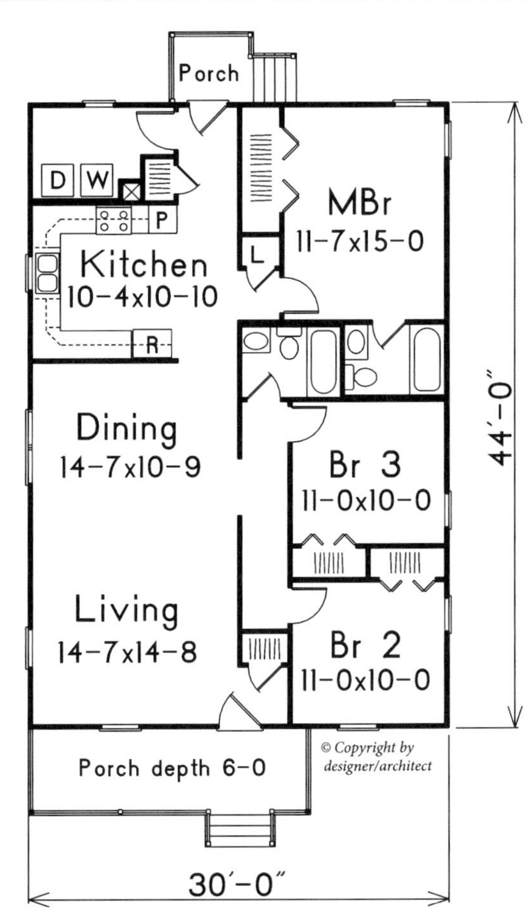

LOWE'S LEGACY SERIES

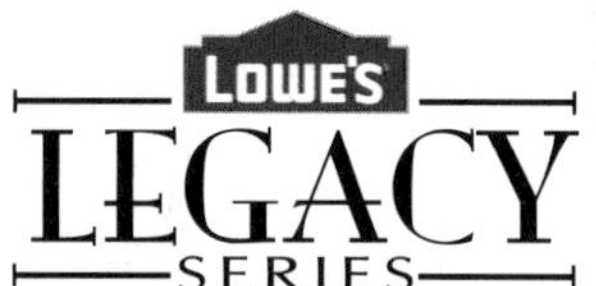

Plan #541-017D-0001 • Price Code D

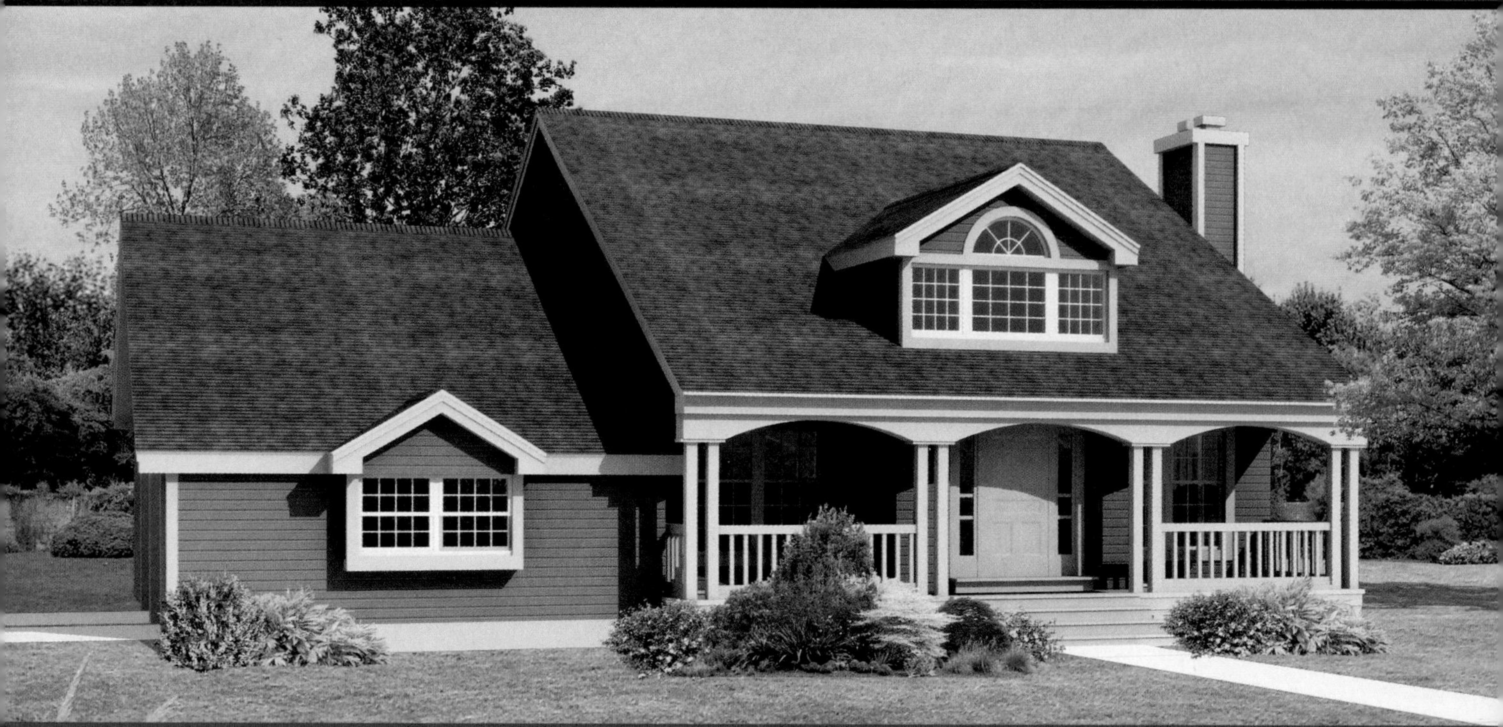

Welcoming Front Porch, A Country Touch

- 2,043 total square feet of living area
- Energy efficient home with 2" x 6" exterior walls
- Two-story central foyer includes two coat closets
- Large combined space is provided by the kitchen, family and breakfast rooms
- Breakfast nook for informal dining looks out to the deck and screened porch
- 3 bedrooms, 2 1/2 baths, 2-car side entry garage
- Basement foundation, drawings also include slab foundation

Second Floor
534 sq. ft.

First Floor
1,509 sq. ft.

• To Order See Page 288 or Call Toll-Free 1-877-379-3420

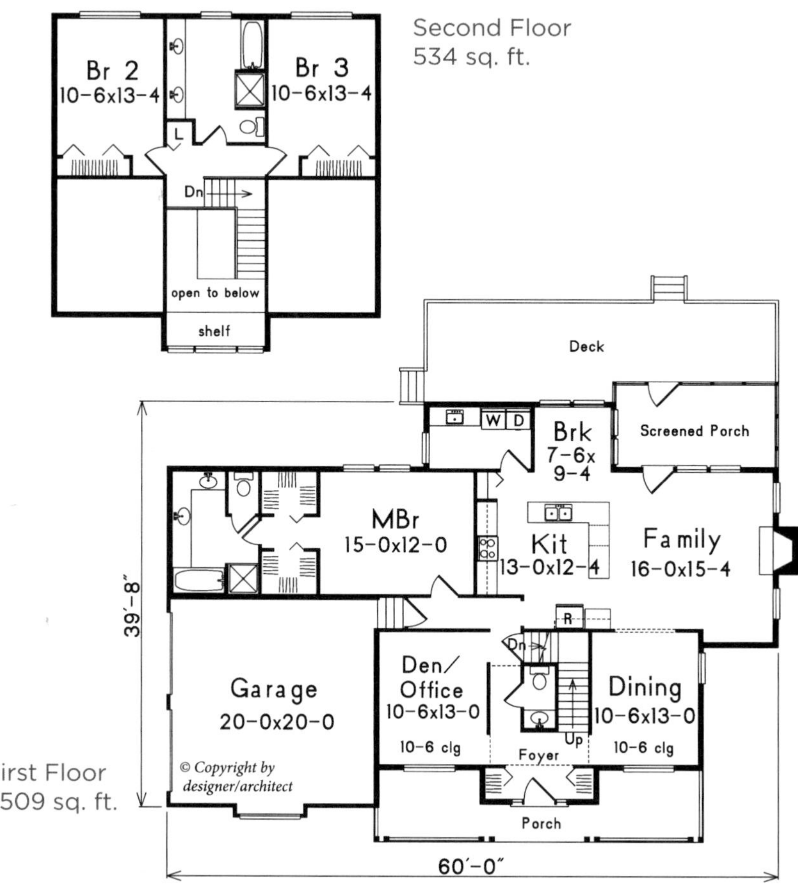

Plan #541-037D-0001 • Price Code B

LOWE'S LEGACY SERIES

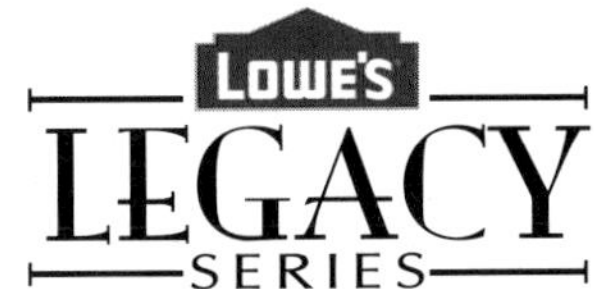

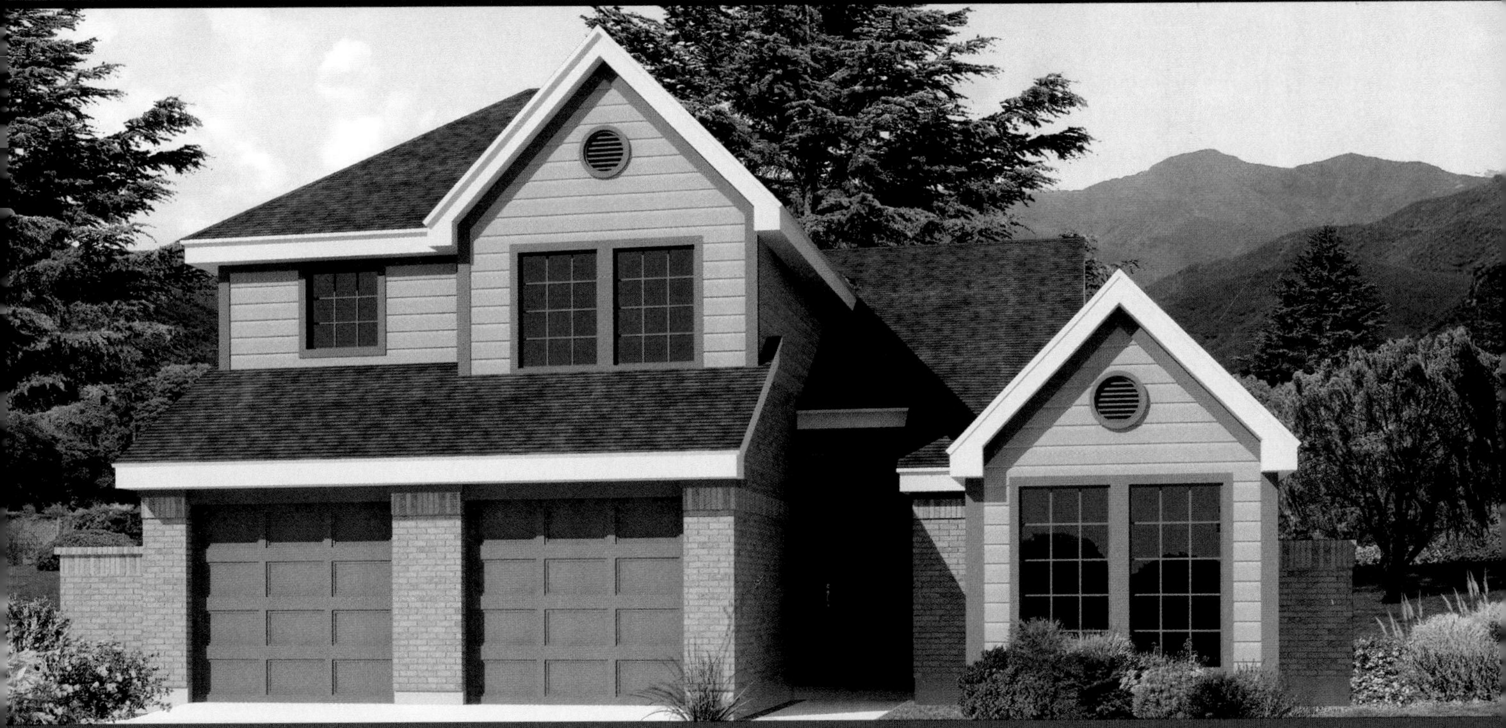

Corner Windows Brighten This Charming Home

- 1,703 total square feet of living area
- A large fireplace, plant shelf and access onto the patio enhance the spacious living room
- Protected front entry includes a raised ceiling in the foyer
- Master bedroom enjoys a walk-in closet, vaulted ceiling and window seats
- Plan is well-suited for a narrow lot
- 3 bedrooms, 2 1/2 baths, 2-car garage
- Slab foundation, drawings also include crawl space foundation

First Floor
1,163 sq. ft.

Second Floor
540 sq. ft.

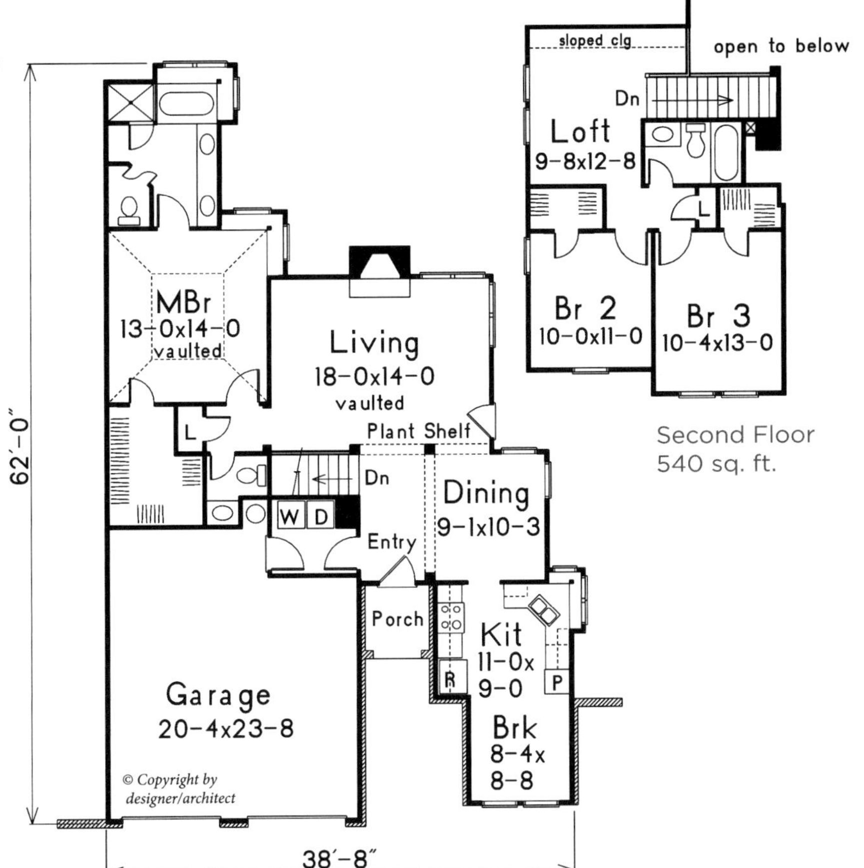

Plan #541-007D-0053 • Price Code D

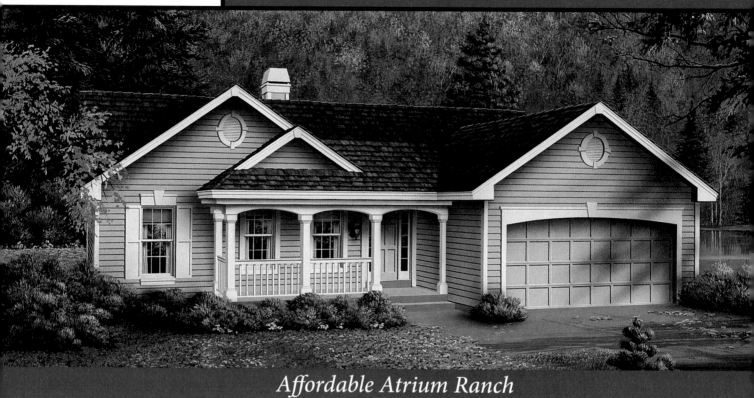

Affordable Atrium Ranch

- 2,432 total square feet of living area
- Roomy front porch gives home a country flavor
- Vaulted great room boasts a fireplace, TV alcove, pass-through snack bar to kitchen and atrium featuring bayed window wall and a descending stair to the family room
- Oversized master bedroom features a vaulted ceiling, double-door entry and large walk-in closet
- 3 bedrooms, 2 baths, 2-car garage
- Walk-out basement foundation

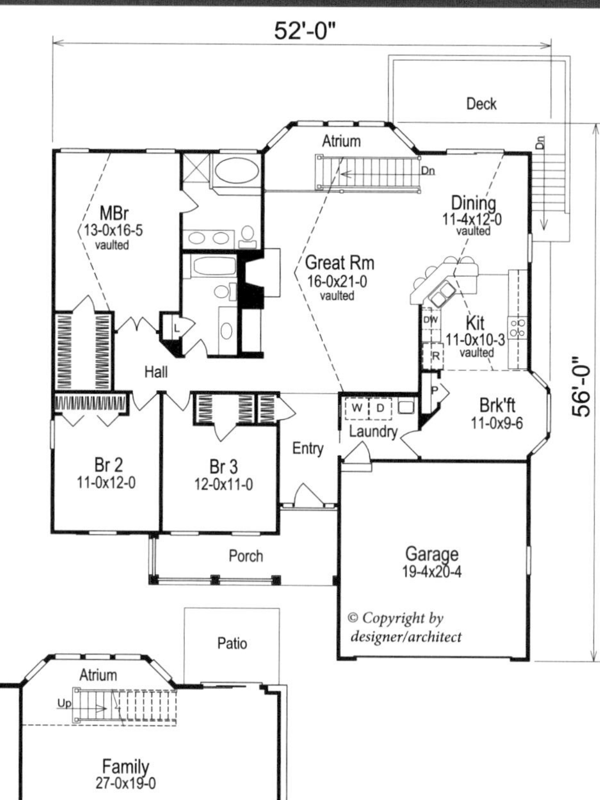

First Floor
1,885 sq. ft.

Lower Level
547 sq. ft.

• To Order See Page 288 or Call Toll-Free 1-877-379-3420

Plan #541-027D-0006 • Price Code C

LOWE'S LEGACY SERIES

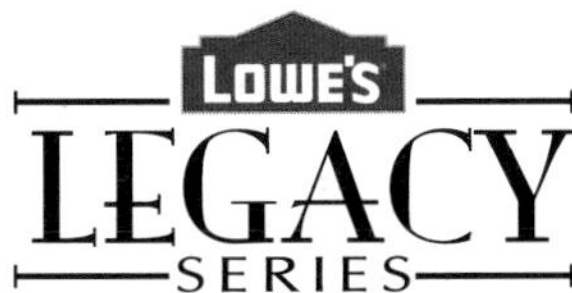

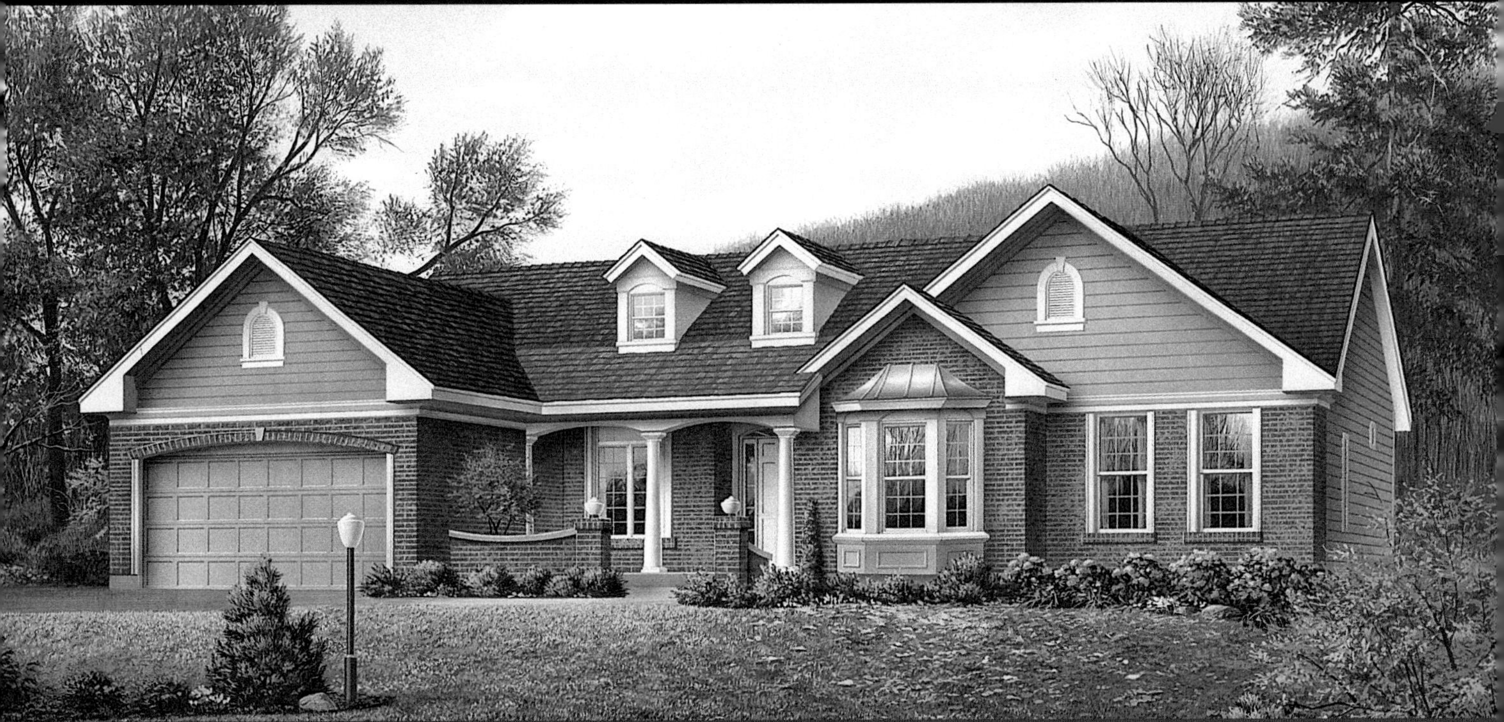

Great Room Forms Core Of This Home

- 2,076 total square feet of living area
- Vaulted great room has a fireplace flanked by windows and skylights that welcome the sun
- Kitchen leads to the vaulted breakfast room and rear deck
- Study located off the foyer provides a great location for a home office
- Large bay windows grace the master bedroom and bath
- 3 bedrooms, 2 baths, 2-car garage
- Basement foundation

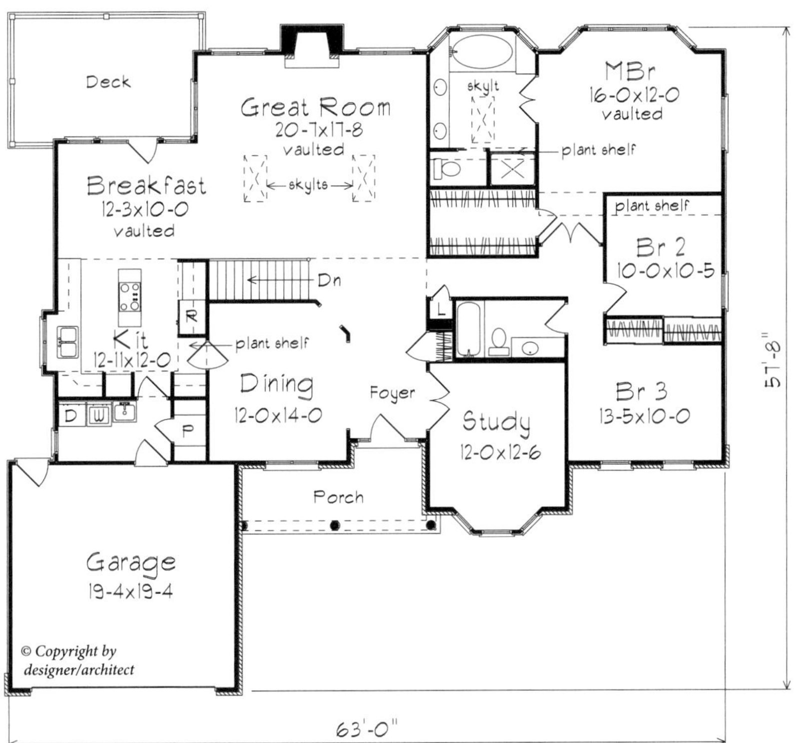

LOWE'S LEGACY SERIES

Plan #541-053D-0010 • Price Code A

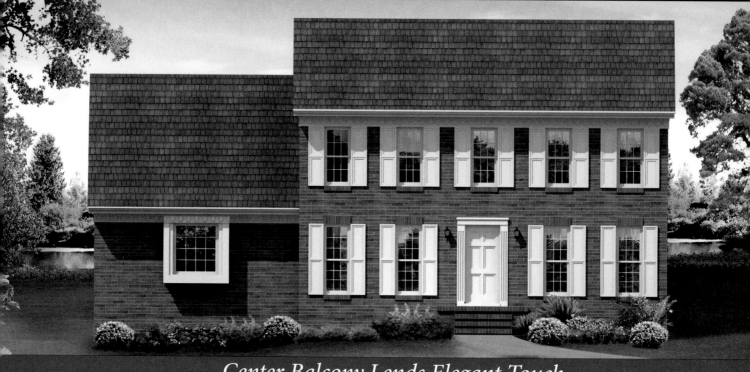

Center Balcony Lends Elegant Touch

- 1,983 total square feet of living area
- Second floor balcony overlooks first floor adding spaciousness
- Traditional styling with a contemporary interior flair
- Isolated first floor master bedroom suite for privacy
- Secondary bedrooms both have large walk-in closets
- 3 bedrooms, 2 1/2 baths, 2-car drive under garage
- Basement foundation

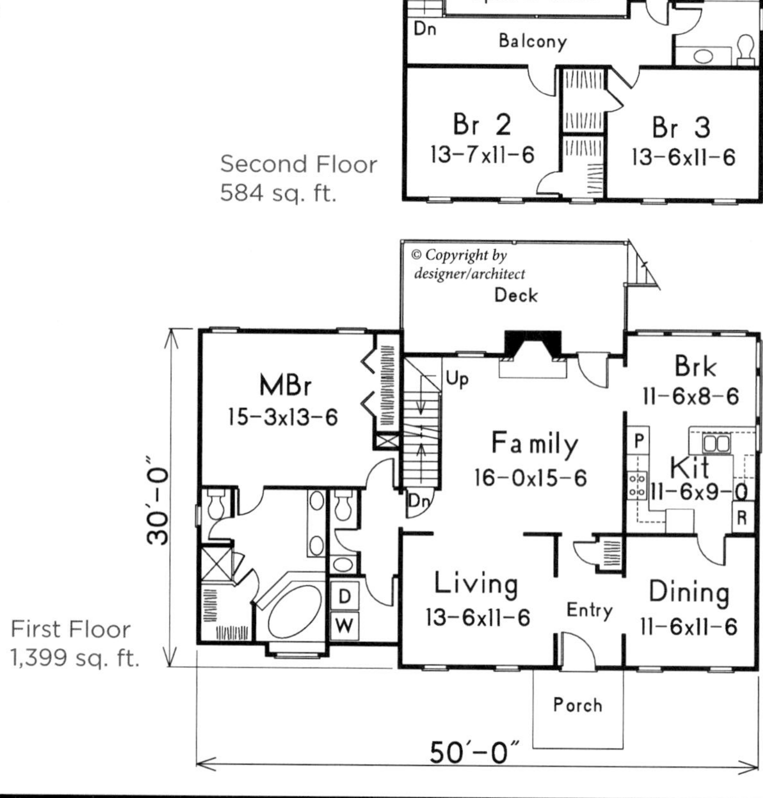

To Order See Page 288 or Call Toll-Free 1-877-379-3420

Plan #541-068D-0010 • Price Code C

Bedrooms Separate From Rest Of Home

- 1,849 total square feet of living area
- Enormous laundry room has many extras including a storage area and half bath
- Lavish master bath has a corner whirlpool tub, double sinks, separate shower and walk-in closet
- Secondary bedrooms include walk-in closets
- Kitchen has a wrap-around eating counter and is positioned between the formal dining area and breakfast room for convenience
- 3 bedrooms, 2 1/2 baths, 2-car side entry garage
- Slab foundation, drawings also include crawl space foundation

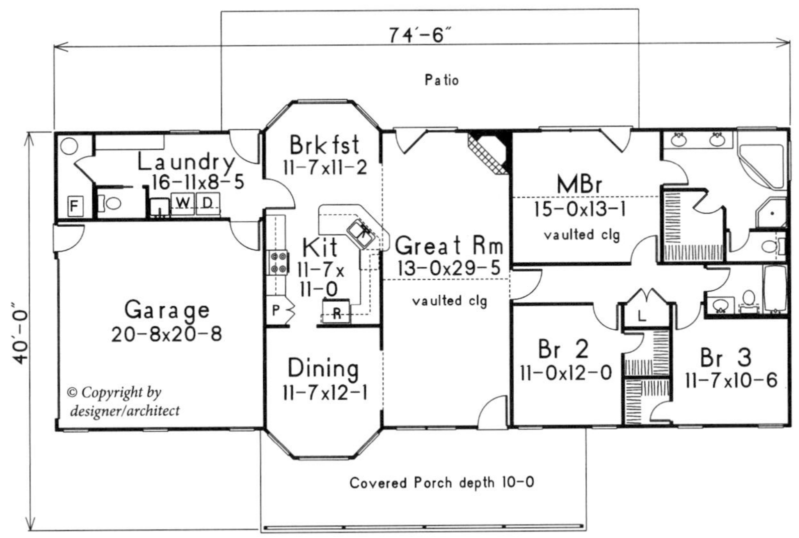

Plan #541-045D-0009 • Price Code B

See-Through Fireplace Joins Gathering Rooms

- 1,684 total square feet of living area
- The bayed dining area boasts convenient double-door access onto the large deck
- The family room features several large windows for brightness
- Bedrooms are separate from living areas for privacy
- Master bedroom offers a bath with walk-in closet, double-bowl vanity and both a shower and a whirlpool tub
- 3 bedrooms, 2 1/2 baths, 2-car garage
- Basement foundation

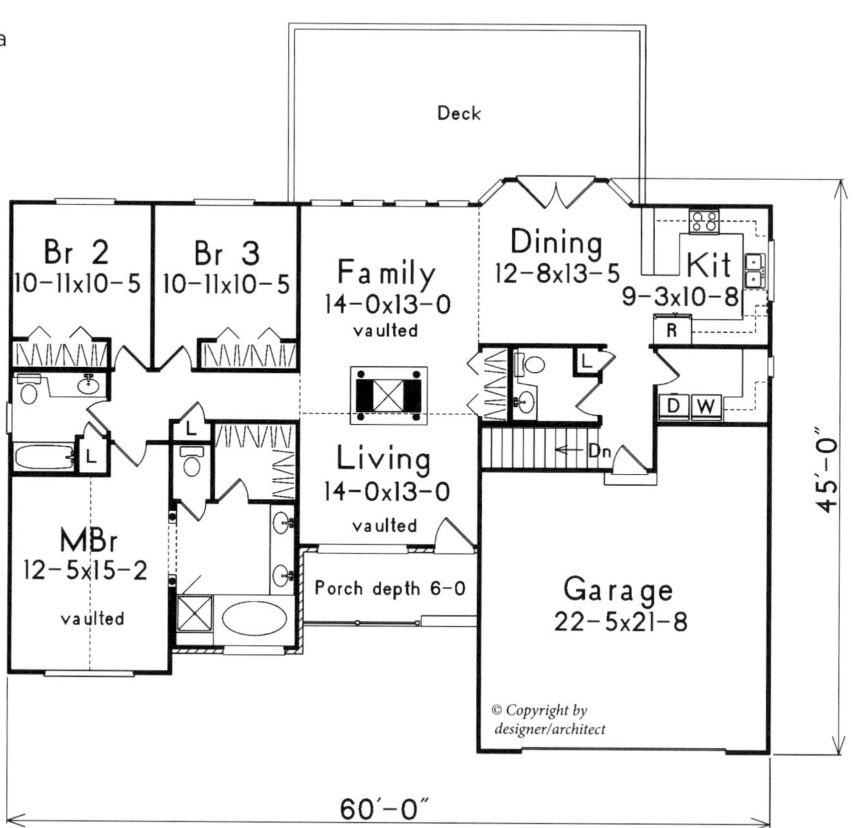

• To Order See Page 288 or Call Toll-Free 1-877-379-3420

Plan #541-121D-0001 • Price Code C

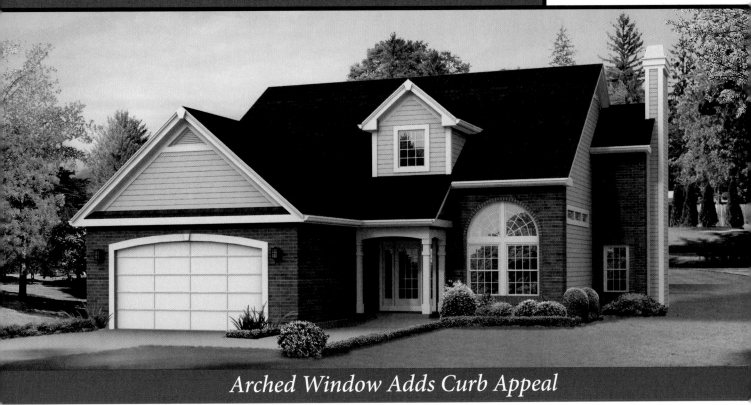

Arched Window Adds Curb Appeal

- 2,360 total square feet of living area
- The U-shaped kitchen enjoys the convenience of a large walk-in pantry, desk area and extended counterspace with enough casual dining space for three people
- An enormous hearth room extends off the bayed breakfast area and features a cozy fireplace on one wall and an oversized bay window on another
- Terrific luxury can be found in the second floor master bedroom including his and her walk-in closets and a private bath with a corner spa style tub
- Balcony overlooks the spacious living room with large arched window and has views out the active dormer
- 3 bedrooms, 2 1/2 baths, 2-car garage
- Basement foundation

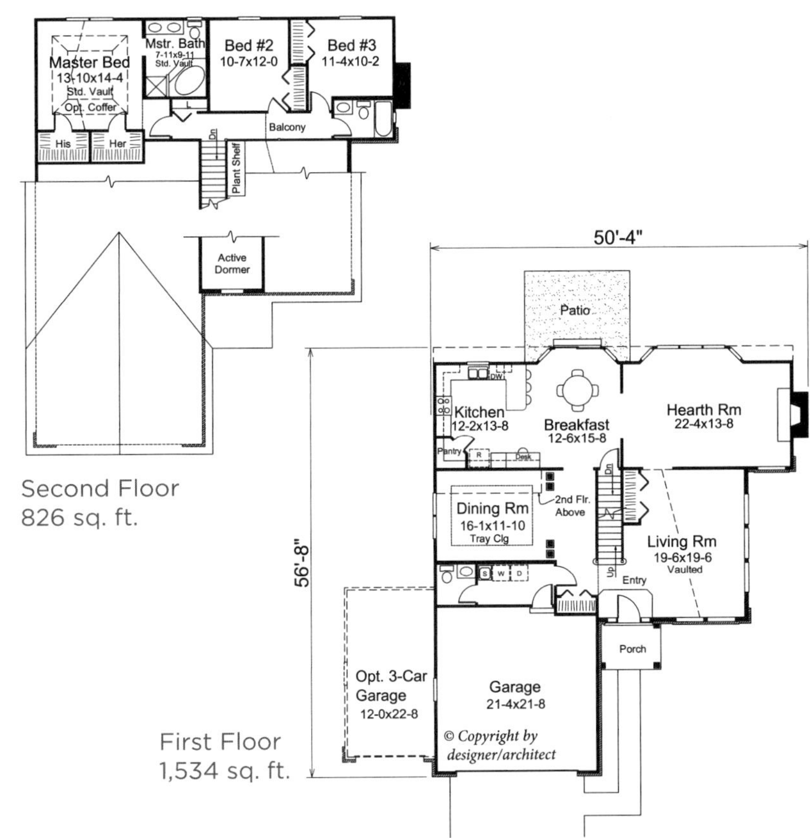

Second Floor
826 sq. ft.

First Floor
1,534 sq. ft.

Plan #541-057D-0043 • Price Code B

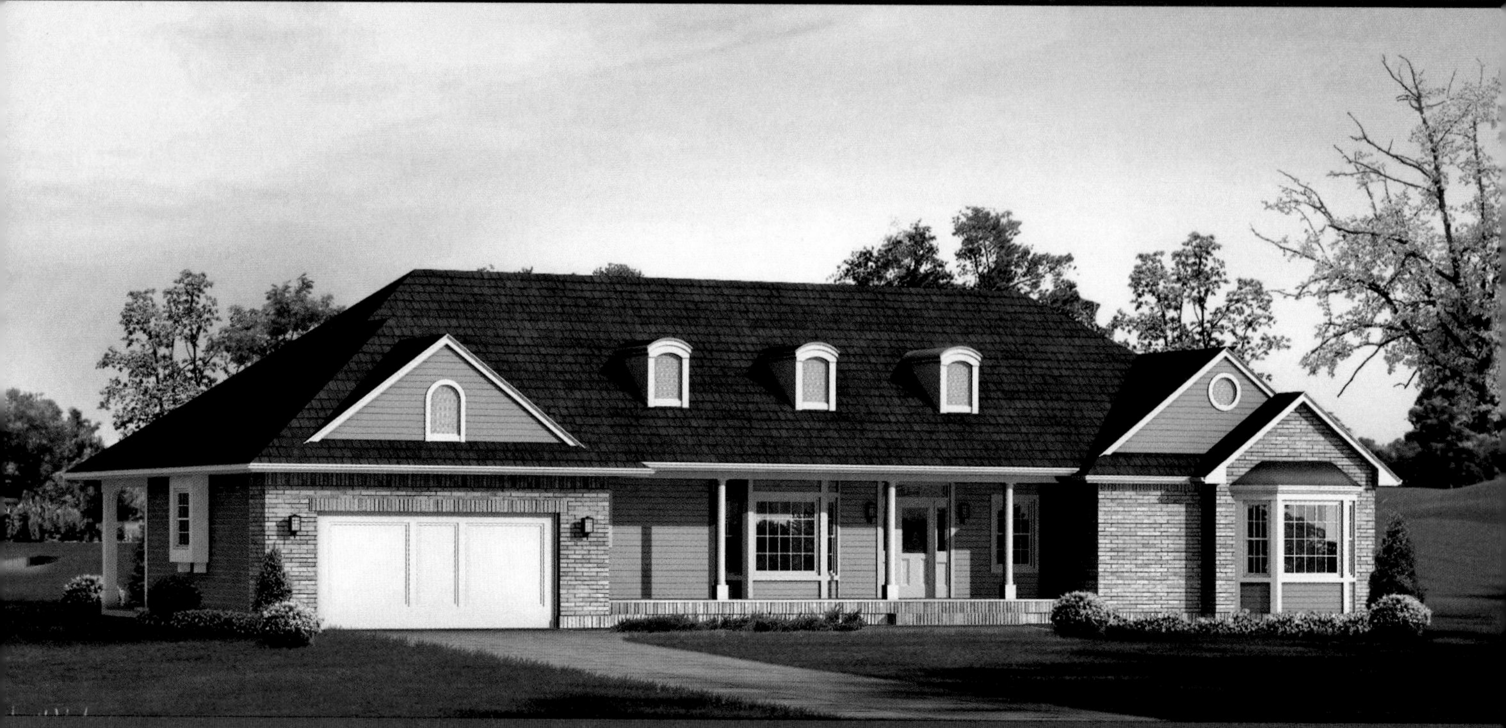

Dignified Ranch Exterior

- 2,024 total square feet of living area
- Lovely covered porch provides weather protection
- Living room features a vaulted ceiling, built-in bar and double French doors to the adjoining deck
- Beautiful three-season porch features an abundance of windows
- 3 bedrooms, 2 baths, 2-car garage
- Basement foundation

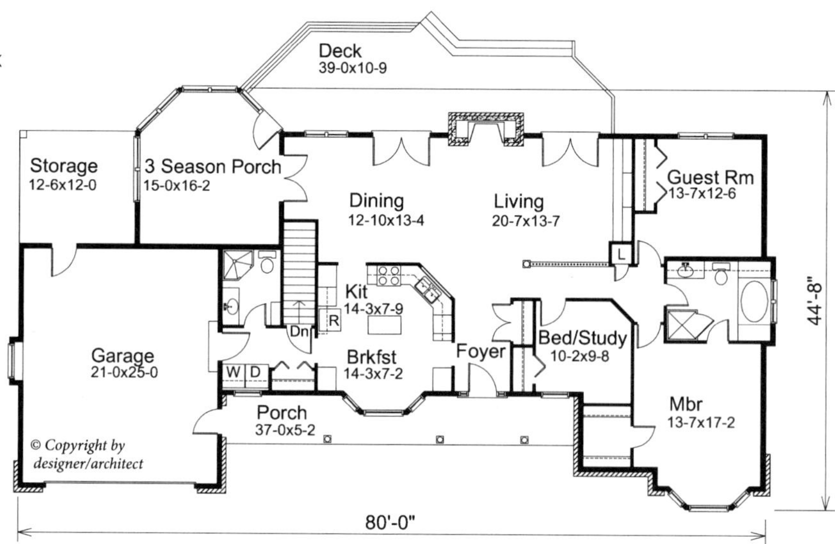

Plan #541-001D-0081 • Price Code AA

Large Great Room And Dining Area

- 1,160 total square feet of living area
- U-shaped kitchen includes a breakfast bar and convenient laundry closet
- Master bedroom features a private half bath and large closet
- Dining room has outdoor access
- Dining and great rooms combine to create an open living atmosphere
- 3 bedrooms, 1 1/2 baths
- Crawl space foundation, drawings also include basement and slab foundations

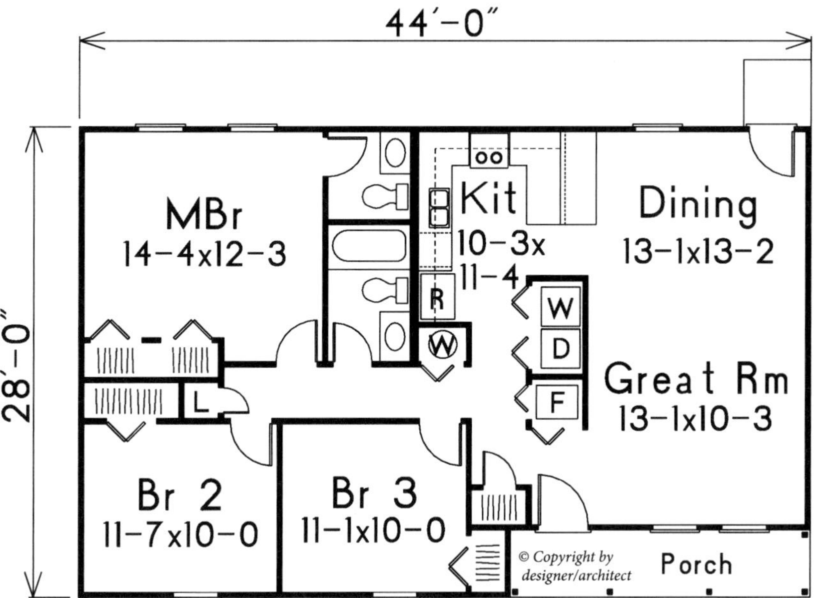

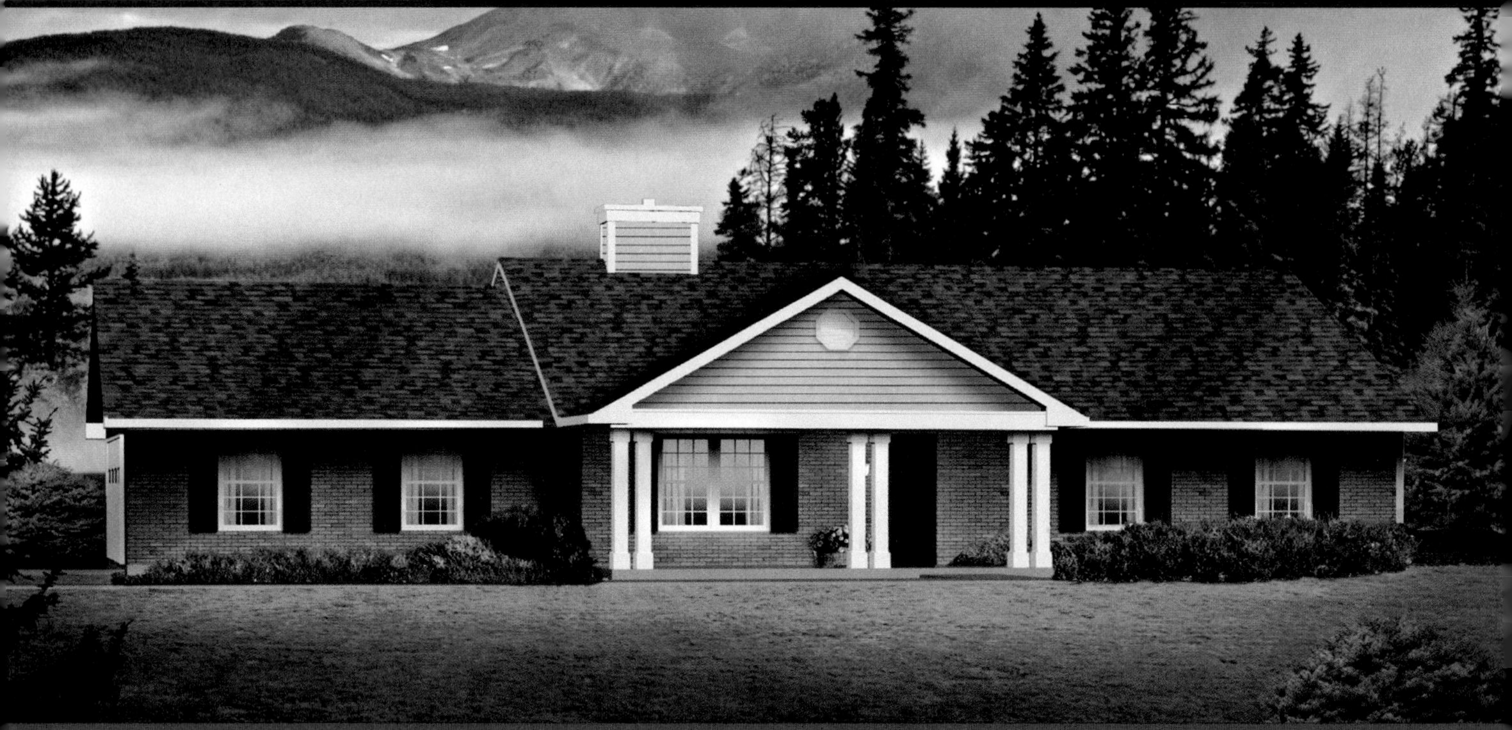

Graciously Designed Traditional Ranch

- 1,477 total square feet of living area
- Energy efficient home with 2" x 6" exterior walls
- Oversized porch provides protection from the elements
- Innovative kitchen employs step-saving design
- Kitchen has a snack bar which opens to the breakfast room with bay window
- 3 bedrooms, 2 baths, 2-car side entry garage with storage area
- Basement foundation

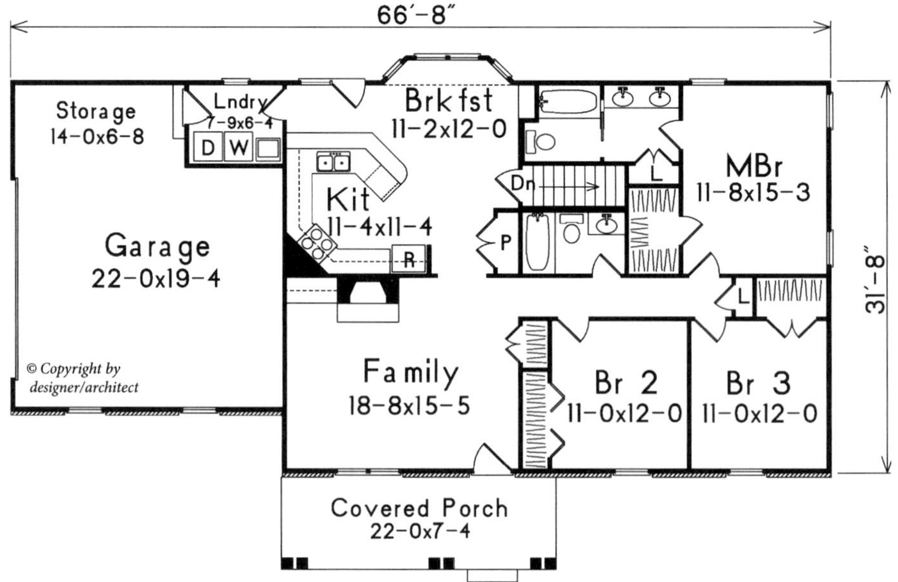

To Order See Page 288 or Call Toll-Free 1-877-379-3420

Formal Dining Room

- 2,096 total square feet of living area
- The foyer opens to the great room which features a fireplace and built-in bookshelves
- The secondary bedrooms are secluded with a central bath and laundry room
- The grand kitchen has an eating counter, pantry, optional island and connects to the bayed breakfast room
- 3 bedrooms, 2 1/2 baths, 3-car side entry garage
- Slab, crawl space, basement or walk-out basement foundation, please specify when ordering

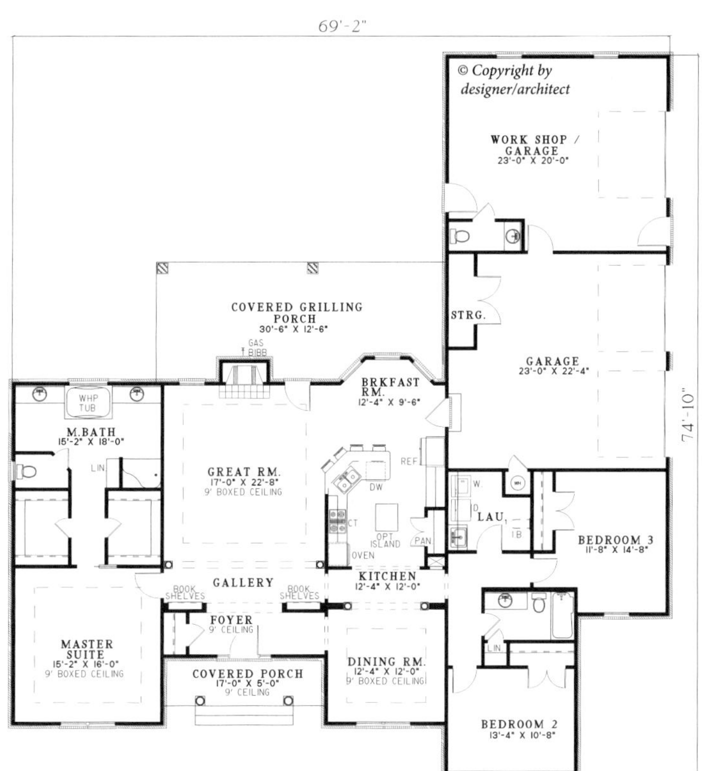

Plan #541-053D-0004 • Price Code A

Front Features Handsome Mullioned Windows

- 1,740 total square feet of living area
- The dining room boasts a coffered ceiling and specially treated ceilings grace the living room and master bedroom
- Master bedroom features a large bath with walk-in closet, double-vanity, separate shower and tub
- Both secondary bedrooms have ample closet space
- Large breakfast area is convenient to the laundry closet, pantry and rear deck
- 3 bedrooms, 2 baths, 2-car drive under garage
- Basement foundation

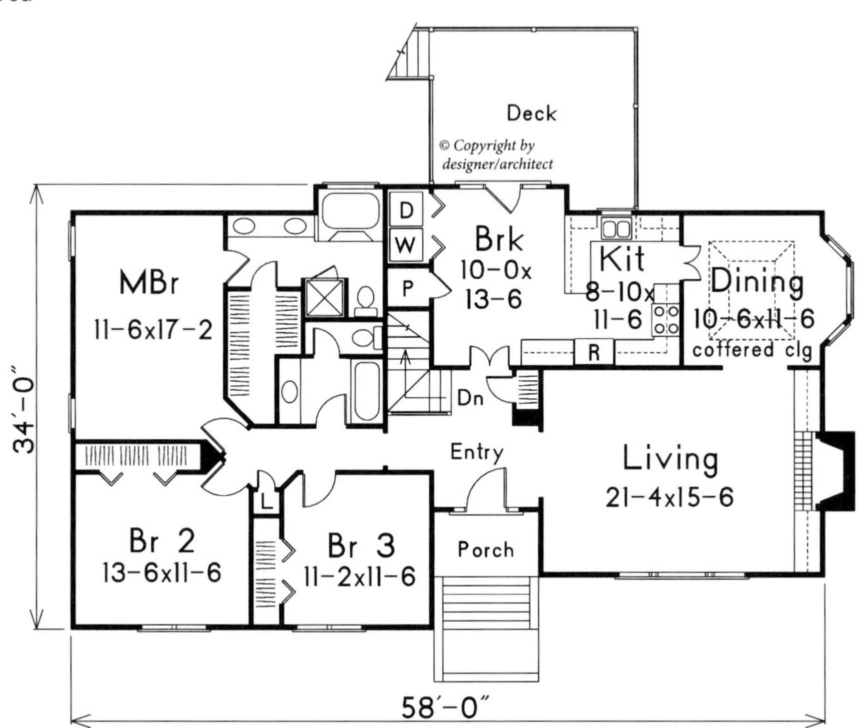

• To Order See Page 288 or Call Toll-Free 1-877-379-3420

Plan #541-008D-0013 • Price Code A

Terrific Design For Family Living

- 1,345 total square feet of living area
- Brick front details add a touch of elegance
- Master bedroom has a private full bath
- Great room combines with the dining area creating a sense of spaciousness
- Garage includes a handy storage area that could easily be converted to a workshop space
- 3 bedrooms, 2 baths, 2-car side entry garage
- Basement foundation, drawings also include crawl space and slab foundations

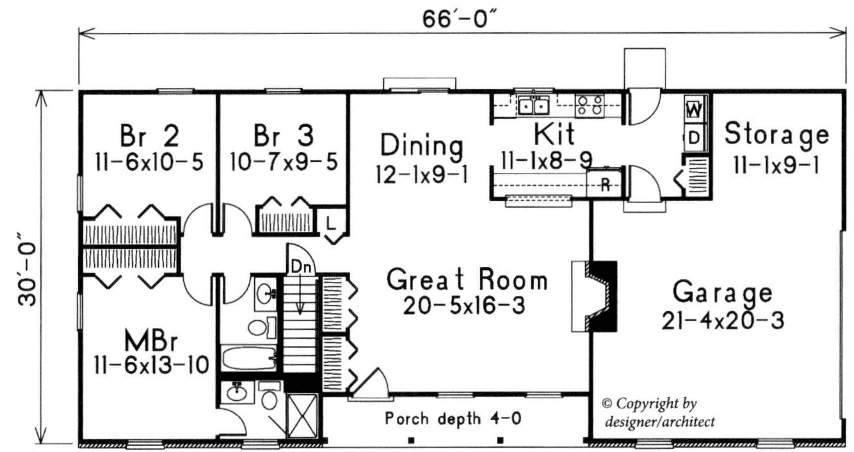

Plan #541-037D-0006 • Price Code C

Old-Fashioned Comfort And Privacy

- 1,772 total square feet of living area
- Extended porches in the front and rear provide a charming touch
- Large bay windows lend distinction to the dining room and bedroom #3
- Efficient U-shaped kitchen with plenty of storage
- Master bedroom includes two walk-in closets
- A full corner fireplace warms the family room
- 3 bedrooms, 2 baths, 2-car detached garage
- Slab foundation, drawings also include crawl space foundation

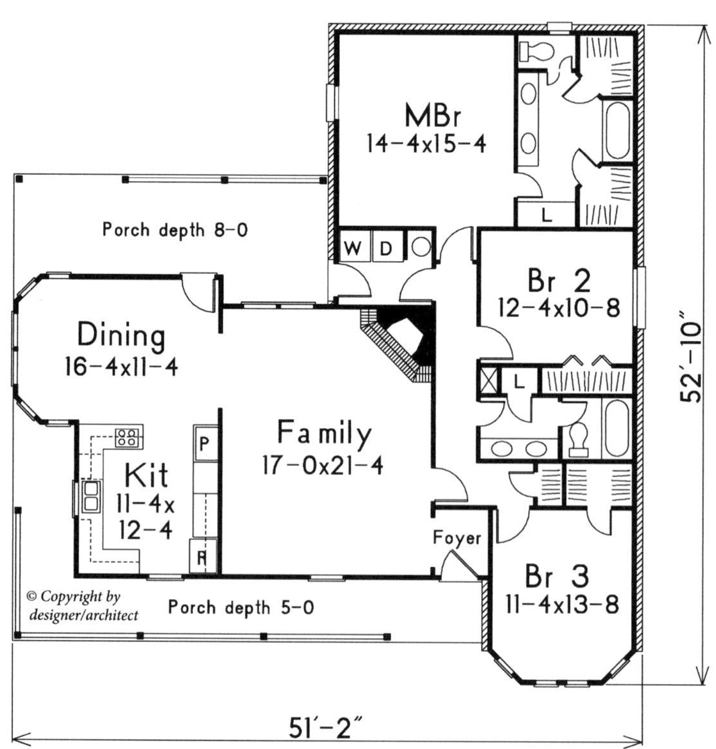

• To Order See Page 288 or Call Toll-Free 1-877-379-3420

Plan #541-058D-0168 • Price Code AA

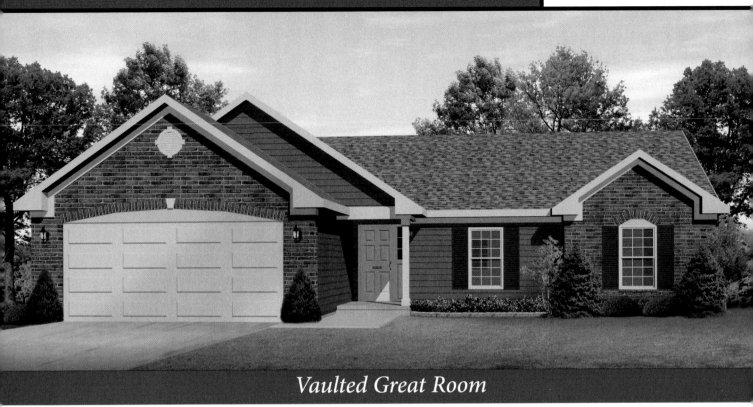

Vaulted Great Room

- 1,568 total square feet of living area
- Family and friends will love to gather around the kitchen snack bar that is open to the dining and great rooms
- A half bath, walk-in pantry and laundry area at the garage entrance adds simplicity to family functions
- A vaulted ceiling crowns the master bedroom, and the deluxe bath makes this area a luxurious suite
- 3 bedrooms, 2 1/2 baths, 2-car garage
- Basement foundation

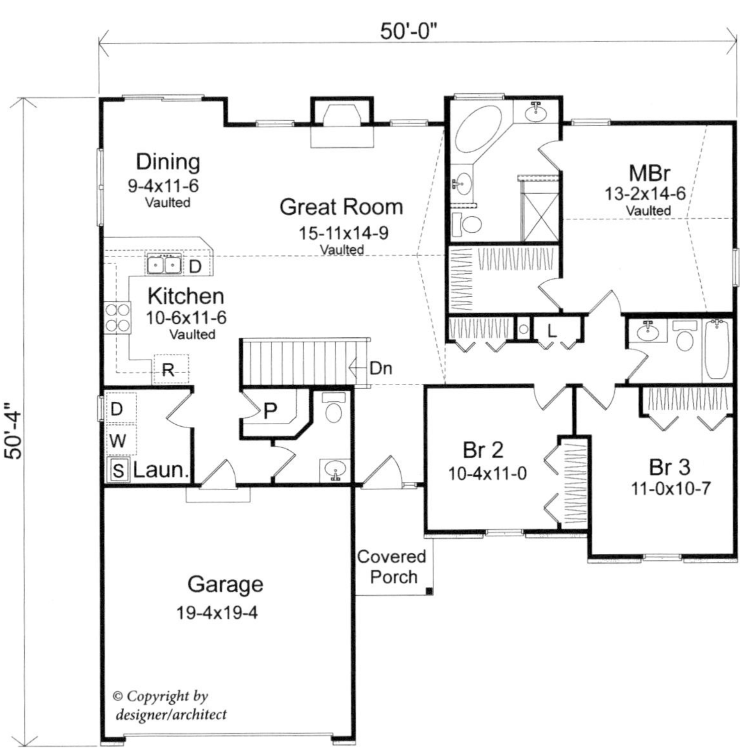

Plan #541-053D-0032 • Price Code A

Welcoming Front Porch

- 1,404 total square feet of living area
- Split-foyer entrance
- Bayed living area features a unique vaulted ceiling and fireplace
- Wrap-around kitchen has corner windows for added sunlight and a bar that overlooks the dining area
- Master bath features a garden tub with separate shower
- Rear deck provides handy access to the dining room and kitchen
- 3 bedrooms, 2 baths, 2-car drive under garage
- Basement foundation, drawings also include partial crawl space foundation

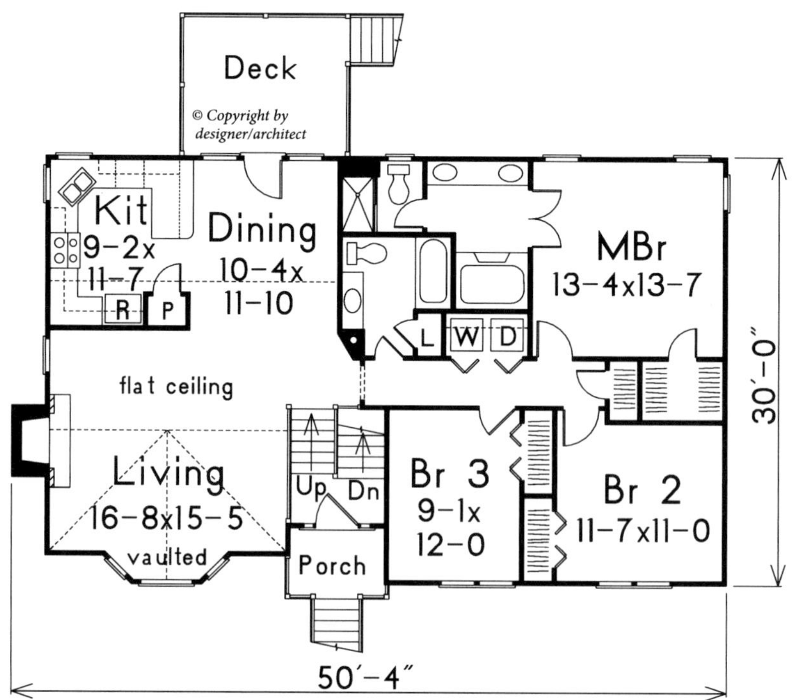

• To Order See Page 288 or Call Toll-Free 1-877-379-3420

Plan #541-001D-0126 • Price Code C

Angled Walls Create Dramatic Layout

- 2,080 total square feet of living area
- Energy efficient home with 2" x 6" exterior walls
- Combined design elements create a unique facade
- Foyer leads into the large living room with direct view to the patio
- Master bedroom includes a spacious bath with garden tub, separate shower, walk-in closet and dressing area
- 4 bedrooms, 2 baths, 2-car side-entry garage
- Crawl space foundation, drawings also include basement and slab foundations

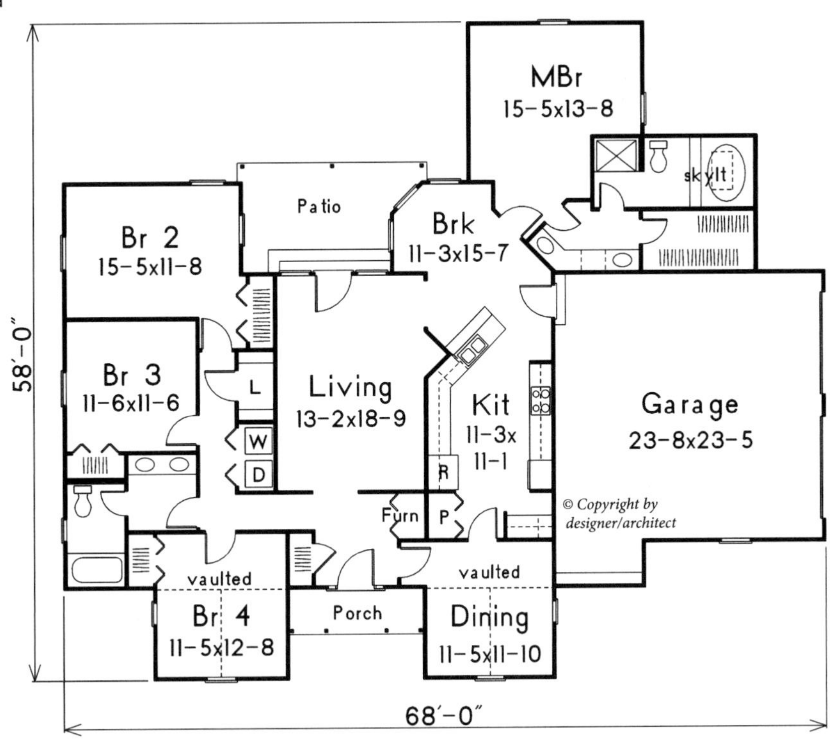

Plan #541-023D-0012 • Price Code D

Fully Columned Front Entrance

- 2,365 total square feet of living area
- 9' ceilings throughout the home
- Expansive central living room is complemented by a corner fireplace
- Breakfast bay overlooks the rear covered porch
- Master bedroom features a bath with two walk-in closets and vanities, a separate tub and shower and handy linen closet
- Peninsula keeps kitchen private
- 4 bedrooms, 2 baths, 2-car carport
- Slab foundation

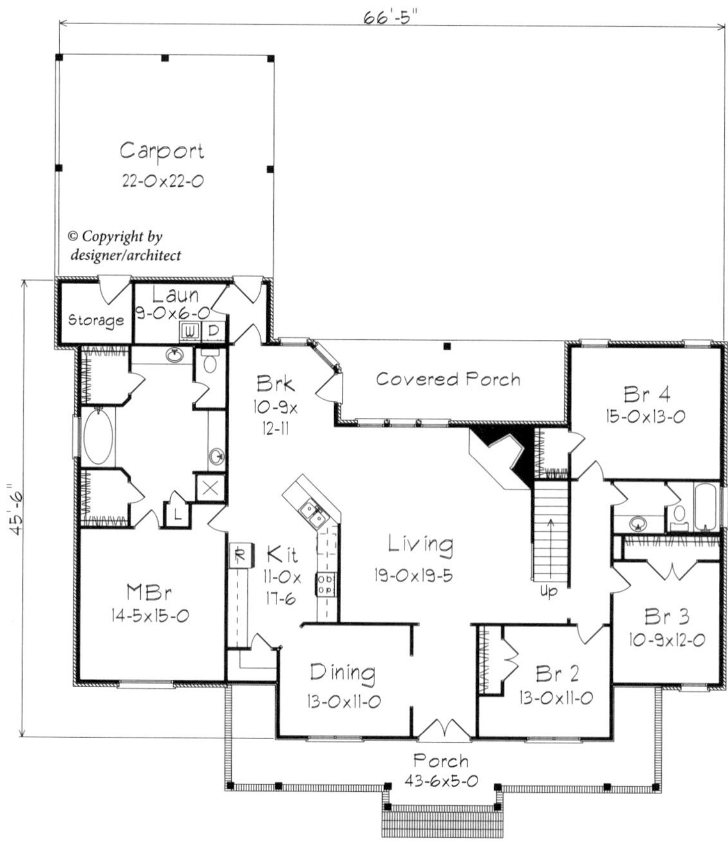

• To Order See Page 288 or Call Toll-Free 1-877-379-3420

Plan #541-053D-0029 • Price Code AA

Compact Home For Functional Living

- 1,220 total square feet of living area
- A vaulted ceiling adds luxury to the living room and master bedroom
- Spacious living room is accented with a large fireplace and hearth
- The kitchen/dining area offers direct access onto the outdoor deck
- The washer and dryer closet is handy to the bedrooms
- Covered porch entry adds appeal
- Rear deck adjoins dining area
- 3 bedrooms, 2 baths, 2-car side entry drive under garage
- Basement foundation

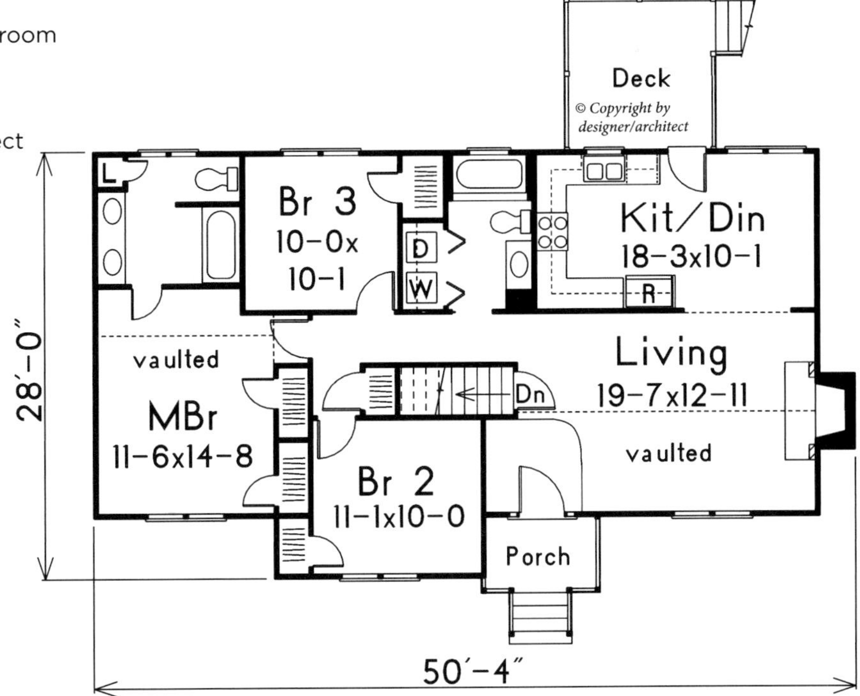

Plan #541-003D-0002 • Price Code B

Vaulted Ceilings Add Light And Dimension

- 1,676 total square feet of living area
- The living area skylights and large kitchen/breakfast area with bay window provide plenty of sunlight
- The master bedroom has a walk-in closet and both the secondary bedrooms have large closets
- Vaulted ceilings, plant shelving and a fireplace provide a quality living area
- 3 bedrooms, 2 baths, 2-car garage
- Basement foundation, drawings also include crawl space and slab foundations

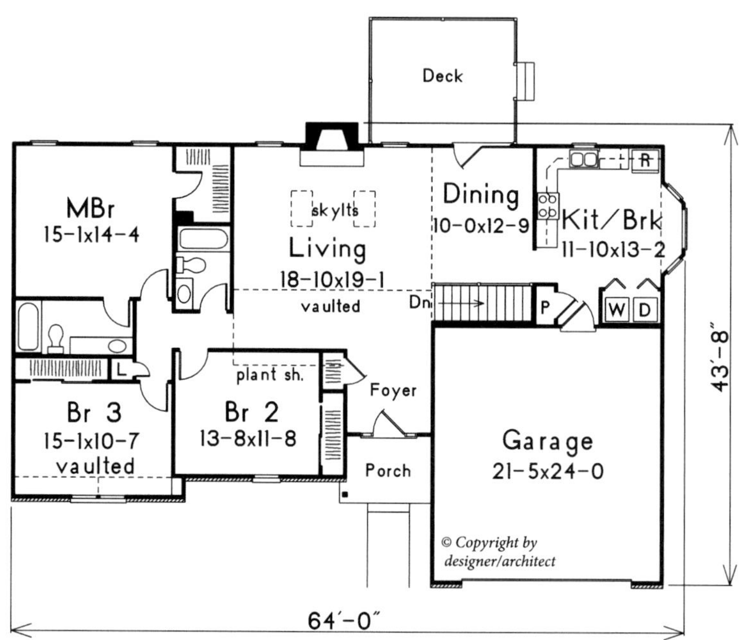

• To Order See Page 288 or Call Toll-Free 1-877-379-3420

Plan #541-007D-0185 • Price Code B

Fireplace Shared By Breakfast And Great Rooms

- 1,977 total square feet of living area
- The impressive great room includes a vaulted ceiling, fireplace and 10′ high feature windows
- A center island, built-in pantry and corner sink with windows are a few amenities of the kitchen that has access to a large deck
- The morning/breakfast room includes a see-through fireplace and balcony overlook of the atrium and rear yard through a 13′ x 14′ feature window wall
- The master bedroom suite offers an expansive bay window, convenient linen closet and luxury bath
- 4 bedrooms, 2 1/2 baths, 2-car side entry garage
- Walk-out basement foundation, drawings also include slab and crawl space foundations

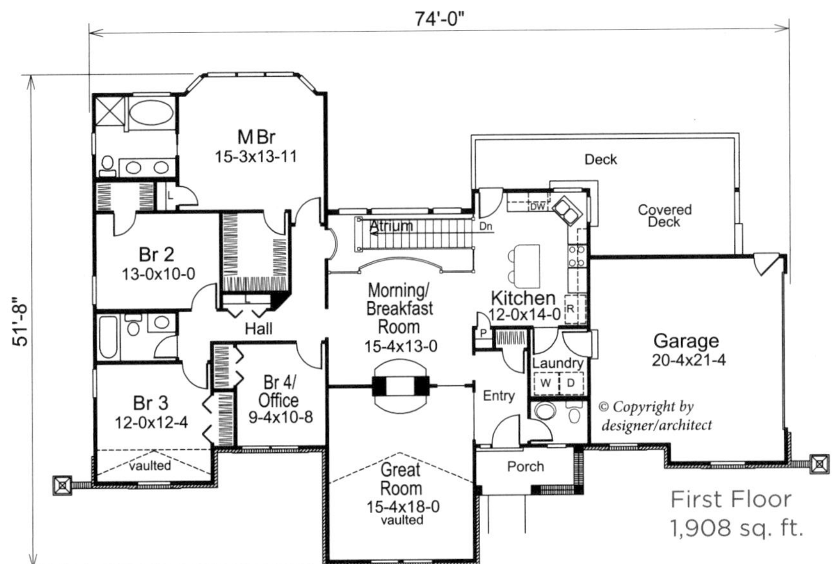

First Floor
1,908 sq. ft.

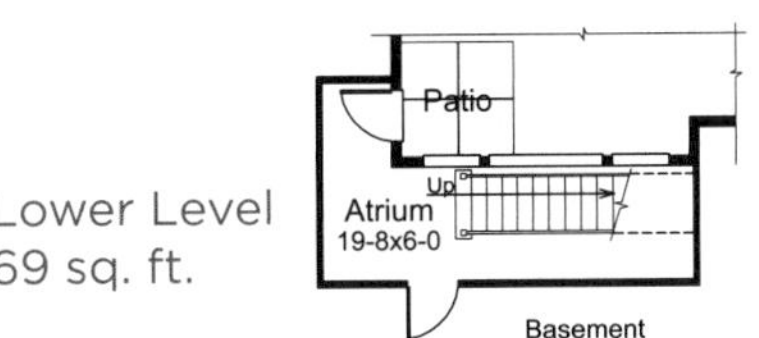

Lower Level
69 sq. ft.

Plan #541-007D-0067 • Price Code B

Small Ranch For A Perfect Country Haven

- 1,761 total square feet of living area
- Exterior window dressing, roof dormers and planter boxes provide visual warmth and charm
- Great room boasts a vaulted ceiling, fireplace and opens to a pass-through kitchen
- The vaulted master bedroom includes a luxury bath and walk-in closet
- Home features an abundance of storage
- Plan also available with energy efficient R-Control® SIPs (Structural Insulated Panels), please call 1-877-379-3420 for more information
- 4 bedrooms, 2 baths, 2-car side entry garage
- Basement foundation

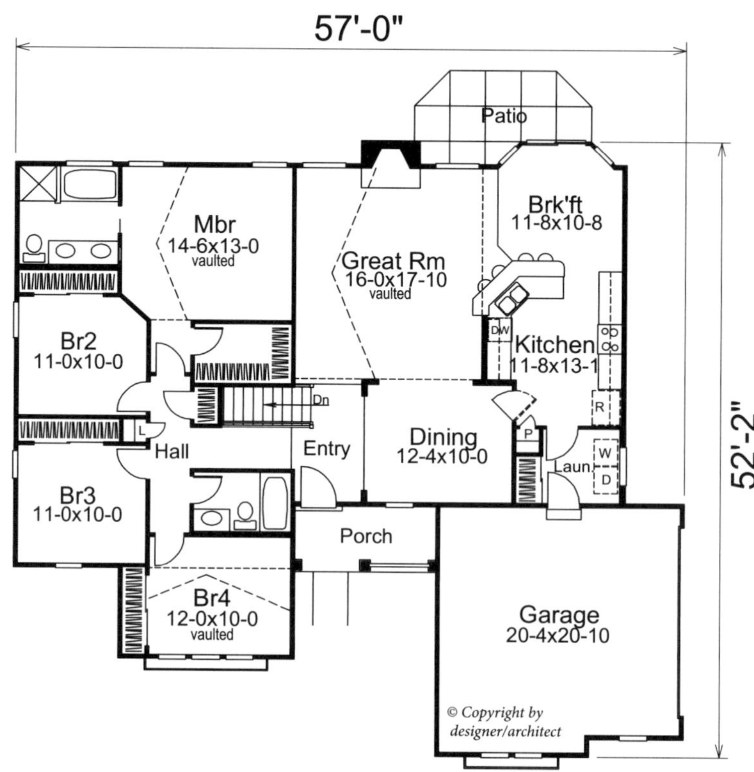

• To Order See Page 288 or Call Toll-Free 1-877-379-3420

Plan #541-053D-0058 • Price Code A

Dormers Accent This Country Home

- 1,818 total square feet of living area
- The breakfast room is tucked behind the kitchen and has a laundry closet and deck access
- Living and dining areas share a vaulted ceiling and fireplace
- Master bedroom has two closets, a large double-bowl vanity and a separate tub and shower
- Large front porch wraps around the home
- 4 bedrooms, 2 1/2 baths, 2-car drive under side entry garage
- Walk-out basement foundation

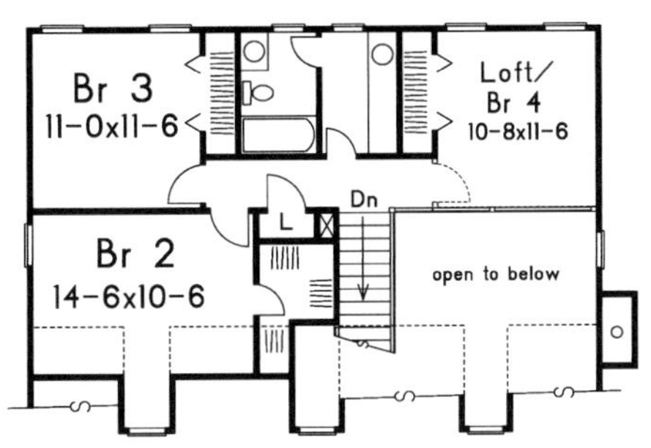

Second Floor
686 sq. ft.

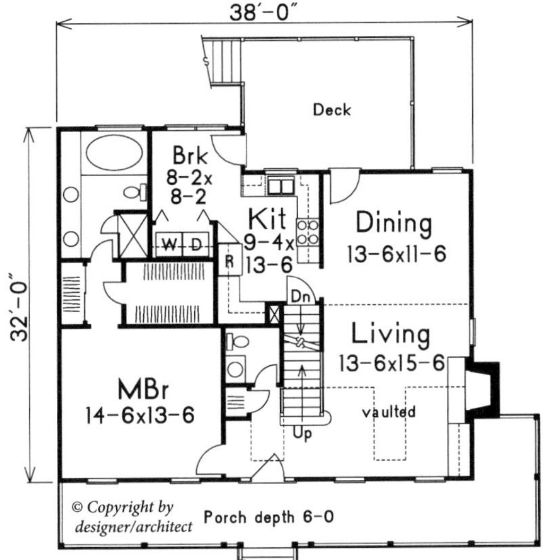

First Floor
1,132 sq. ft.

Plan #541-058D-0022 • Price Code B

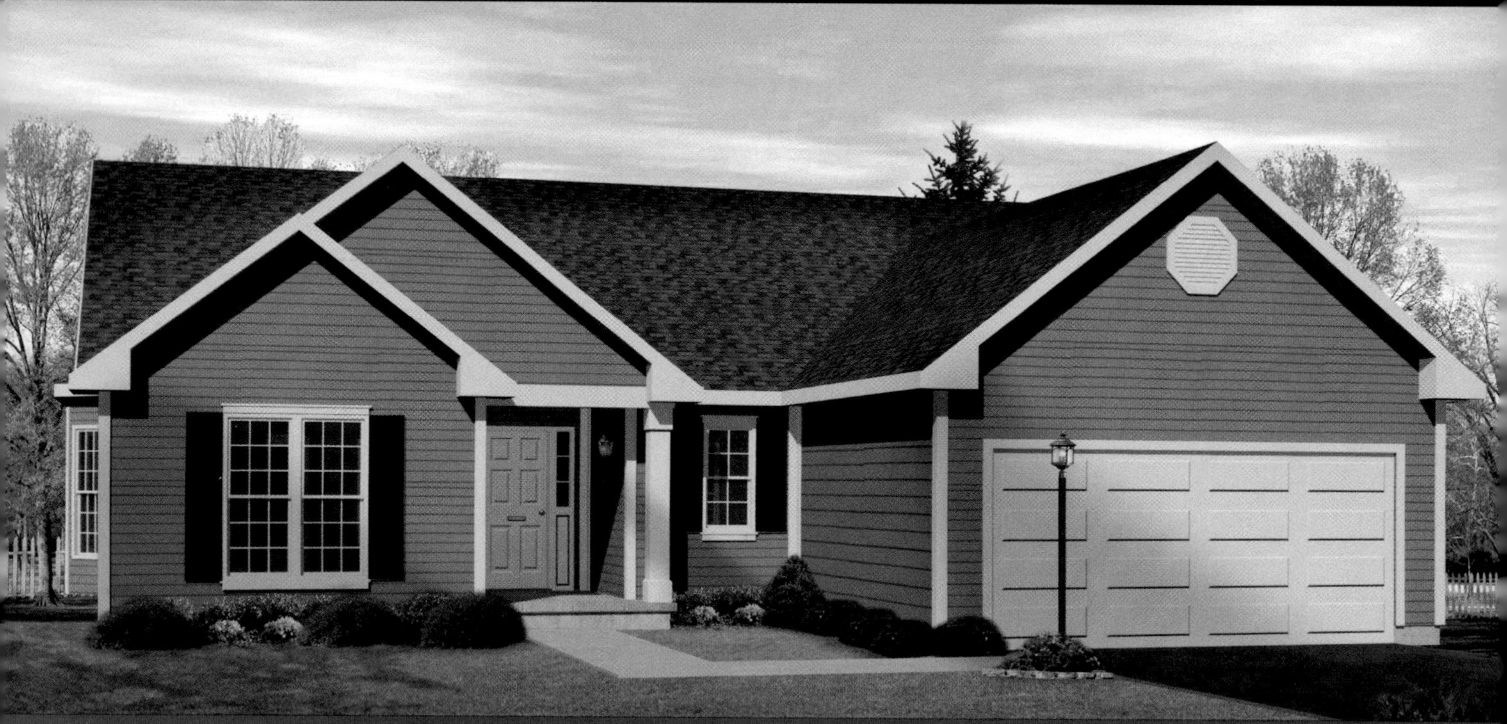

Designed For Handicap Access

- 1,578 total square feet of living area
- Plenty of closet, linen and storage space
- Covered porches in the front and rear of home add charm to this design
- Open floor plan has a unique angled layout
- 3 bedrooms, 2 baths, 2-car garage
- Basement foundation

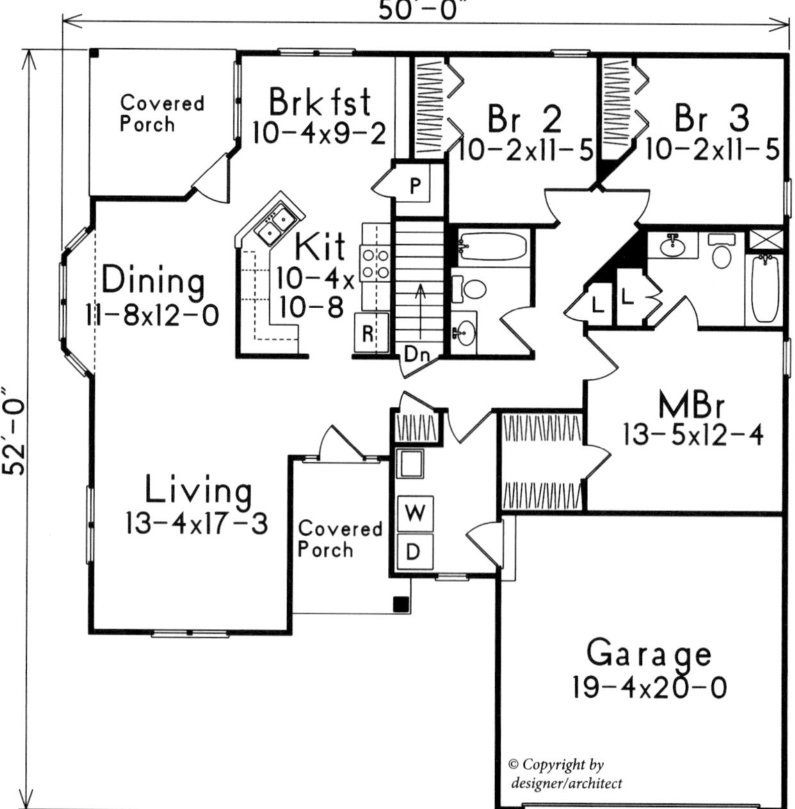

Plan #541-053D-0031 • Price Code A

Handsome Facade Welcomes Guests

- 1,908 total square feet of living area
- Distinguished front entry features circle-top window and prominent center gable
- Deck is nestled between living areas for easy access
- Oversized two-car garage has large work/storage area and convenient laundry room access
- Vaulted ceiling and floor-to-ceiling windows in the family and breakfast rooms create an open, unrestricted space
- Master bedroom has a deluxe bath, large walk-in closet and recessed ceiling
- 3 bedrooms, 2 baths, 2-car garage
- Crawl space foundation, drawings also include slab foundation

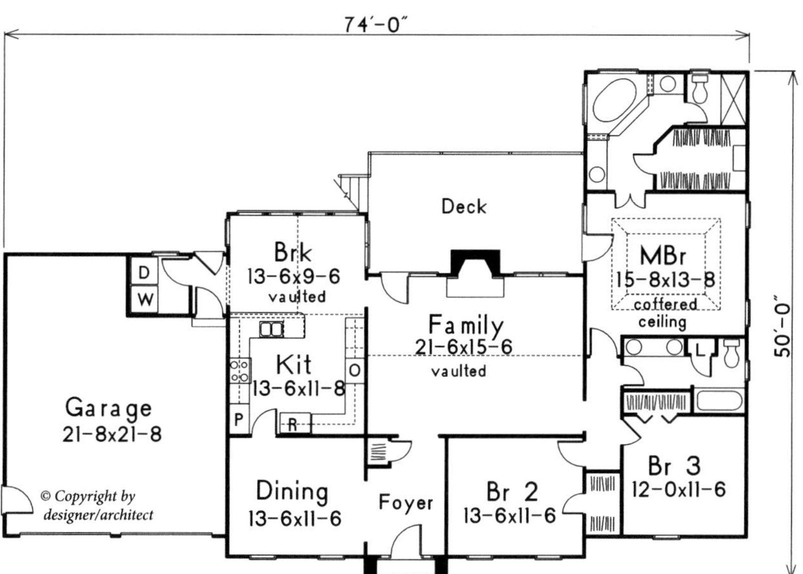

LOWE'S LEGACY SERIES

Plan #541-077L-0156 • Price Code E

Grand One-Level Home

- 2,200 total square feet of living area
- Step inside this inviting home to find an exquisite great room topped with a tray ceiling and featuring a gas fireplace flanked by built-in shelves
- The nearby kitchen is centrally located, offering a walk-in pantry and raised snack bar, and easily serves both the formal dining room and the casual breakfast area
- The master bedroom pampers with two walk-in closets and a compartmented bath equipped with a jet tub and twin vanity
- The optional second floor has an additional 371 square feet of living area
- 4 bedrooms, 2 1/2 baths, 2-car side entry garage
- Crawl space foundation, drawings also include slab foundation

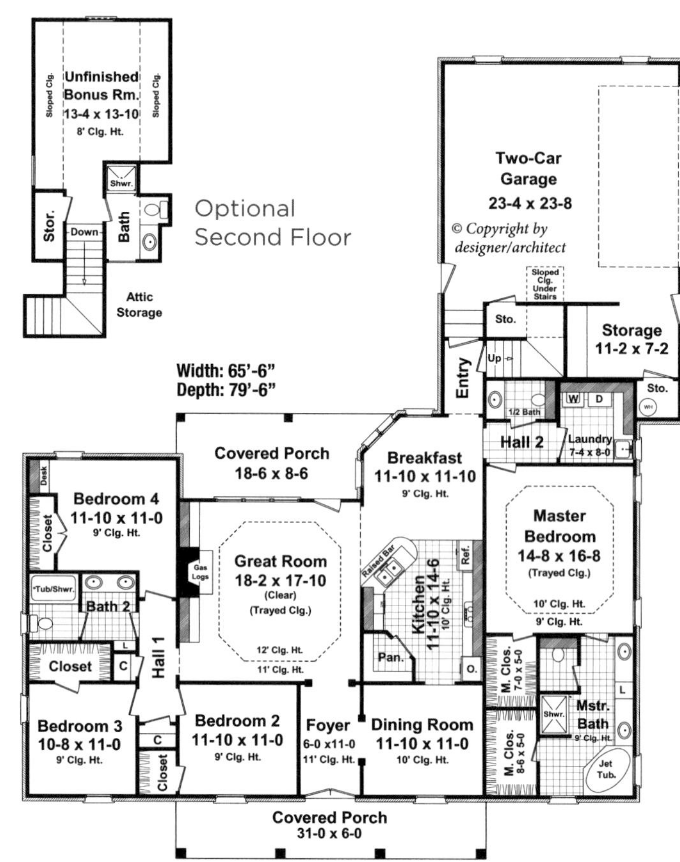

First Floor
2,200 sq. ft.

• To Order See Page 288 or Call Toll-Free 1-877-379-3420

Plan #541-001D-0053 • Price Code A

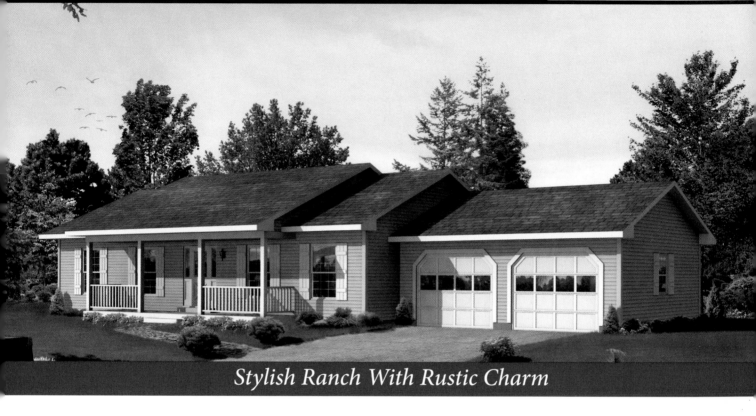

Stylish Ranch With Rustic Charm

- 1,344 total square feet of living area
- Family/dining room has sliding glass doors to the outdoors
- Master bedroom features a private bath
- Hall bath includes a double-bowl vanity for added convenience
- U-shaped kitchen features a large pantry and laundry area
- 2″ x 6″ exterior walls available, please order plan #541-001D-0108
- 3 bedrooms, 2 baths, 2-car garage
- Crawl space foundation, drawings also include basement and slab foundations

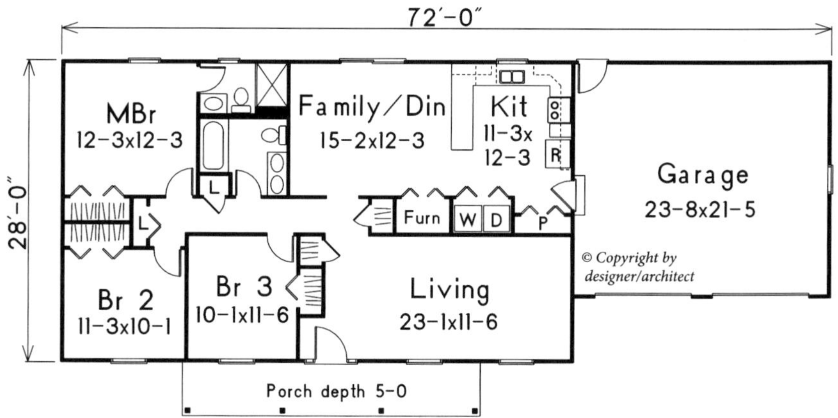

• To Order See Page 288 or Call Toll-Free 1-877

LOWE'S LEGACY SERIES

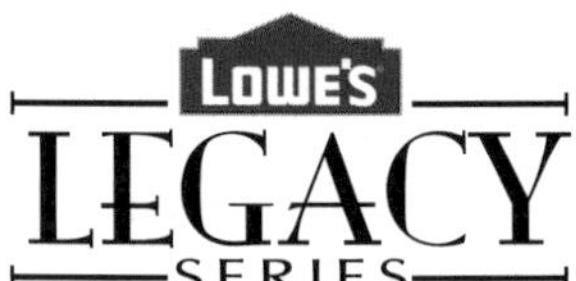

Plan #541-077L-0178 • Price Code D

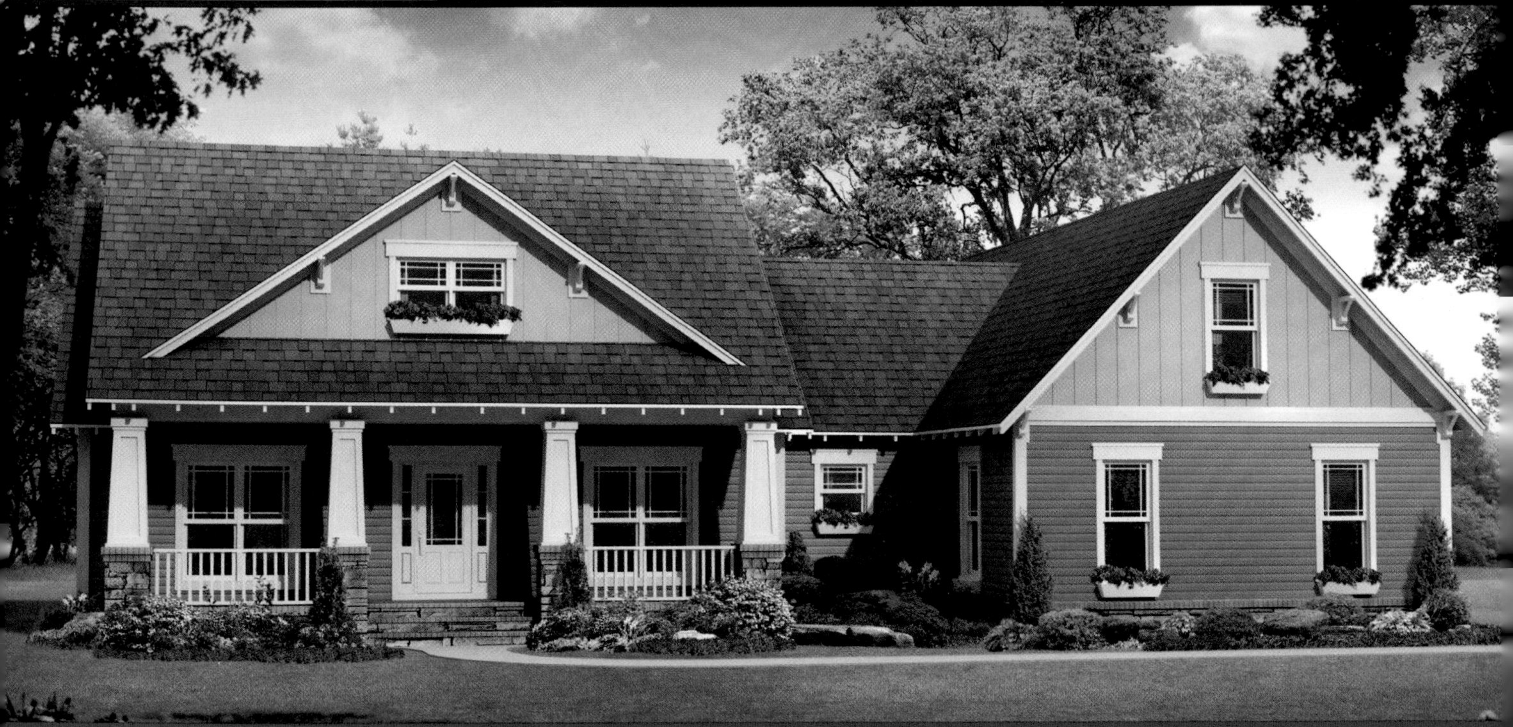

Charming Curb Appeal

- 1,900 total square feet of living area
- The breakfast area enjoys the view of the large fireplace located in the great room
- The master bedroom is separated from the other bedrooms for privacy and features a luxury bath and two walk-in closets
- The dining/office is a versatile space that can adapt to your needs
- The bonus room above the garage has an additional 348 square feet of living area
- 3 bedrooms, 2 1/2 baths, 2-car side entry garage
- Slab foundation, drawings also include crawl space foundation

Optional Second Floor

First Floor
1,900 sq. ft.

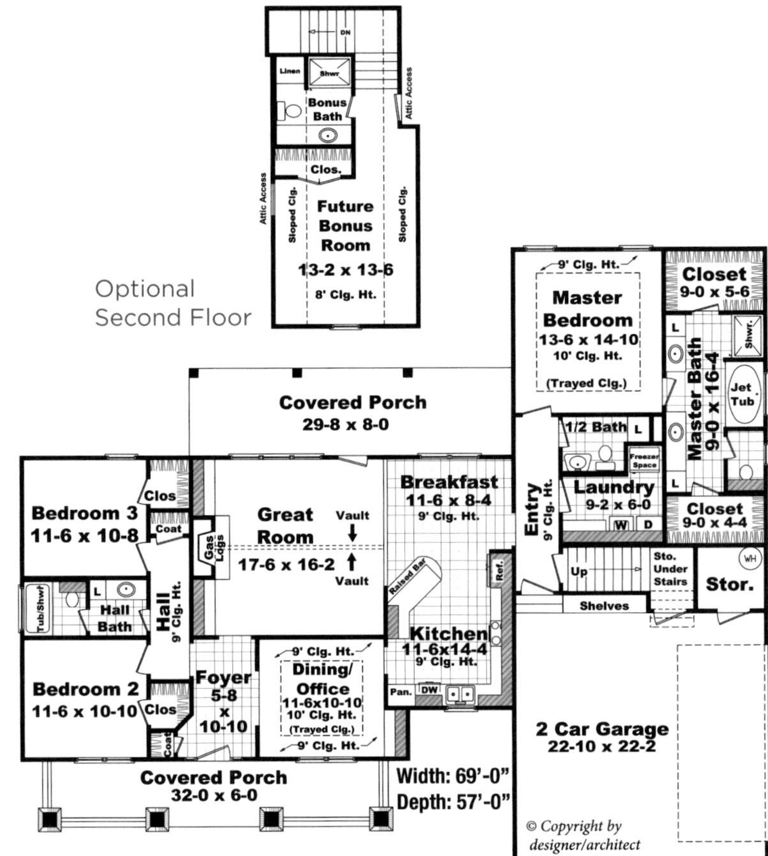

• To Order See Page 288 or Call Toll-Free 1-877-379-3420

Plan #541-010D-0005 • Price Code A

Stonework Entry Adds Character To This Home

- 1,358 total square feet of living area
- Vaulted master bath has a walk-in closet, double-bowl vanity, large tub, shower and toilet area
- Galley kitchen opens to both the living room and the breakfast area
- A vaulted ceiling joins the dining and living rooms
- Breakfast room has a full wall of windows
- 3 bedrooms, 2 baths, 2-car garage
- Slab foundation

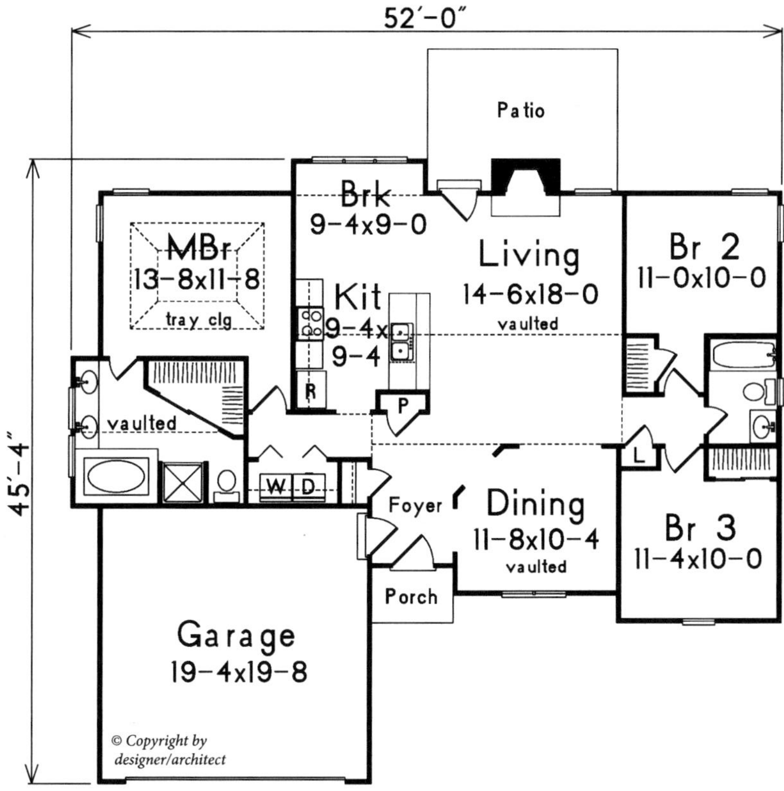

Plan #541-058D-0129 • Price Code A

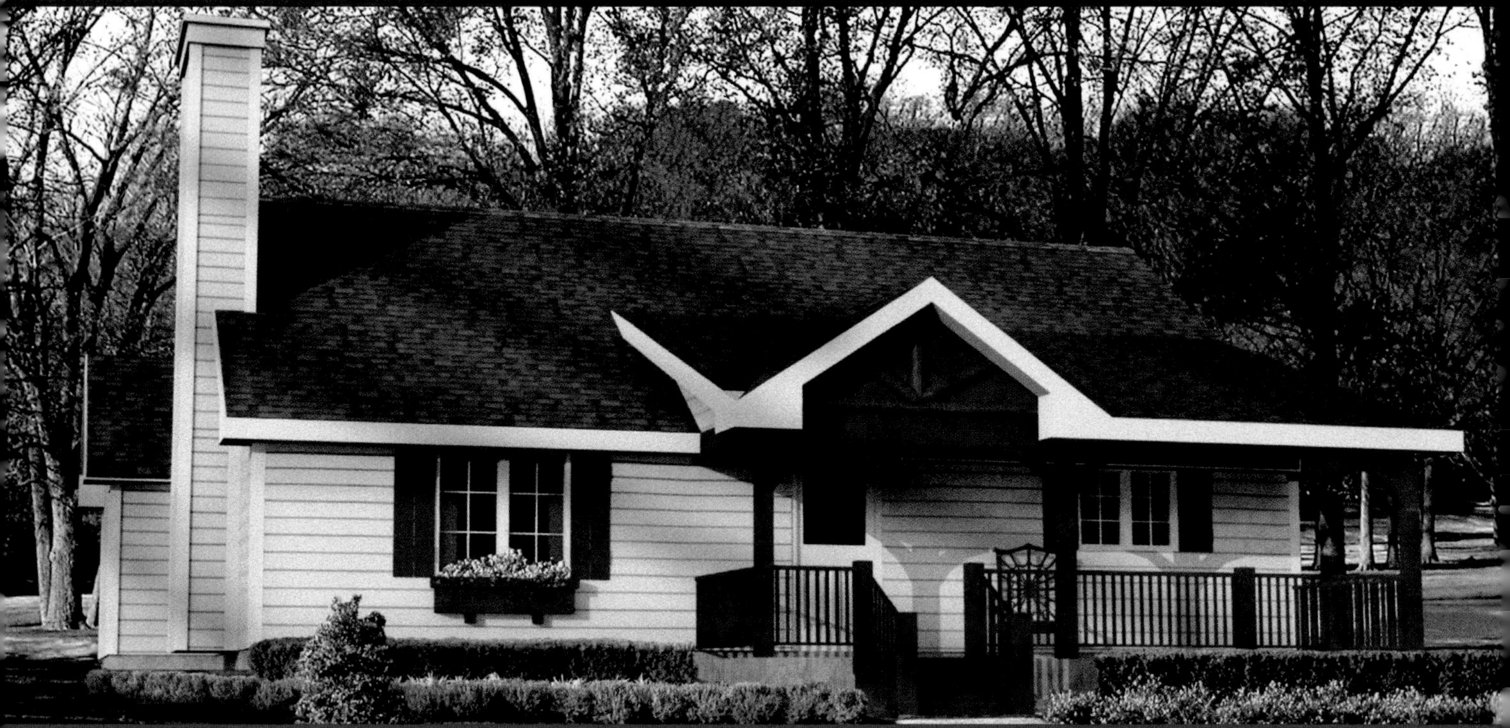

Family And Kitchen/Breakfast Area Combination

- 1,217 total square feet of living area
- Energy efficient home with 2" x 6" exterior walls
- The covered porch welcomes guests into this lovely cottage
- Inside, the massive living area includes the combined kitchen/breakfast room and family room, all warmed by a grand fireplace
- The master bedroom enjoys a walk-in closet and private bath
- 2 bedrooms, 2 baths
- Basement foundation

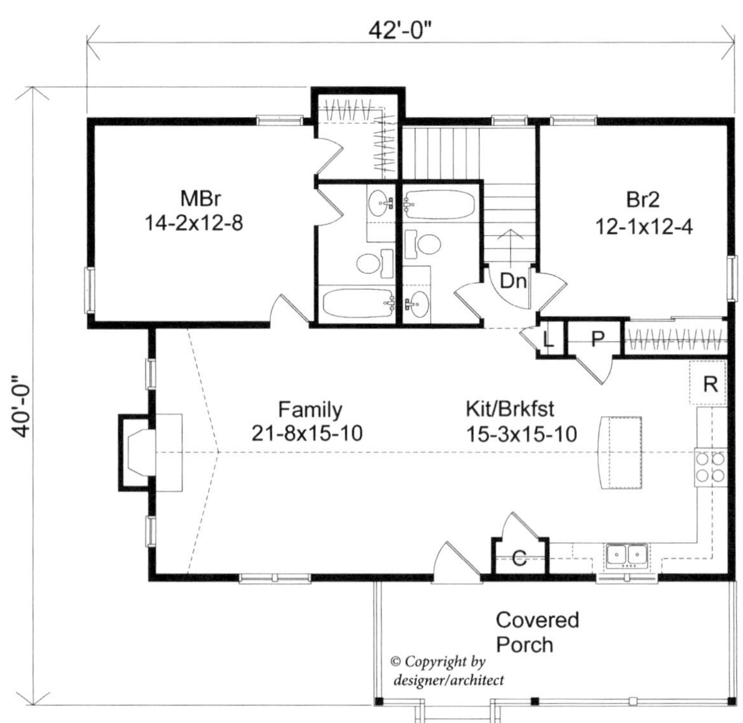

Plan #541-040D-0030 • Price Code B

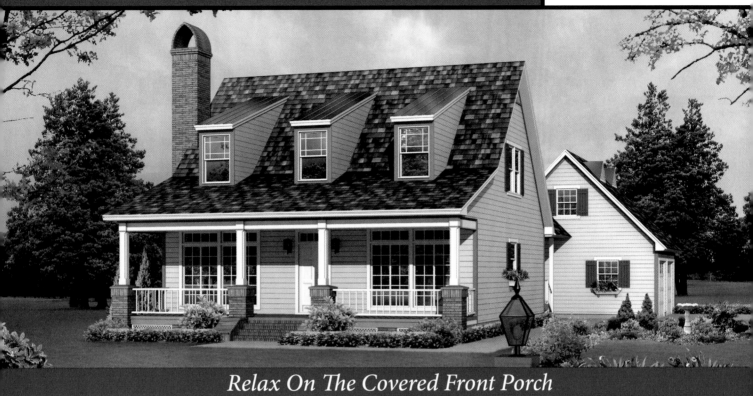

Relax On The Covered Front Porch

- 1,543 total square feet of living area
- Fireplace serves as the focal point of the large family room
- Efficient floor plan keeps hallways at a minimum
- Laundry room connects the kitchen to the garage
- Private first floor master bedroom has a walk-in closet and bath
- 3 bedrooms, 2 1/2 baths, 2-car detached side entry garage
- Slab foundation, drawings also include crawl space foundation

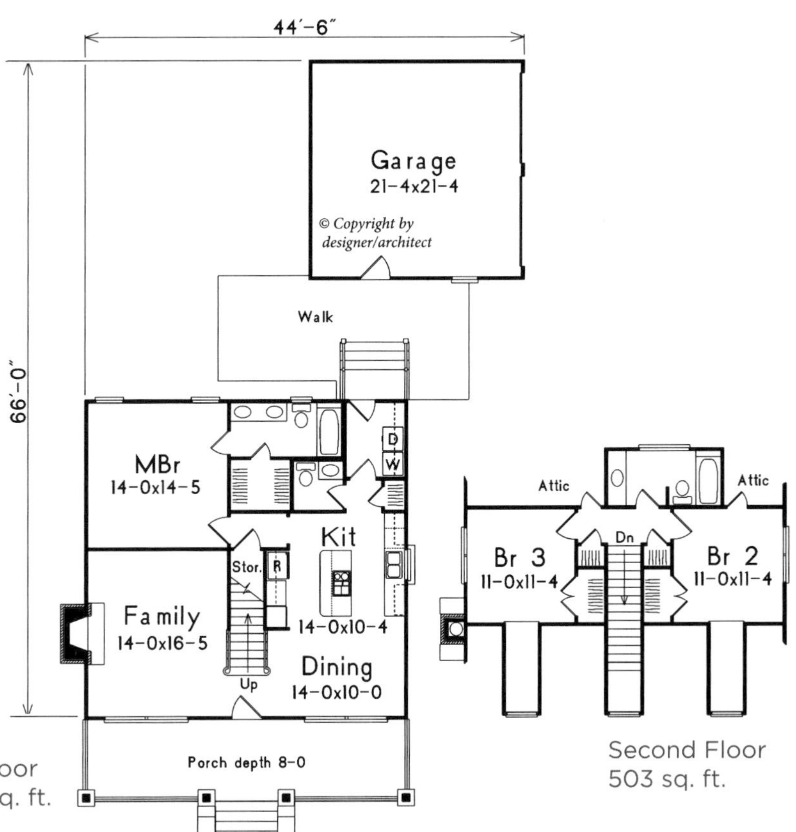

First Floor
1,040 sq. ft.

Second Floor
503 sq. ft.

Plan #541-065L-0027 • Price Code B

Covered Porch Adds Charm

- 1,595 total square feet of living area
- The front secondary bedroom could easily convert to a library or home office especially with its convenient double-door entry option
- An expansive deck is enjoyed by the open great room and bayed dining area
- A walk-in closet organizes the master bedroom
- 3 bedrooms, 2 baths, 2-car garage
- Walk-out basement foundation

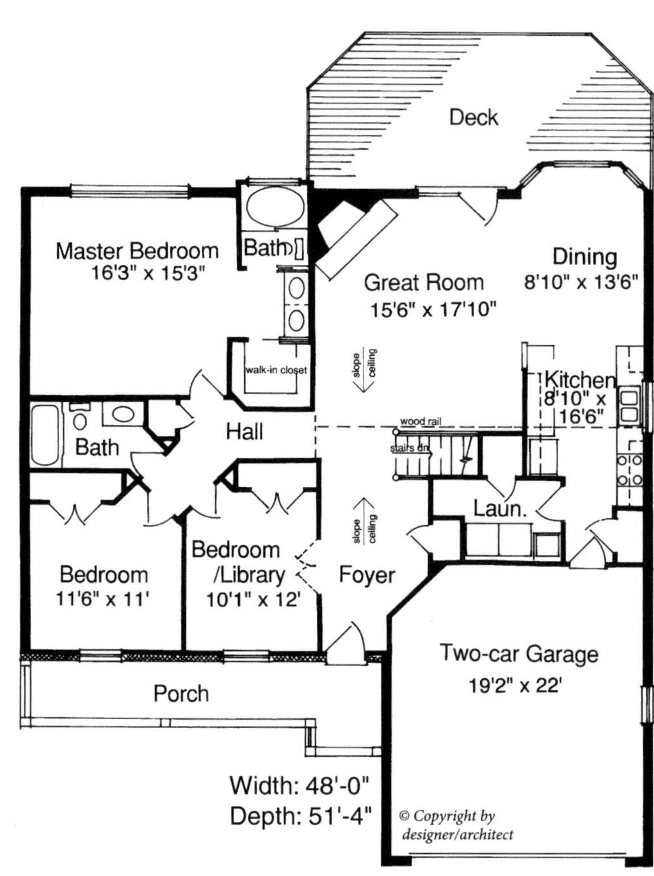

• To Order See Page 288 or Call Toll-Free 1-877-379-3420

Plan #541-007D-0123 • Price Code A

Affordable Two-Story Has It All

- 1,308 total square feet of living area
- Multi-gabled facade and elongated porch create a pleasing country appeal
- Large dining room with bay window and view to rear patio opens to a full-functional kitchen with snack bar
- An attractive U-shaped staircase with hall overlook leads to the second floor
- 3 bedrooms, 1 full bath, 2 half baths, 2-car garage
- Basement foundation

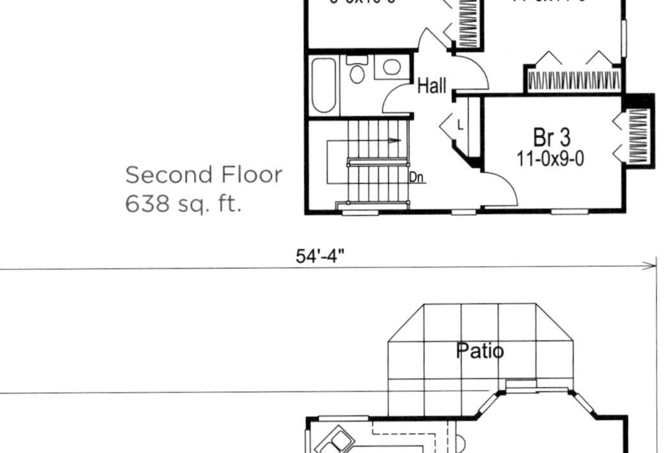

Second Floor
638 sq. ft.

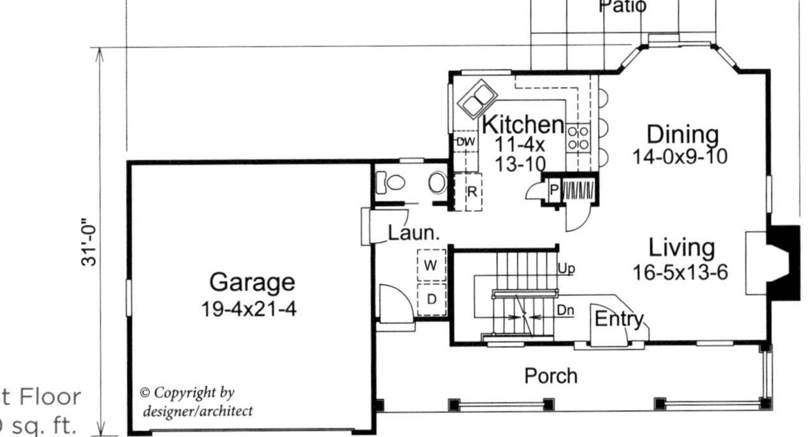

First Floor
670 sq. ft.

LOWE'S LEGACY SERIES

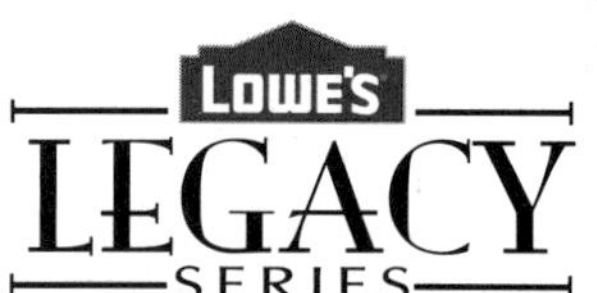

Plan #541-023D-0016 • Price Code B

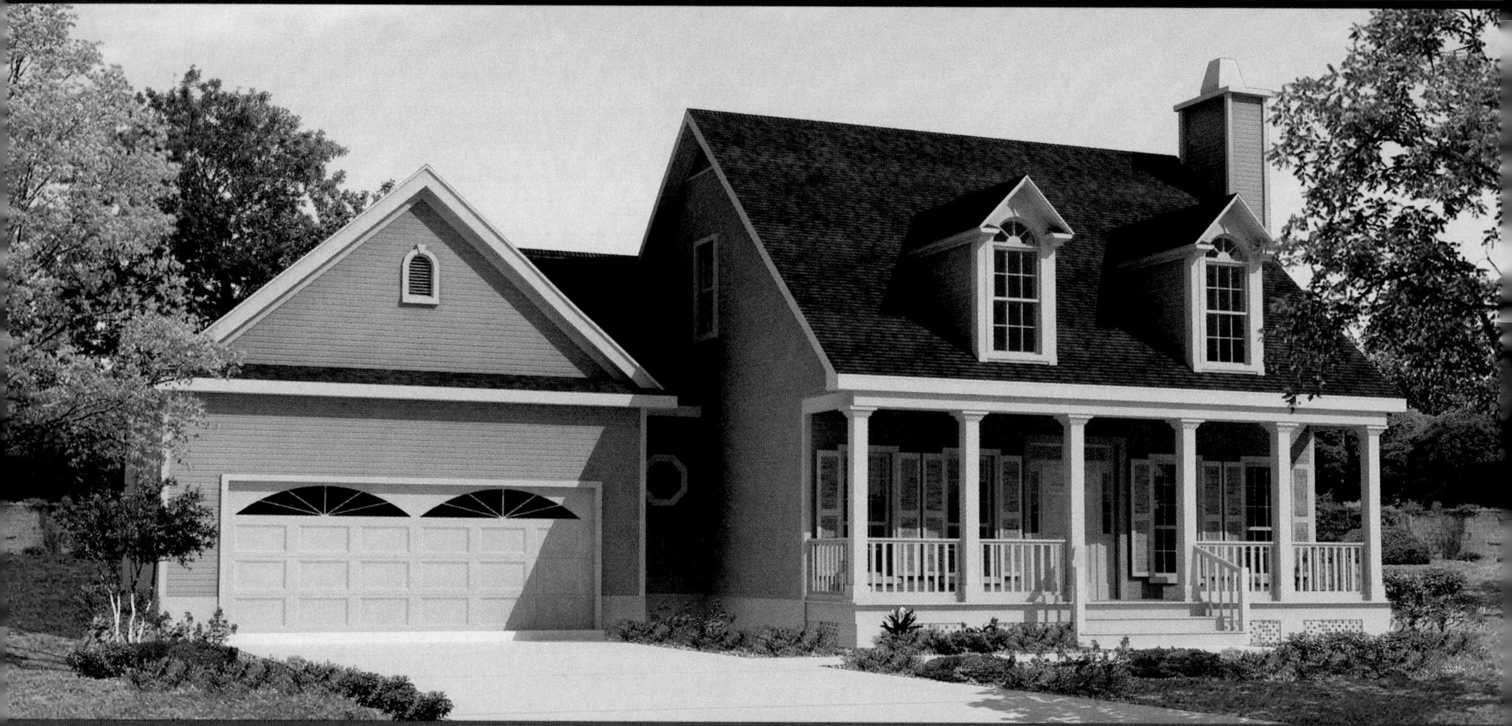

Charming Home Arranged For Open Living

- 1,609 total square feet of living area
- Kitchen captures full use of space with pantry, ample cabinets and workspace
- Master bedroom is well secluded with a walk-in closet and private bath
- Large utility room includes a sink and extra storage
- Attractive bay window in the dining area provides light
- 3 bedrooms, 2 1/2 baths, 2-car garage
- Slab foundation, drawings also include crawl space foundation

Second Floor
537 sq. ft.

First Floor
1,072 sq. ft.

• To Order See Page 288 or Call Toll-Free 1-877-379-3420

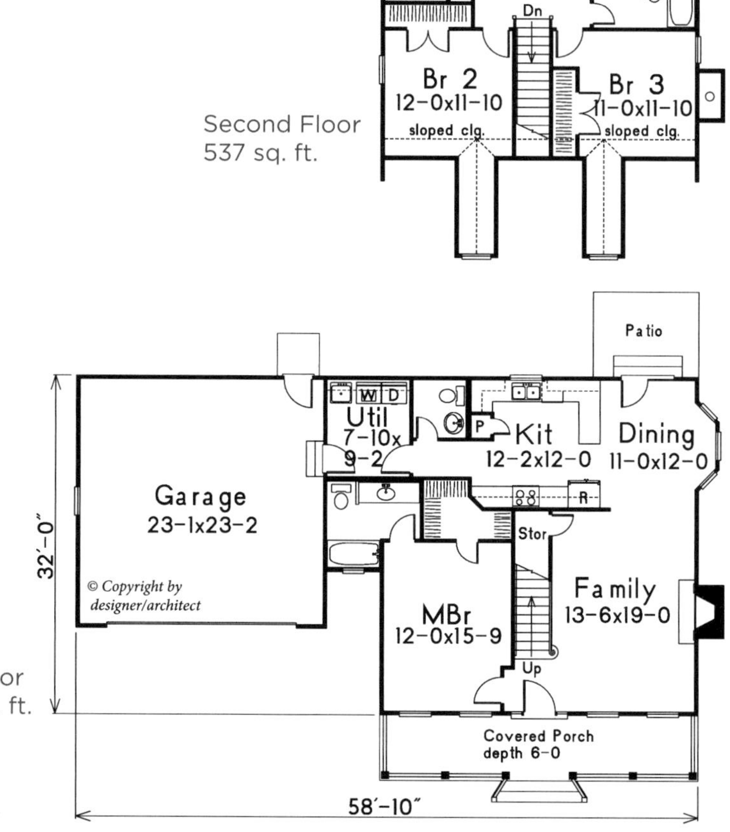

Plan #541-055L-0508 • Price Code C

This Country Style Home Has A High-Pitched Roof

- 1,894 total square feet of living area
- The center fireplace warms the entire great room that spans the entire depth of this home
- The second floor master suite is topped with a tray ceiling and has an amenity-filled private bath
- The extended counter in the kitchen features enough casual dining space for four people
- 3 bedrooms, 2 1/2 baths, 2-car garage
- Crawl space or slab foundation, please specify when ordering

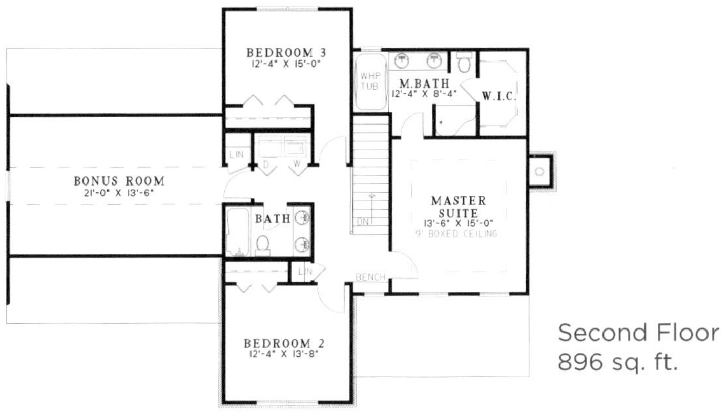

Second Floor
896 sq. ft.

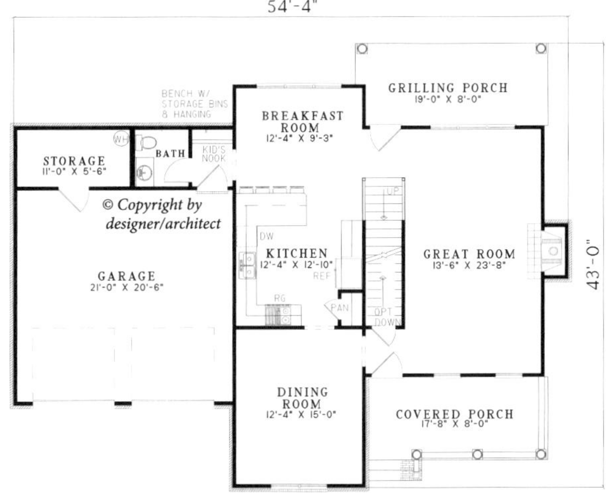

First Floor
998 sq. ft.

Plan #541-001D-0029 • Price Code A

Central Fireplace Warms Living Area

- 1,260 total square feet of living area
- Spacious kitchen/dining area features a large pantry, storage area and easy access to the garage and laundry room
- Pleasant covered front porch adds a practical touch
- Master bedroom with a private bath adjoins two other bedrooms, all with plenty of closet space
- 3 bedrooms, 2 baths, 2-car garage
- Basement foundation, drawings also include crawl space and slab foundations

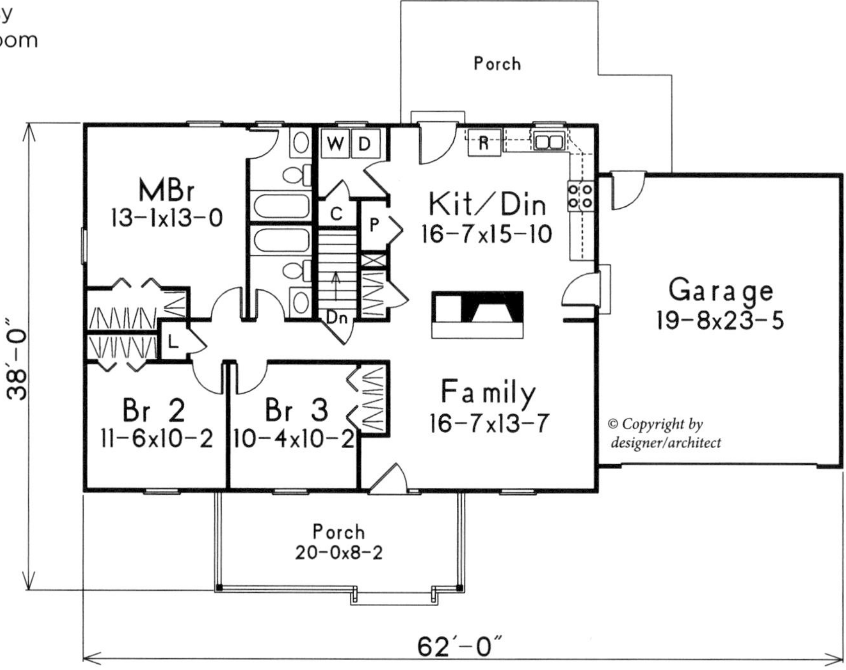

• To Order See Page 288 or Call Toll-Free 1-877-379-3420

Plan #541-087L-1672 • Price Code E

Quaint Front Covered Porch

- 1,659 total square feet of living area
- The large family room enjoys the warmth of the fireplace flanked by built-in bookcases
- The porte-cochere has extra storage and access into the home near the utility room
- The cheerful dining area provides accessibility to the covered rear porch
- 3 bedrooms, 2 1/2 baths, 2-car carport
- Slab foundation

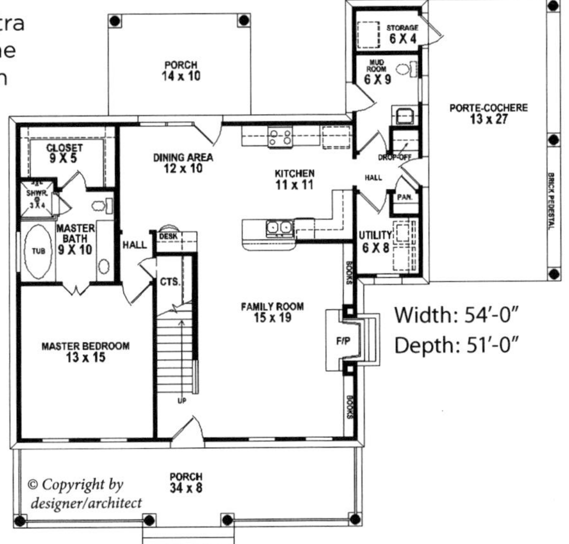

Width: 54'-0"
Depth: 51'-0"

First Floor
1,237 sq. ft.

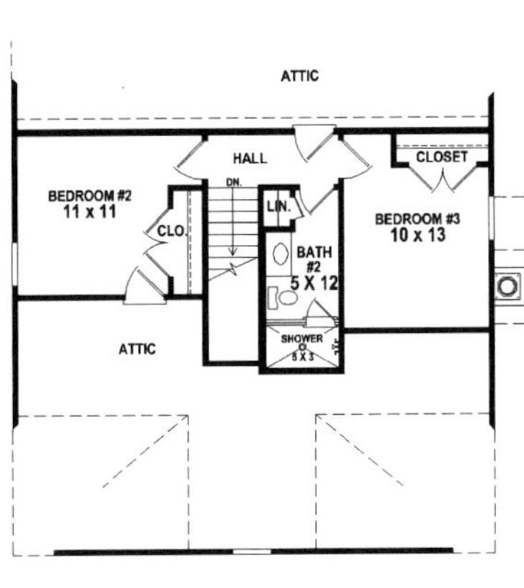

Second Floor
422 sq. ft.

• To Order See Page 288 or Call Toll-Free 1-877-379-3420

Plan #541-057D-0038 • Price Code AA

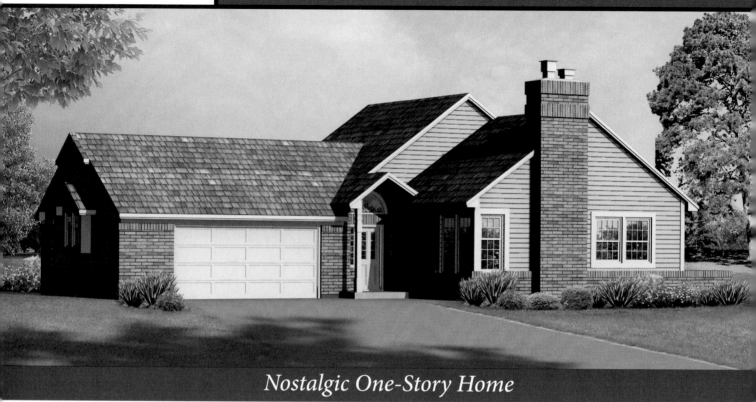

Nostalgic One-Story Home

- 1,229 total square feet of living area
- A spacious foyer includes a coat closet and area for plants
- Living room enjoys a fireplace and a vaulted ceiling
- Abundant storage room and closet located in the garage
- 2 bedrooms, 1 bath, 2-car garage
- Basement foundation

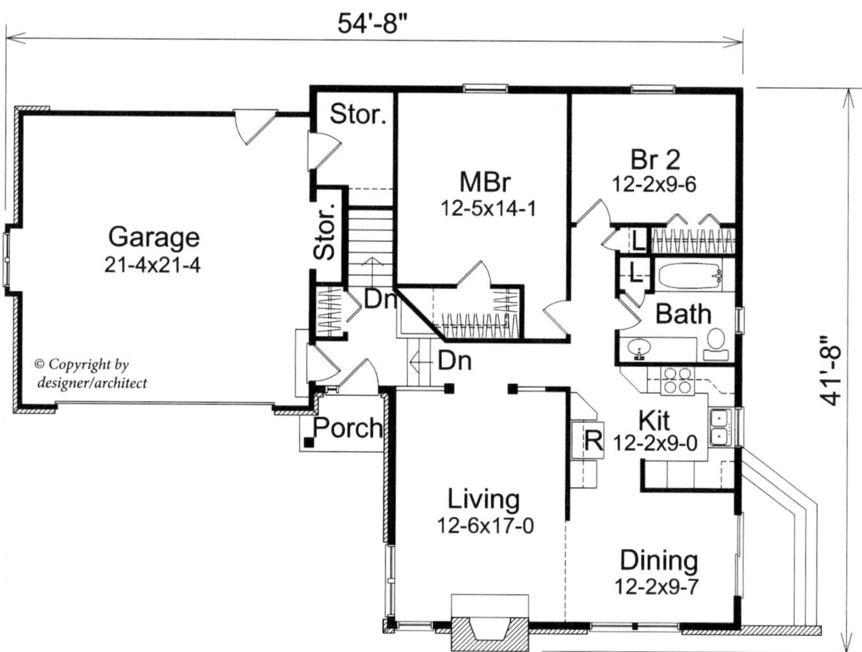

• To Order See Page 288 or Call Toll-Free 1-877-379-3420

Plan #541-007D-0128 • Price Code AA

Complete With Screened Porch, Garage And Shop

- 1,072 total square feet of living area
- Integrated open and screened front porches guarantee comfortable summer enjoyment
- Oversized garage includes area for shop and miscellaneous storage
- U-shaped kitchen and breakfast nook are adjacent to the vaulted living room and have access to the screened porch through sliding glass doors
- 345 square feet of optional living area on the lower level including a third bedroom and a bath
- 2 bedrooms, 2 baths, 2-car side entry garage
- Basement foundation

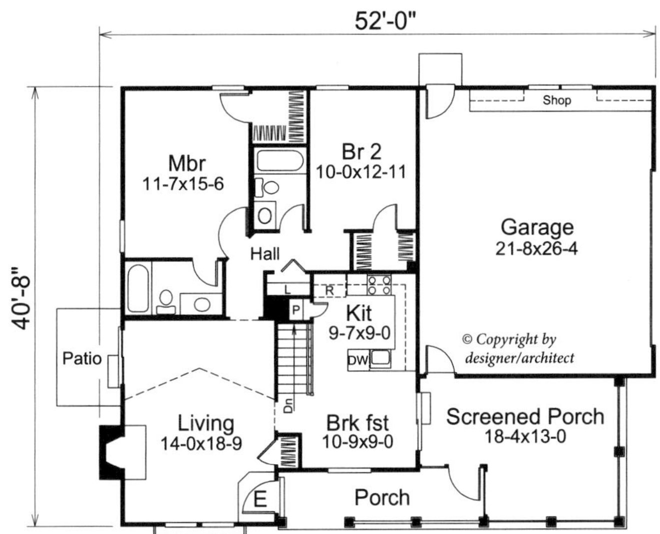

First Floor
1,072 sq. ft.

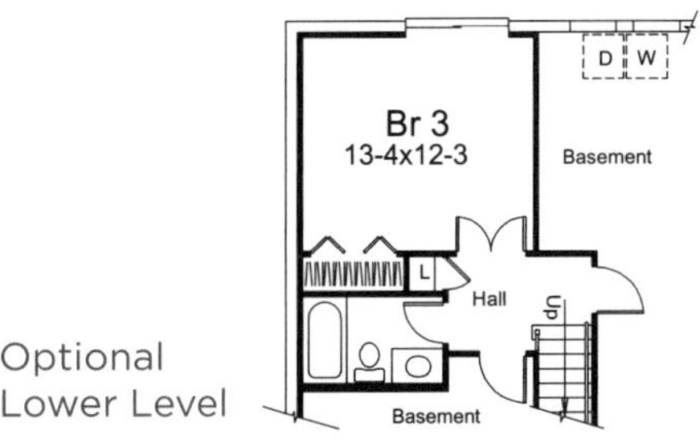

Optional
Lower Level

Plan #541-087L-0095 • Price Code F

Stylish Single Story

- 1,551 total square feet of living area
- A centrally located kitchen is able to effortlessly serve the formal dining room and casual breakfast area
- Four spacious bedrooms offer space for a large family
- The rear of the home includes an essential storage room accessed from the rear yard
- 4 bedrooms, 2 baths
- Slab foundation

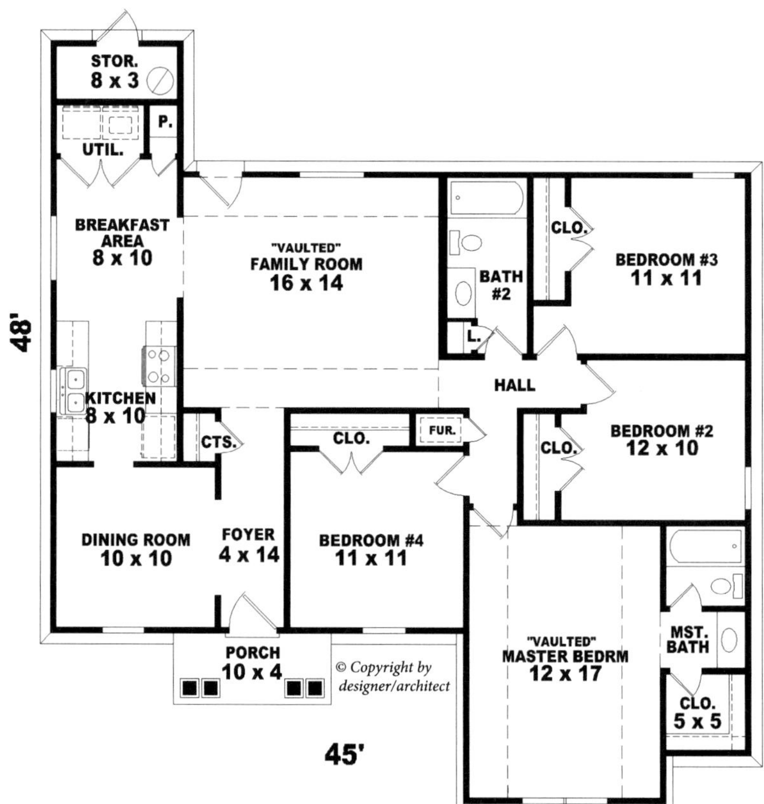

• To Order See Page 288 or Call Toll-Free 1-877-379-3420

Plan #541-007D-0077 • Price Code C

LOWE'S LEGACY SERIES

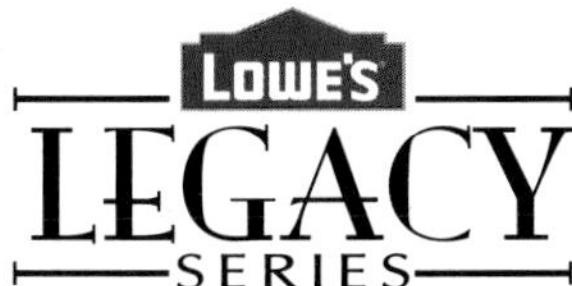

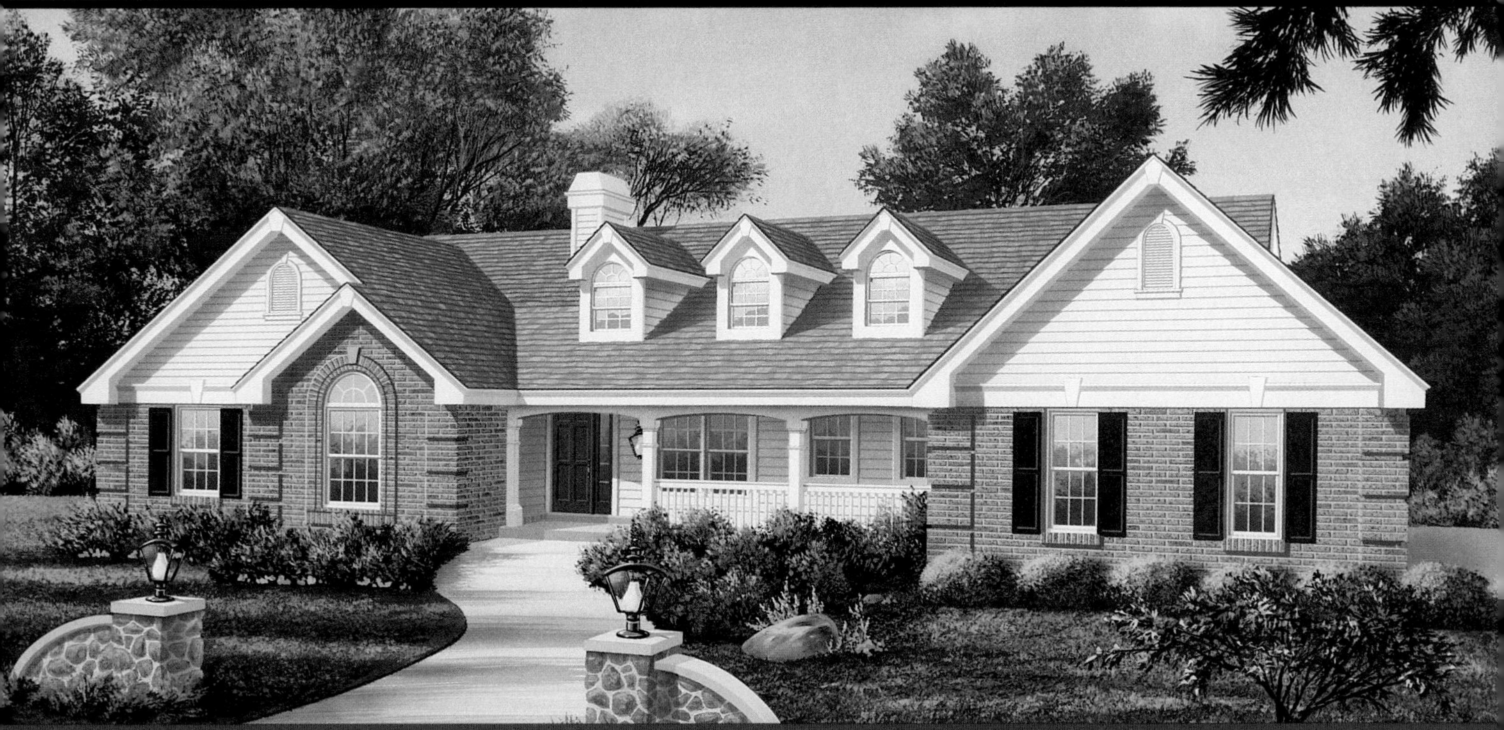

Classic Atrium Ranch With Rooms To Spare

- 1,978 total square feet of living area
- Classic traditional exterior is always in style
- Spacious great room boasts a vaulted ceiling, dining area, atrium with elegant staircase and feature windows
- The lower level has an additional 1,295 square feet of optional living area below that consists of a family room, two bedrooms, two baths and a study
- 2″ x 6″ exterior walls available, please order plan #541-007E-0077
- 4 bedrooms, 2 1/2 baths, 3-car side entry garage
- Walk-out basement foundation

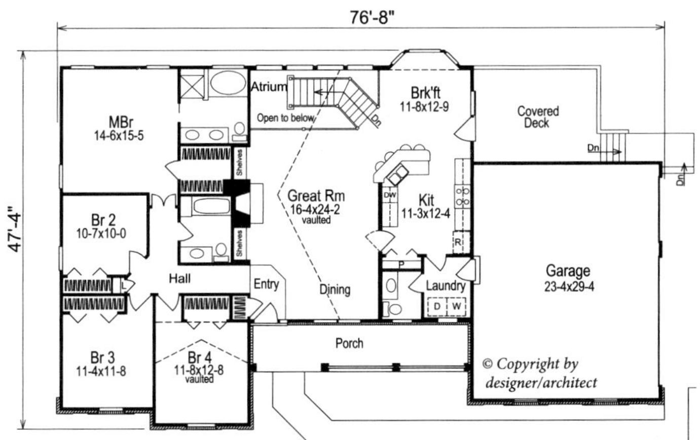

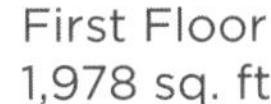

First Floor
1,978 sq. ft.

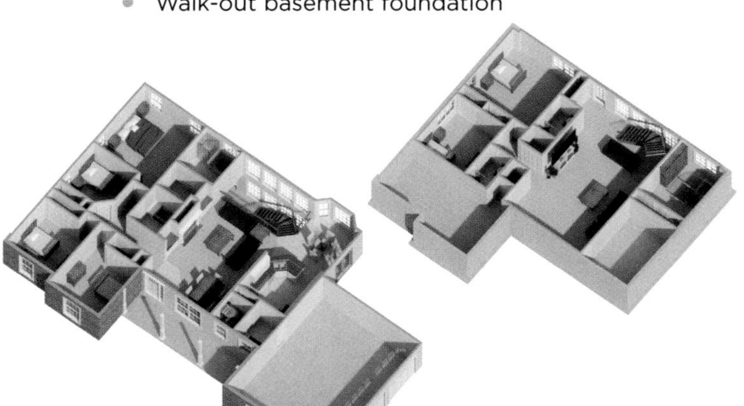

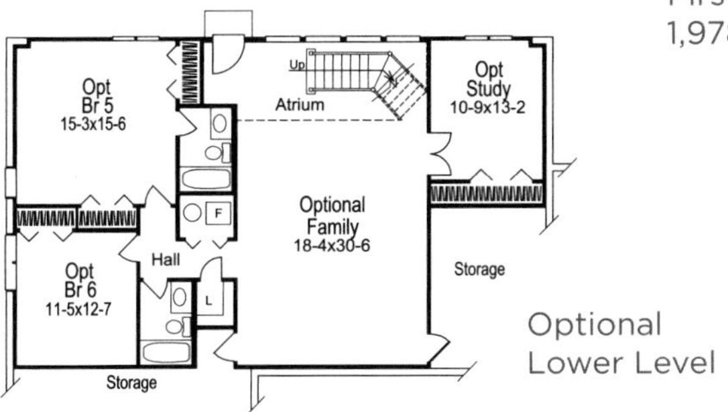

Optional
Lower Level

Plan #541-058D-0056 • Price Code C

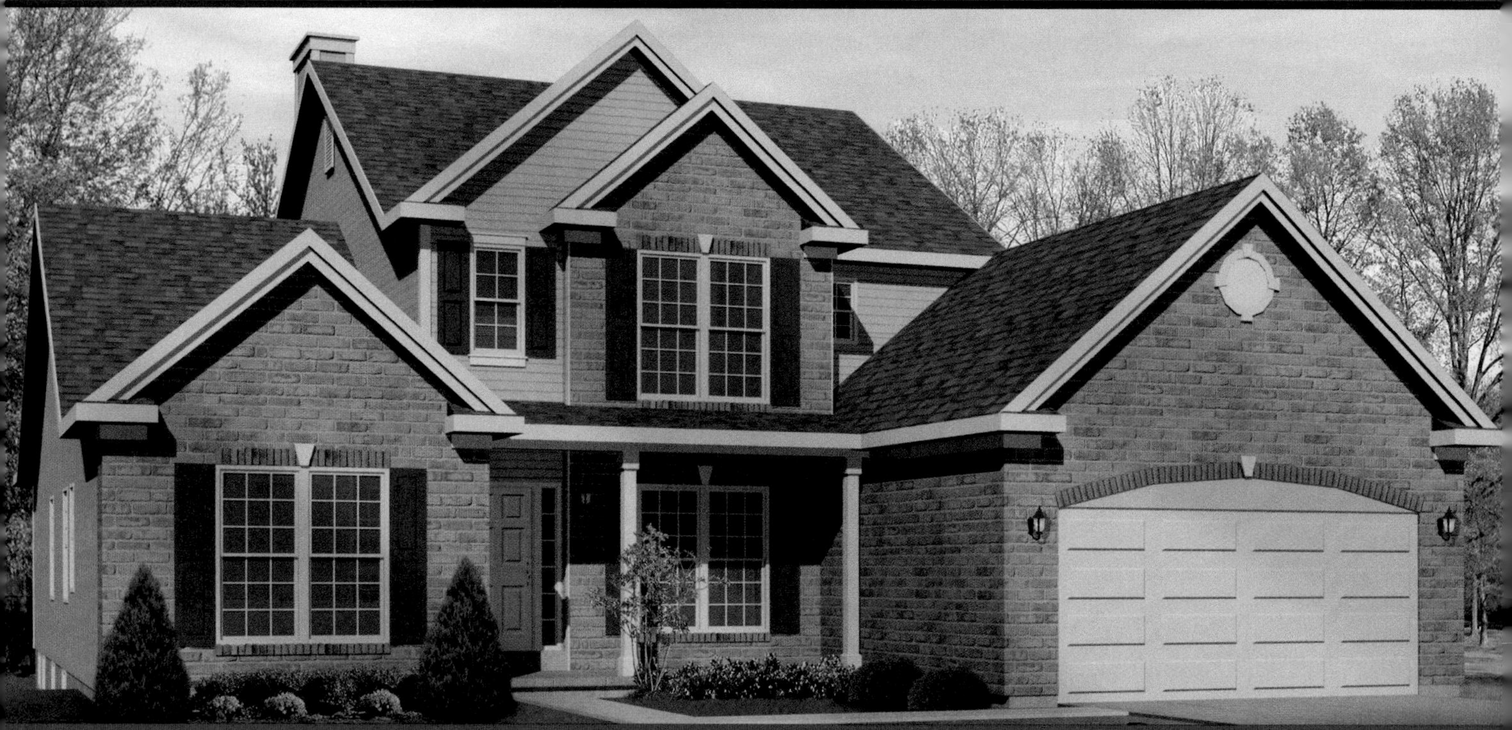

Two-Story Great Room

- 2,150 total square feet of living area
- The centrally located kitchen with pantry serves the breakfast area and formal dining room with ease
- The study located at the front of the house would make an ideal home office
- A coffered ceiling, two walk-in closets and a corner whirlpool tub enhance the master bedroom
- 3 bedrooms, 2 1/2 baths, 3-car garage
- Basement foundation

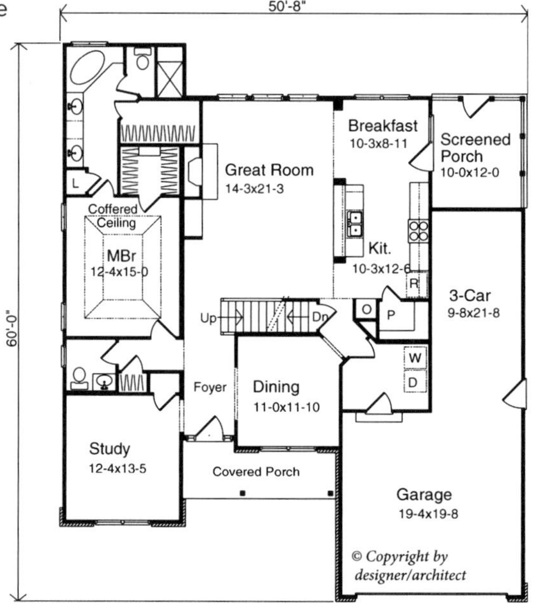

First Floor
1,651 sq. ft.

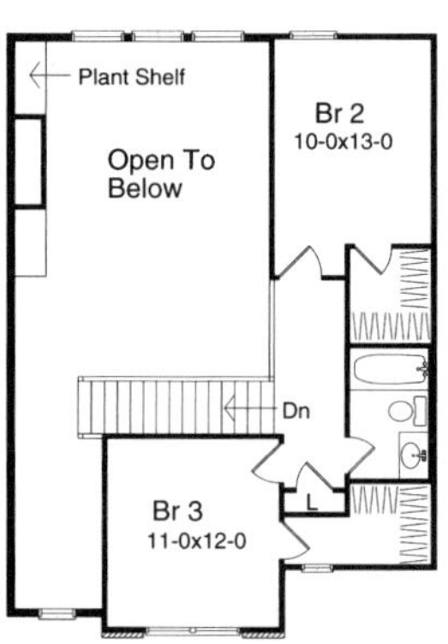

Second Floor
499 sq. ft.

Plan #541-037D-0007 • Price Code D

LOWE'S LEGACY SERIES

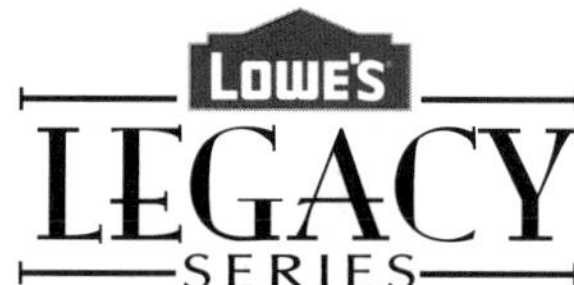

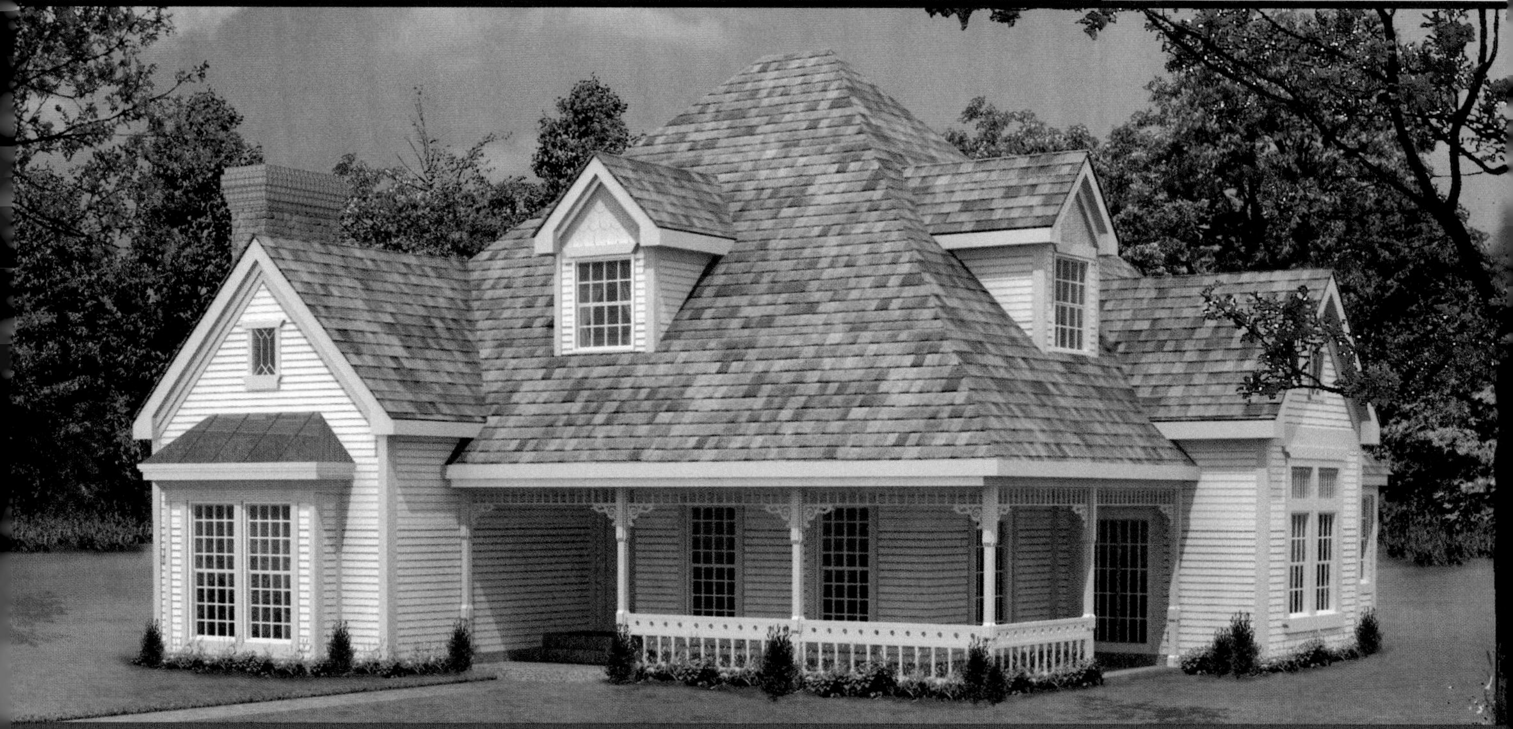

Open Format For Easy Living

- 2,282 total square feet of living area
- Living and dining rooms combine to create a large, convenient entertaining area that includes a fireplace
- Comfortable covered porch allows access from secondary bedrooms
- Second floor game room overlooks the foyer and includes a full bath
- Kitchen and breakfast areas are surrounded by mullioned windows
- 3 bedrooms, 3 baths, 2-car detached garage
- Slab foundation, drawings also include crawl space foundation

Second Floor
445 sq. ft.

First Floor
1,837 sq. ft.

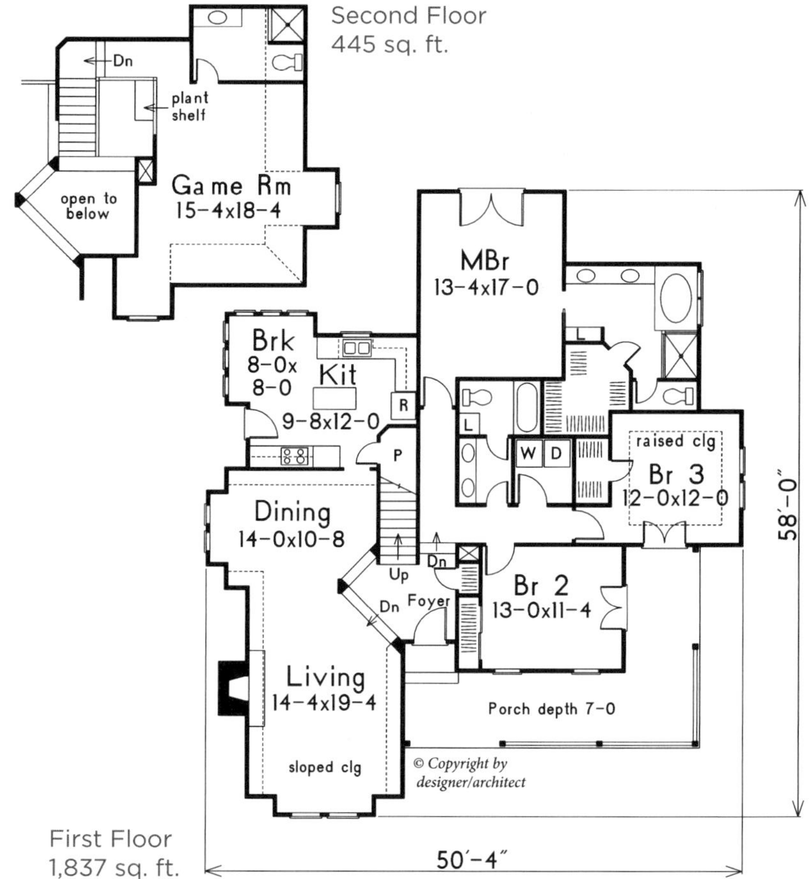

Plan #541-022D-0005 • Price Code A

Distinctive Ranch Has A Larger Look

- 1,360 total square feet of living area
- Double-gabled front facade frames large windows
- The foyer opens to the vaulted great room with a fireplace and access to the rear deck
- Vaulted ceiling and large windows add openness to the kitchen/breakfast room
- Bedroom #3 easily converts to a den
- Plan easily adapts to crawl space or slab construction, with the utilities replacing the stairs
- 3 bedrooms, 2 baths, 2-car garage
- Basement foundation

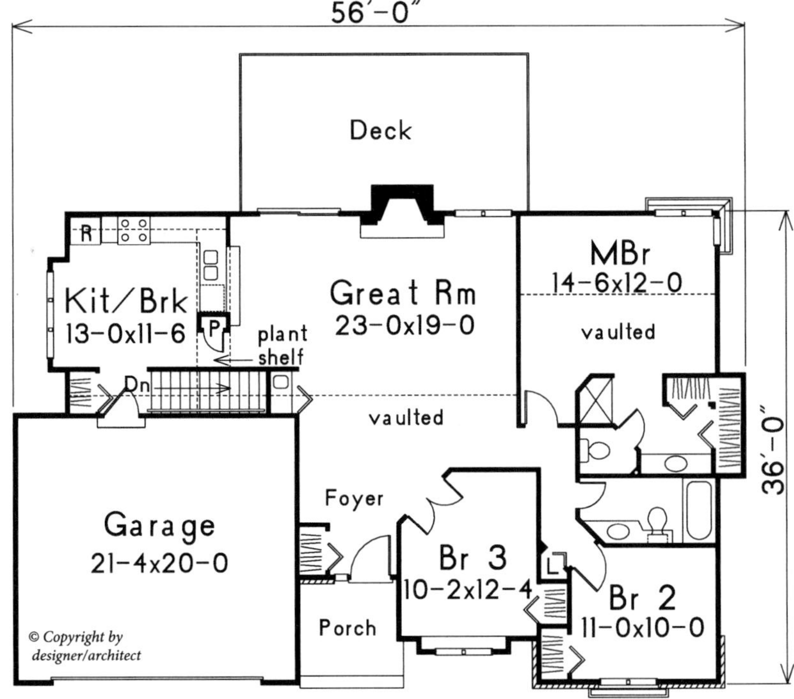

• To Order See Page 288 or Call Toll-Free 1-877-379-3420

Plan #541-022D-0024 • Price Code AA

Charming Exterior And Cozy Interior

- 1,127 total square feet of living area
- A plant shelf joins the kitchen and dining room
- The vaulted master bedroom has double walk-in closets, deck access and a private bath
- Great room features a vaulted ceiling, fireplace and sliding doors to the covered deck
- Ideal home for a narrow lot
- 2 bedrooms, 2 baths, 2-car garage
- Basement foundation

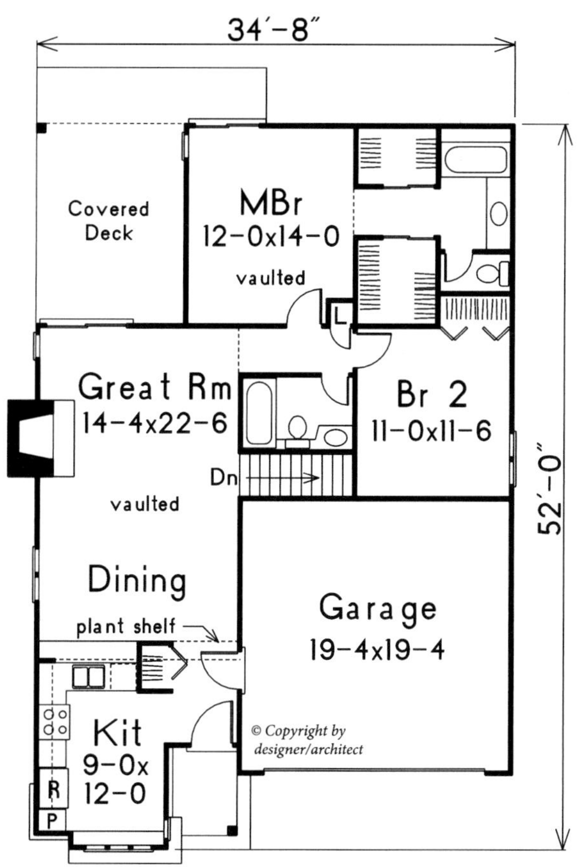

Plan #541-022D-0011 • Price Code B

Open Ranch Design Gives Expansive Look

- 1,630 total square feet of living area
- Crisp facade and full windows front and back offer open viewing
- Wrap-around rear deck is accessible from the breakfast room, dining room and master bedroom
- Vaulted ceilings top the living room and master bedroom
- Sitting area and large walk-in closet complement the master bedroom
- 3 bedrooms, 2 baths, 2-car garage
- Basement foundation

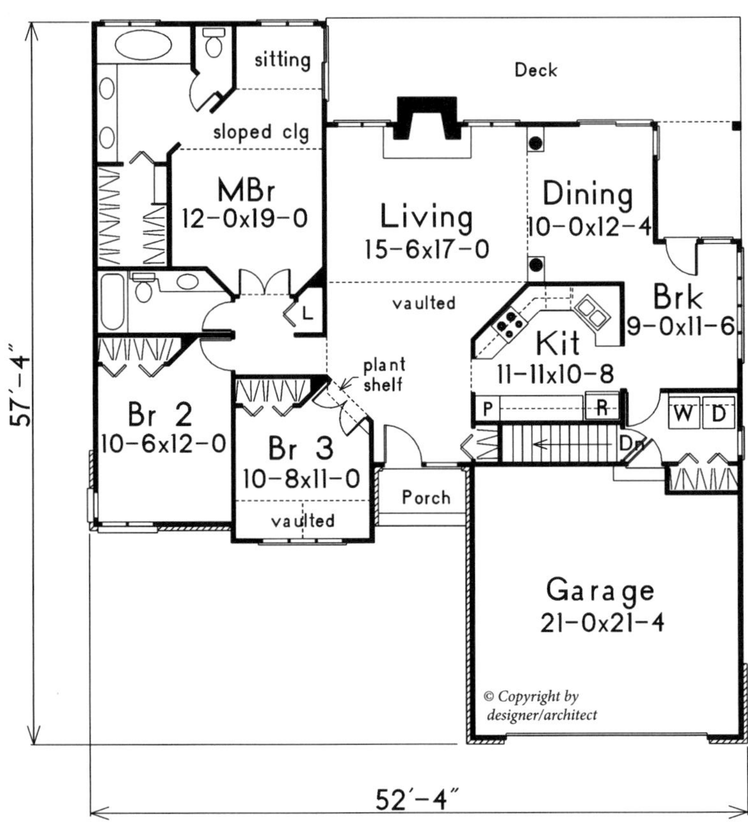

Plan #541-057D-0028 • Price Code A

Elegant French Exterior

- 1,775 total square feet of living area
- Perfect design for a narrow lot
- Abundant kitchen space with a built-in breakfast counter
- Master suite features a luxurious bath and large walk-in closet
- 3 bedrooms, 2 1/2 baths, 2-car garage
- Basement foundation

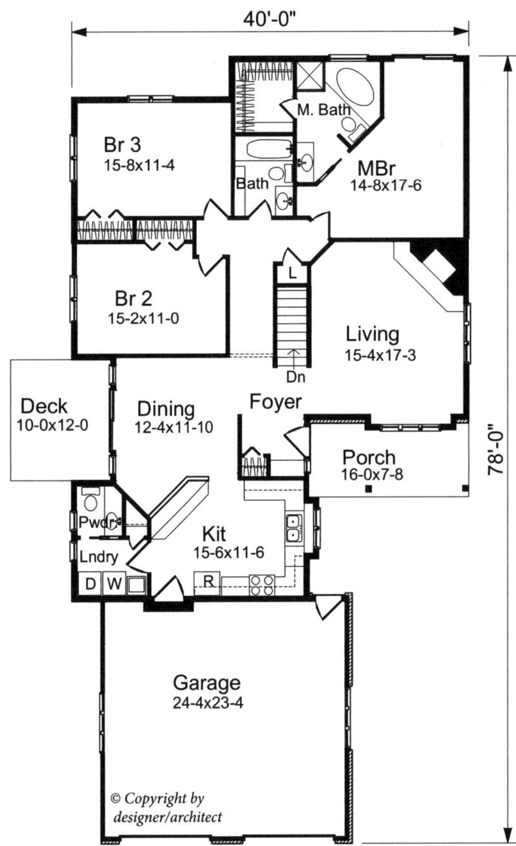

Plan #541-007D-0068 • Price Code B

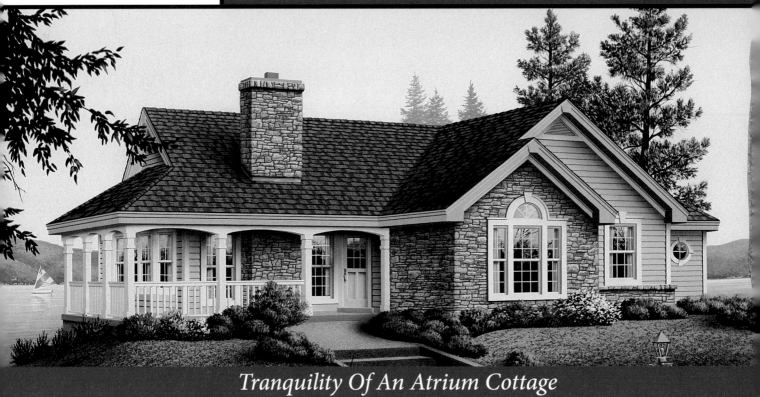

Tranquility Of An Atrium Cottage

- 1,922 total square feet of living area
- Wrap-around country porch for peaceful evenings
- Vaulted great room enjoys a large bay window, stone fireplace, pass-through kitchen and awesome rear views through an atrium window wall
- Master bedroom features a double-door entry, walk-in closet and a fabulous bath
- Plan also available with energy efficient R-Control® SIPs (Structural Insulated Panels), please call 1-877-379-3420 for more information
- 2 bedrooms, 2 baths, 1-car side entry garage
- Walk-out basement foundation

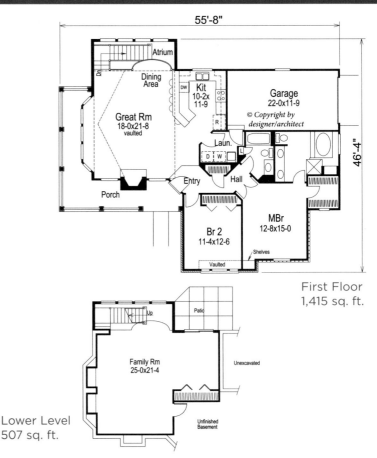

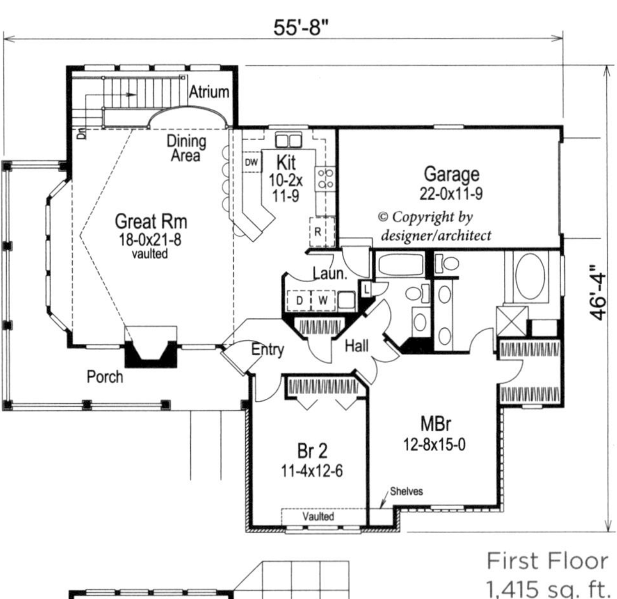

First Floor
1,415 sq. ft.

Patio
Up
Family Rm 25-0x21-4
Unexcavated
Unfinished Basement

Lower Level
507 sq. ft.

• To Order See Page 288 or Call Toll-Free 1-877-379-3420

Plan #541-053D-0015 • Price Code A

Victorian Turret Provides Dramatic Focus

- 2,214 total square feet of living area
- Victorian accents dominate facade
- Covered porches and decks fan out to connect front and rear entries and add to the outdoor living space
- Elegant master bedroom suite features a five-sided windowed alcove and private deck
- Corner kitchen has a sink-top peninsula
- 4 bedrooms, 2 1/2 baths, 2-car side entry drive under garage
- Walk-out basement foundation

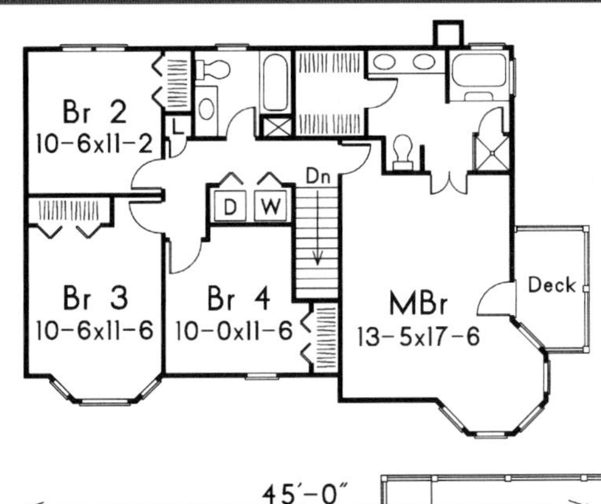

Second Floor
1,085 sq. ft.

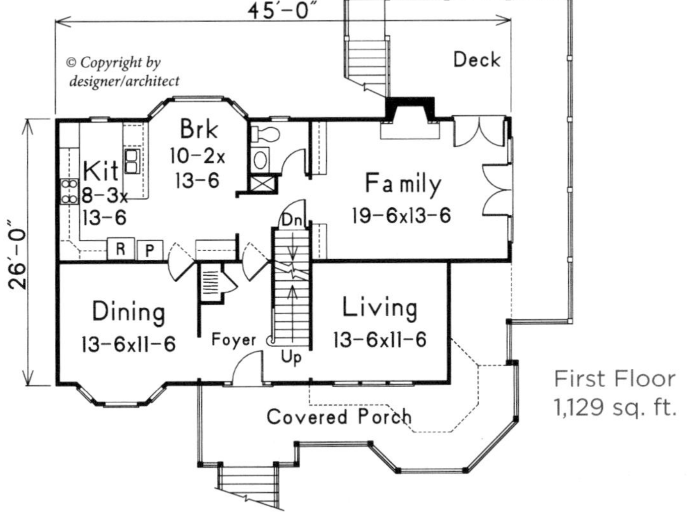

First Floor
1,129 sq. ft.

Plan #541-021D-0016 • Price Code C

Roomy Two-Story Has Covered Porch

- 1,600 total square feet of living area
- Energy efficient home with 2" x 6" exterior walls
- First floor master bedroom is accessible from two points of entry
- Master bath dressing area includes separate vanities and a mirrored makeup counter
- Second floor bedrooms have generous storage space and share a full bath
- 3 bedrooms, 2 baths, 2-car side entry garage
- Crawl space foundation, drawings also include slab foundation

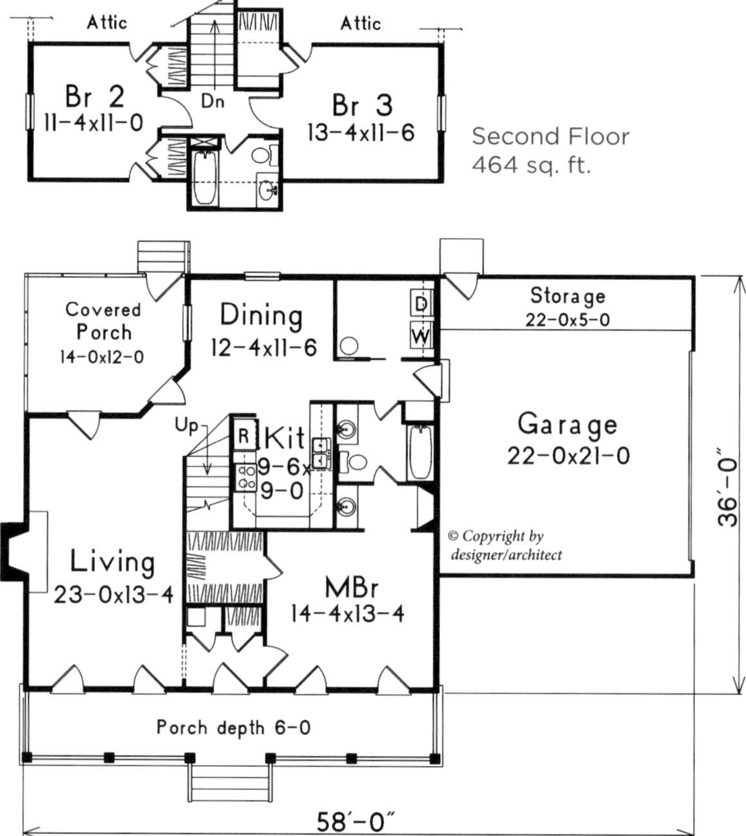

Second Floor
464 sq. ft.

First Floor
1,136 sq. ft.

• To Order See Page 288 or Call Toll-Free 1-877-379-3420

Plan #541-058D-0033 • Price Code A

Flexible Design Is Popular

- 1,440 total square feet of living area
- Open floor plan with access to covered porches in front and back
- Lots of linen, pantry and closet space throughout
- The laundry room located between the kitchen and garage is a convenient feature
- 2 bedrooms, 2 baths, 2-car side entry garage
- Basement foundation

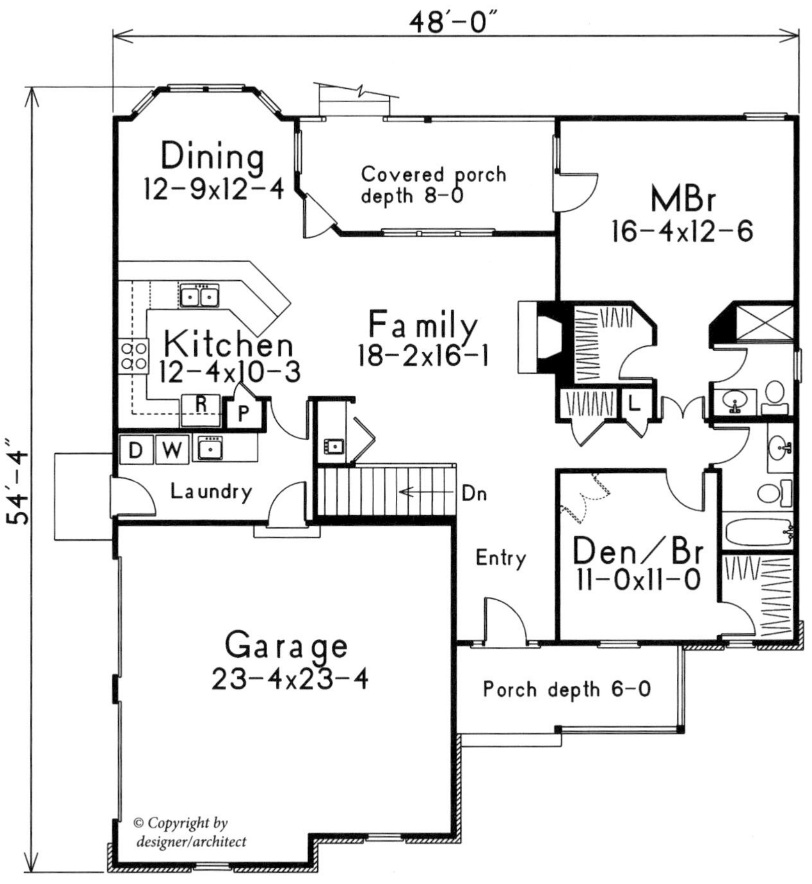

Plan #541-053D-0049 • Price Code AA

Unique Step Up From Entry To Living Space

- 1,261 total square feet of living area
- Great room, brightened by windows and doors, features a raised ceiling, fireplace and access to the deck
- Vaulted master bedroom enjoys a private bath
- Split-level foyer leads to the living space or basement
- Centrally located laundry closet is near the bedrooms
- 3 bedrooms, 2 baths, 2-car drive under garage
- Basement foundation

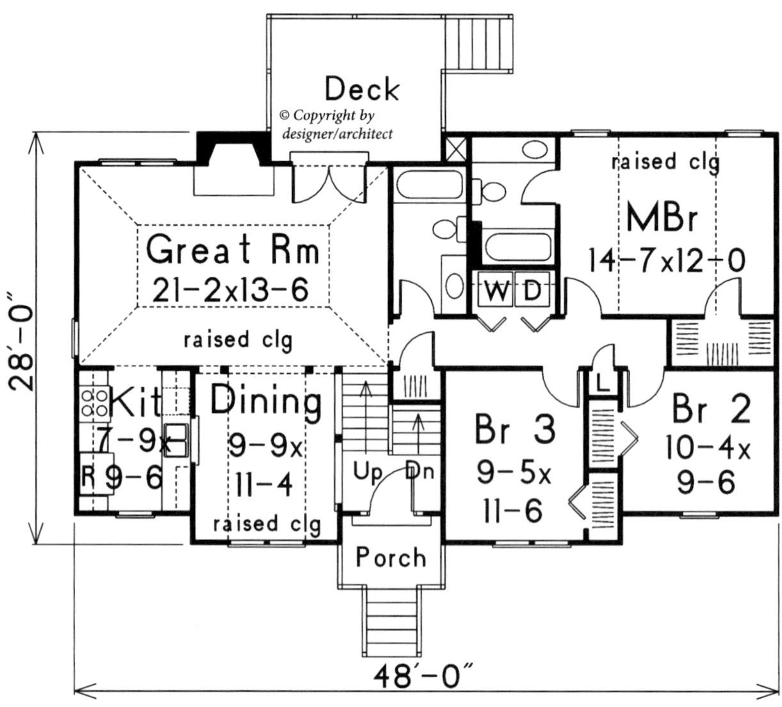

• To Order See Page 288 or Call Toll-Free 1-877-379-3420

Plan #541-007D-0229 • Price Code D

Exciting Design For Views And Entertaining

- 2,014 total square feet of living area
- The front veranda, with its 15′ high volume ceiling receives abundant light from the dormer windows above
- A unique curved wall around the dining, separate entry with coat closet and two 9′ wide glass sliding doors to the front and rear verandas are some of the awesome features of the spacious great room
- The kitchen excels in cabinet storage and includes a useful snack bar
- With a sitting area adjacent to the rear veranda, the master bedroom enjoys two walk-in closets and a luxury bath with a 4′ x 4′ separate shower
- 3 bedrooms, 2 1/2 baths, 2-car side entry garage
- Slab foundation

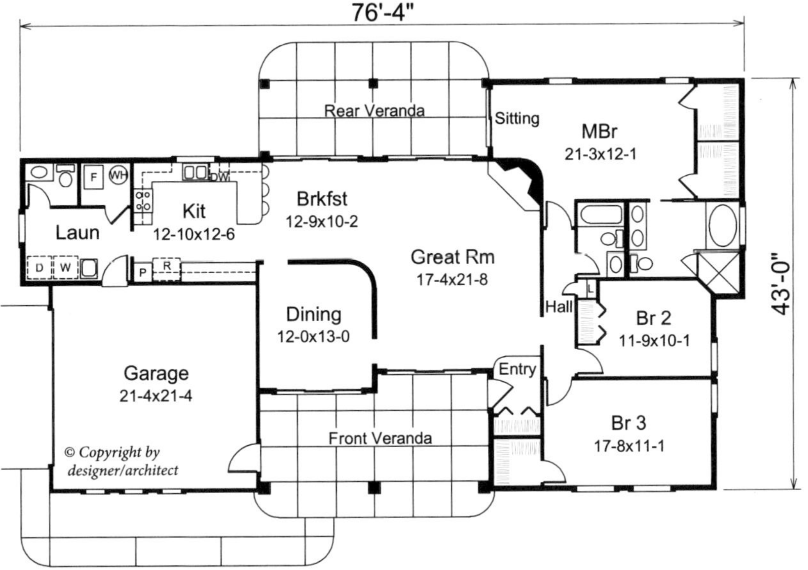

Plan #541-058D-0174 • Price Code D

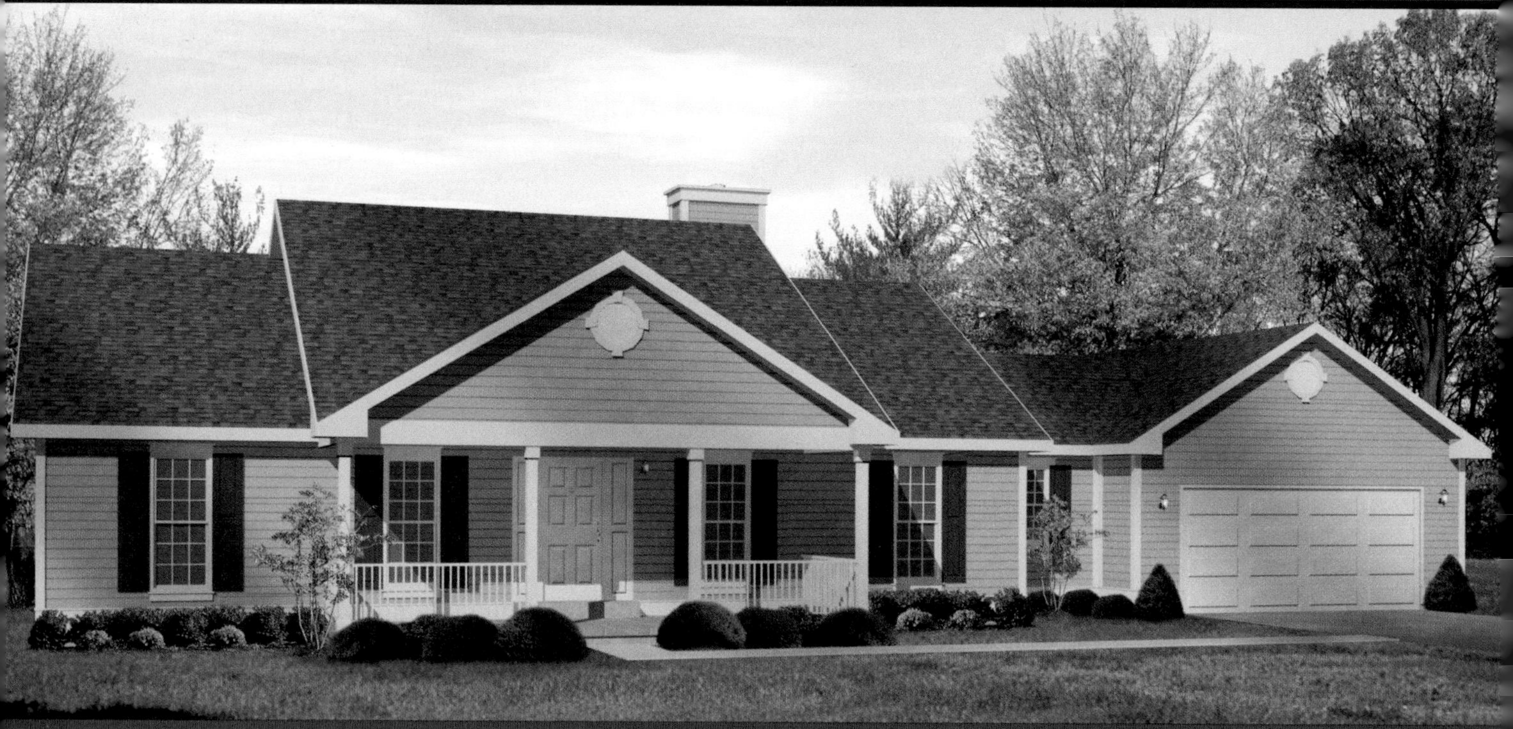

Vaulted Master Bedroom

- 1,682 total square feet of living area
- A covered porch adds charm to the facade and invites guests into this beautiful home
- A vaulted ceiling tops the adjoining kitchen, family and dining rooms adding spaciousness to this area of the home
- Retreat to the master bedroom and find amenities including an oversized walk-in closet and a private bath with double-bowl vanity
- 3 bedrooms, 2 baths, 2-car garage
- Basement foundation

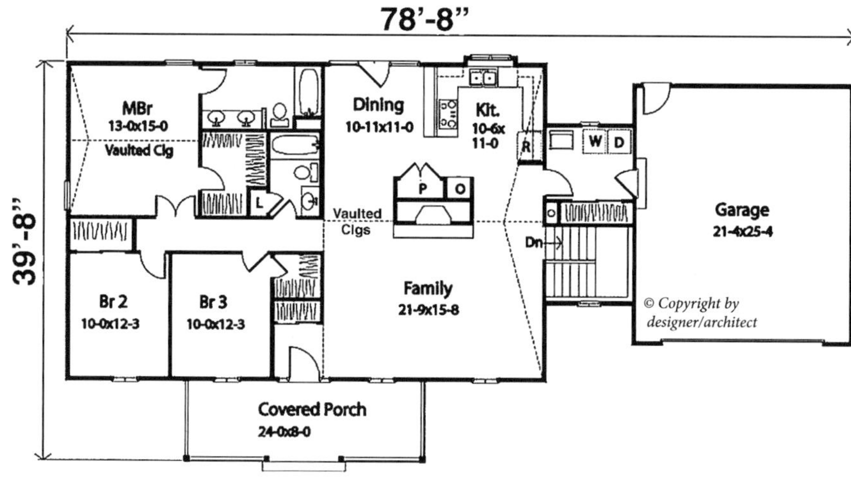

Plan #541-053D-0053 • Price Code B

LOWE'S LEGACY SERIES

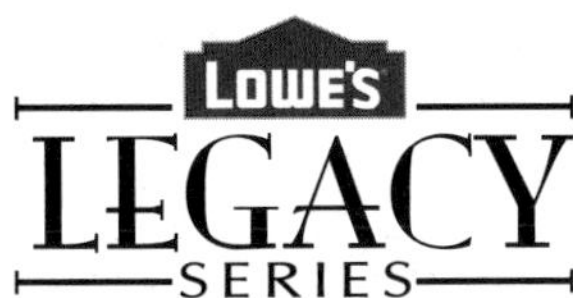

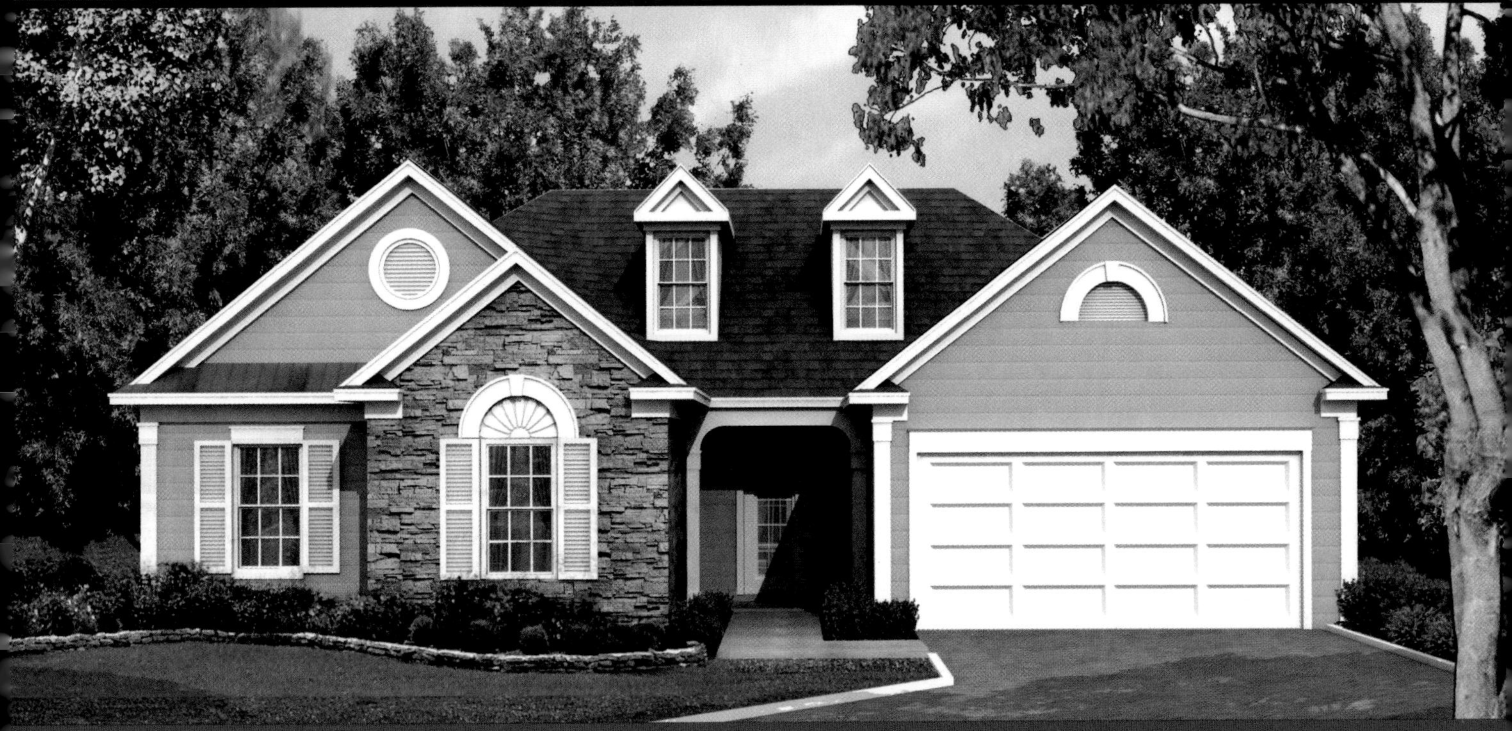

Dormers And Stone Veneer Add Exterior Appeal

- 1,609 total square feet of living area
- Efficient kitchen includes a corner pantry and adjacent laundry room
- Breakfast room boasts plenty of windows and opens onto a rear deck
- Master bedroom features a tray ceiling and private deluxe bath
- Entry opens into large living area with fireplace
- 4 bedrooms, 2 baths, 2-car garage
- Basement foundation, drawings also include walk-out basement, crawl space and slab foundations

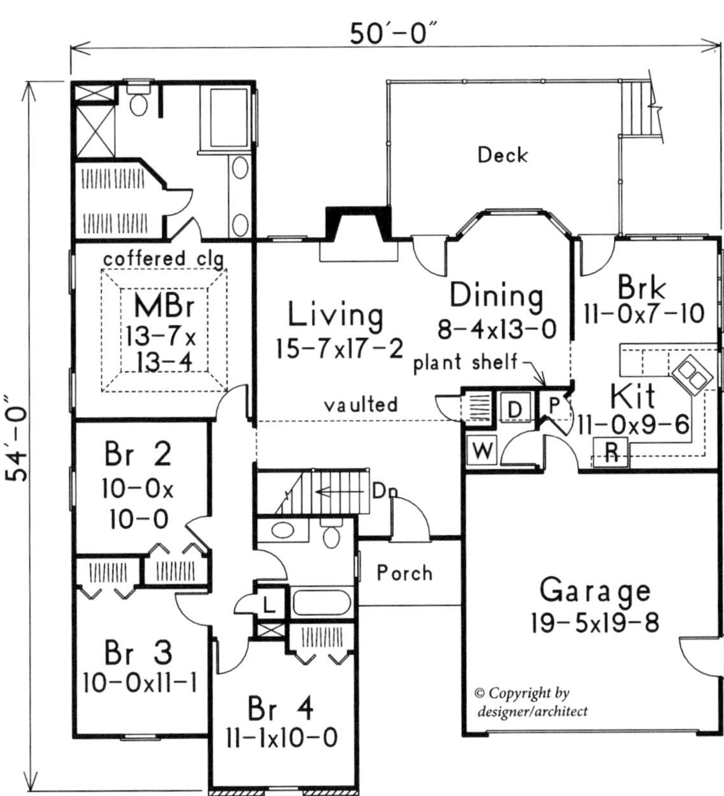

Plan #541-007D-0120 • Price Code C

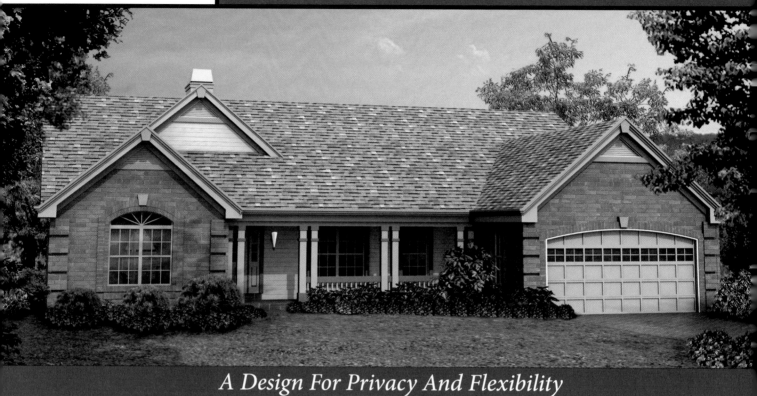

A Design For Privacy And Flexibility

- 1,914 total square feet of living area
- Great room features a vaulted ceiling, dining area, entry foyer, corner fireplace and 9' wide sliding doors to the rear patio
- The secluded secondary bedrooms offer walk-in closets and share a Jack and Jill bath
- A multi-purpose room has a laundry alcove and can easily be used as a hobby room, sewing room or small office
- The bedroom 4/study can be open to the master bedroom suite and utilized as a private home office or nursery
- 4 bedrooms, 3 baths, 2-car garage
- Basement foundation

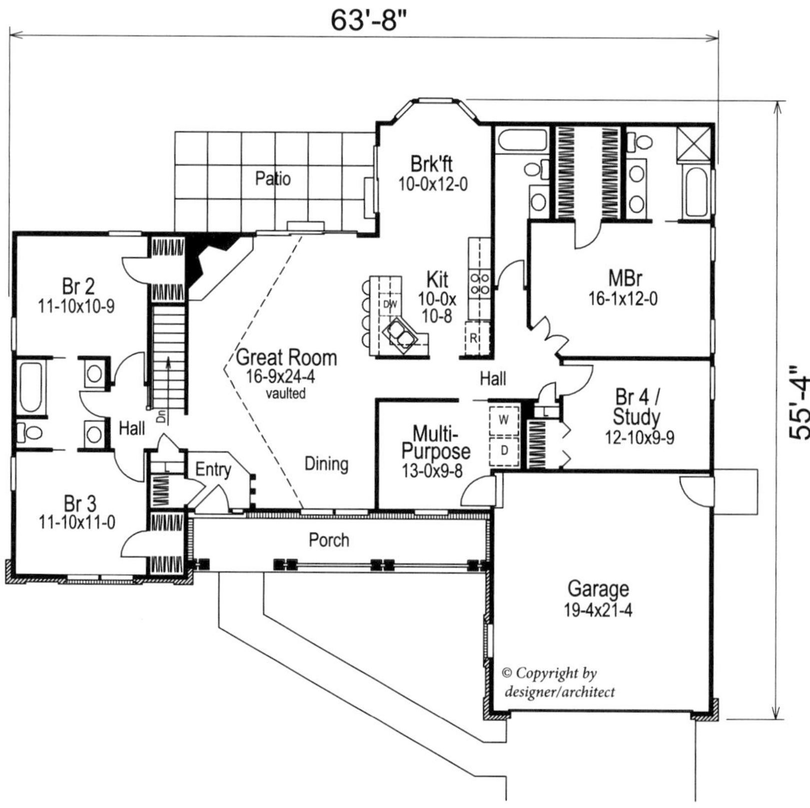

• To Order See Page 288 or Call Toll-Free 1-877-379-3420

Plan #541-053D-0053 • Price Code B

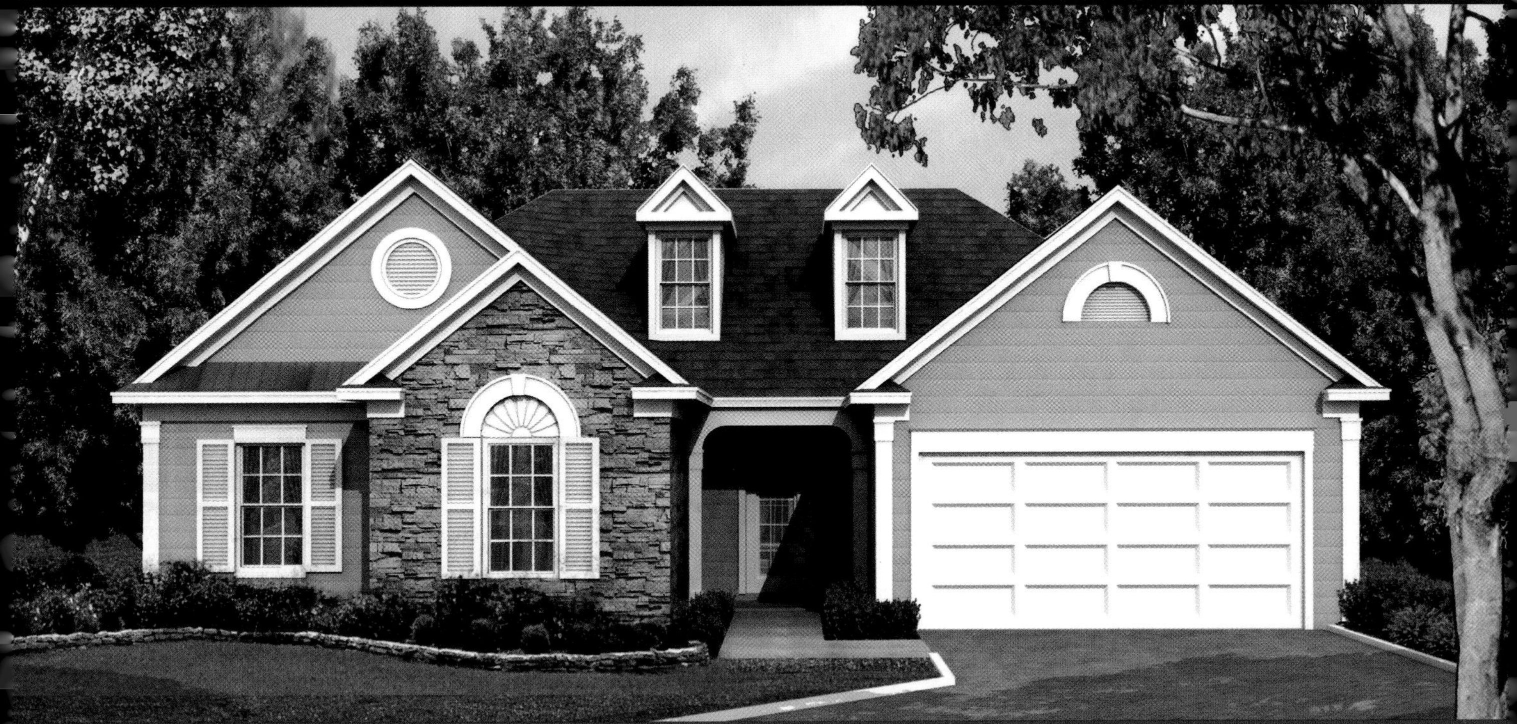

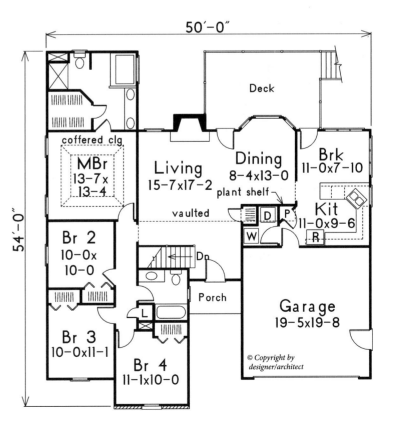

Plan #541-001D-0121 • Price Code B

LOWE'S LEGACY SERIES

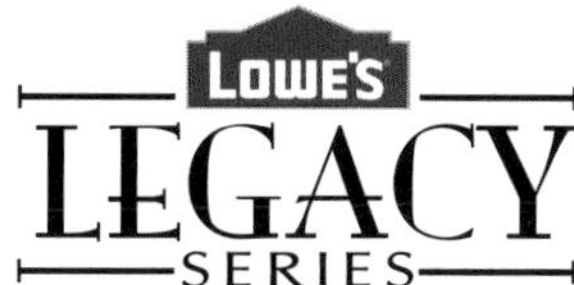

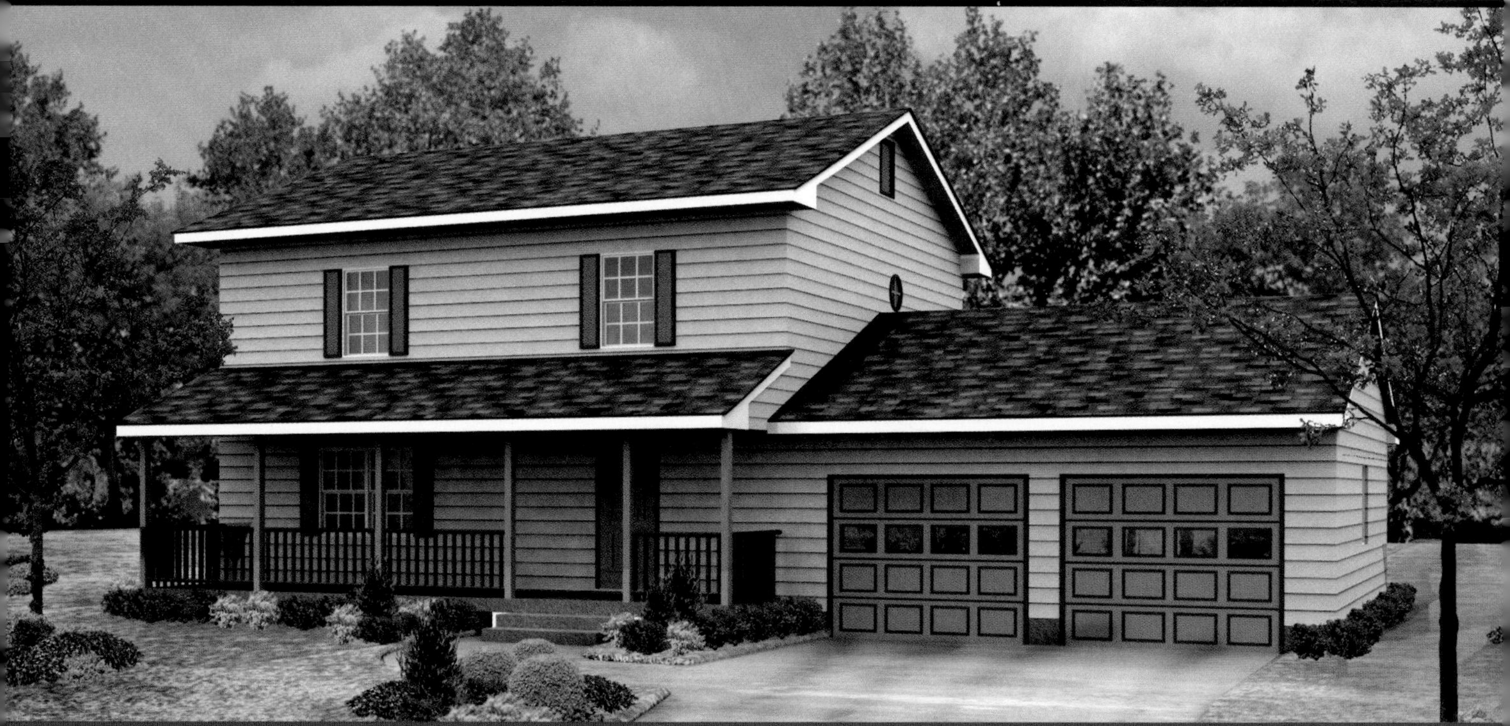

Old-Fashioned Porch Gives Welcoming Appeal

- 1,664 total square feet of living area
- Energy efficient home with 2" x 6" exterior walls
- L-shaped country kitchen includes pantry and cozy breakfast nook
- Bedrooms are located on the second floor for privacy
- Master bedroom includes a walk-in closet, dressing area and bath
- 3 bedrooms, 2 1/2 baths, 2-car garage
- Crawl space foundation, drawings also include basement and slab foundations

Second Floor
832 sq. ft.

First Floor
832 sq. ft.

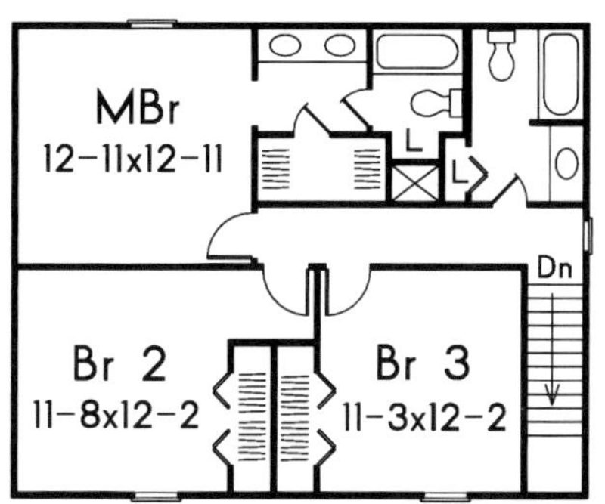

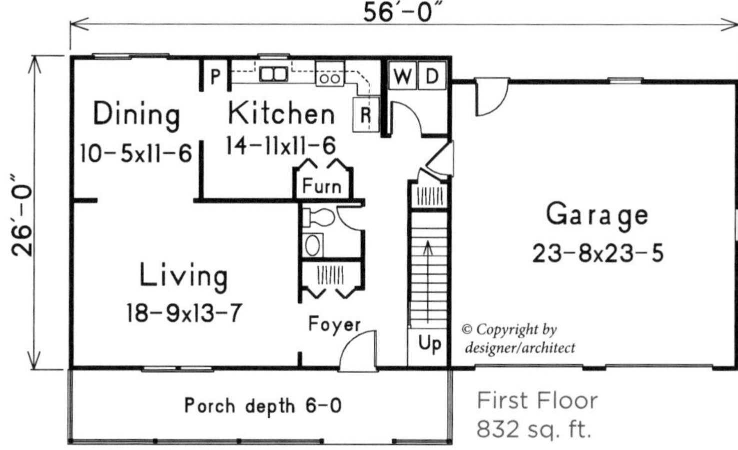

Plan #541-121D-0010 • Price Code AA

Vaulted Living Areas For Added Spaciousness

- 1,281 total square feet of living area
- The functional vaulted kitchen features an angled raised counter perfect for a casual dining option
- The vaulted great room and breakfast area combine maximizing the interior for an open, airy feel
- The vaulted master bedroom enjoys a sizable walk-in closet and its own private bath
- 3 bedrooms, 2 baths, 2-car garage
- Basement foundation

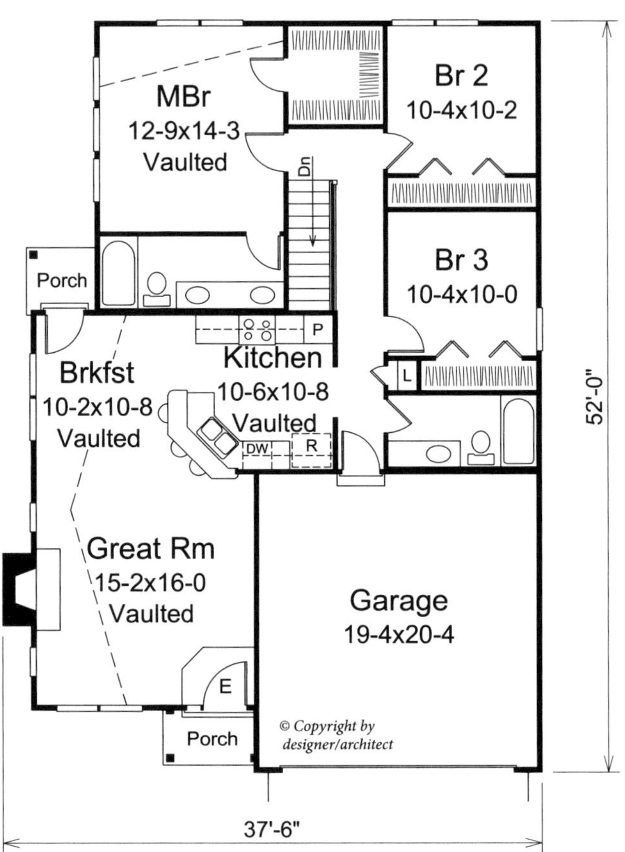

• To Order See Page 288 or Call Toll-Free 1-877-379-3420

Plan #541-058D-0008 • Price Code A

Cozy And Functional Design

- 1,285 total square feet of living area
- Dining nook has a warm feeling with a sunny box-bay window
- Second floor loft is perfect for a recreation space or office hideaway
- Bedrooms include walk-in closets allowing extra storage space
- Kitchen, dining and living areas combine making the perfect gathering place
- 2 bedrooms, 1 bath
- Crawl space foundation

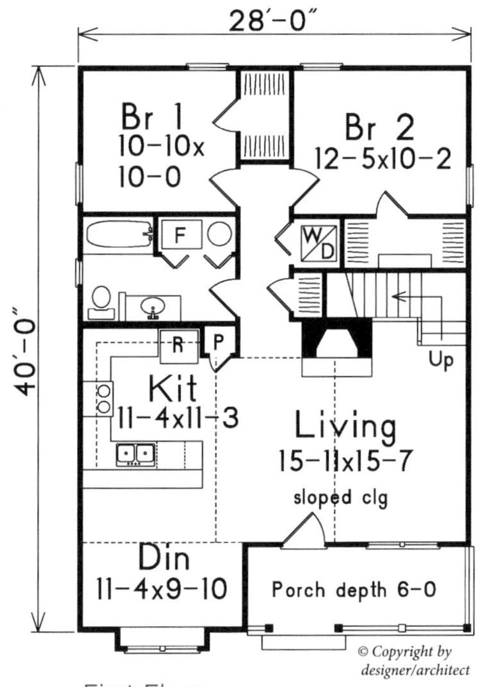

First Floor
1,032 sq. ft.

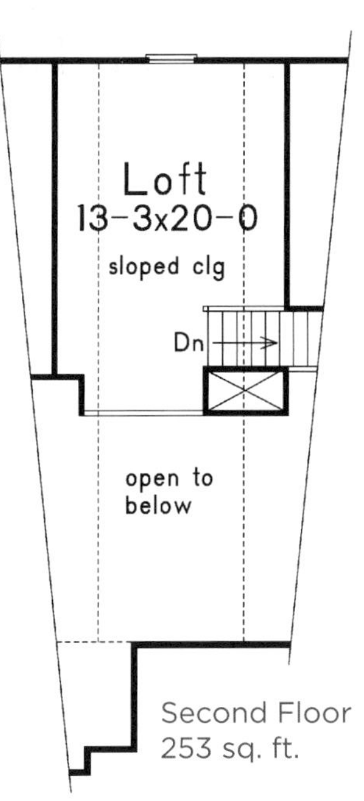

Second Floor
253 sq. ft.

LOWE'S LEGACY SERIES

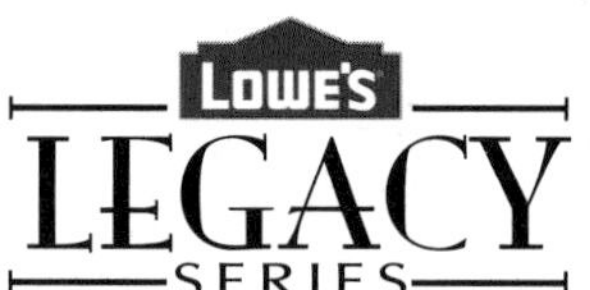

Plan #541-017D-0007 • Price Code C

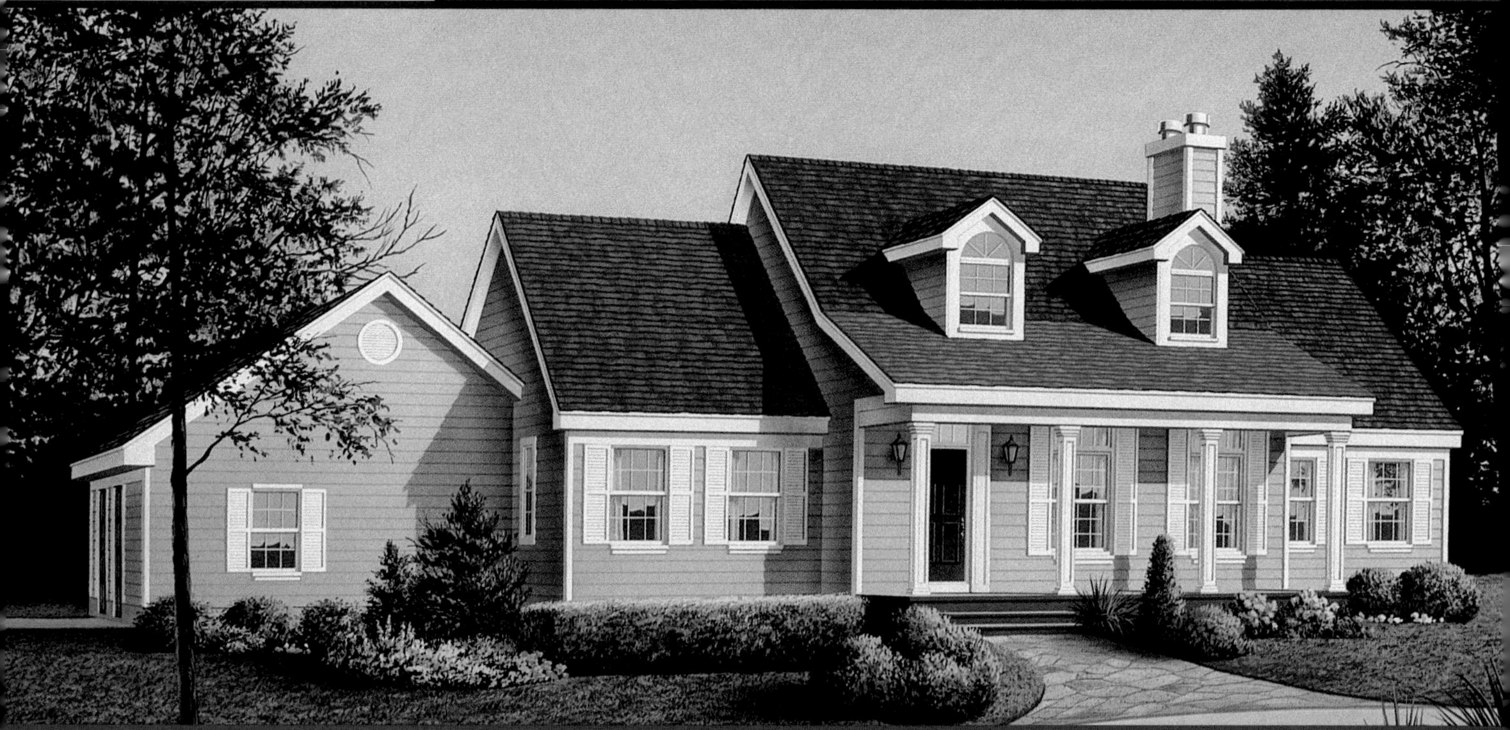

Pillared Front Porch Generates Charm And Warmth

- 1,567 total square feet of living area
- Energy efficient home with 2" x 6" exterior walls
- Living room flows into the dining room shaped by an angled pass-through into the kitchen
- Cheerful, windowed dining area
- Master bedroom is separated from other bedrooms for privacy
- Future area available on the second floor has an additional 338 square feet of living area
- 3 bedrooms, 2 baths, 2-car side entry garage
- Partial basement/crawl space foundation, drawings also include slab foundation

First Floor
1,567 sq. ft.

Optional
Second Floor

• To Order See Page 288 or Call Toll-Free 1-877-379-3420

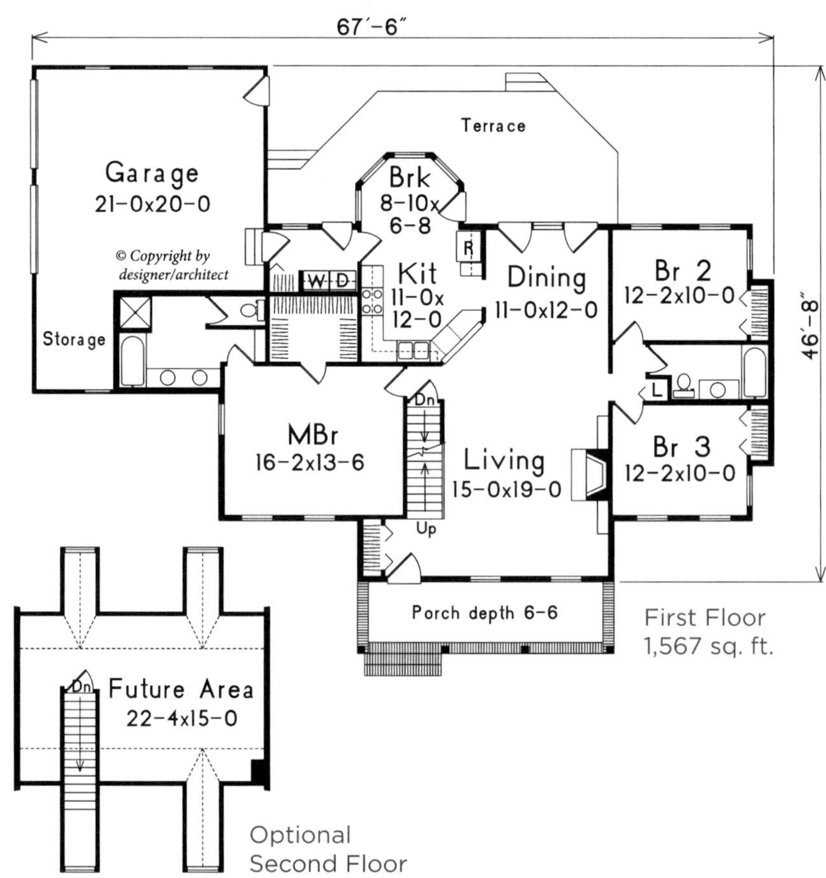

Plan #541-001D-0110 • Price Code B

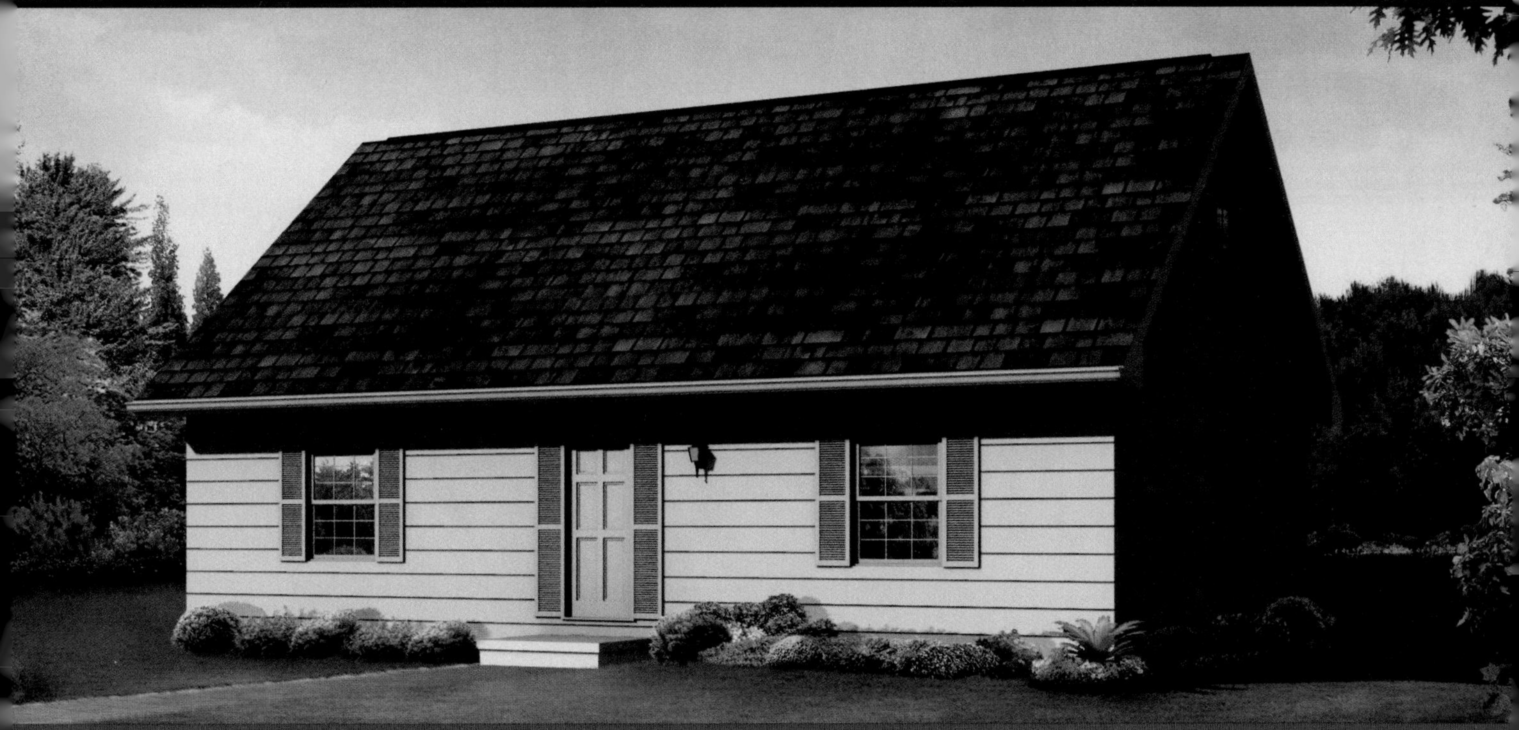

Plenty Of Room For The Growing Family

- 1,705 total square feet of living area
- Energy efficient home with 2" x 6" exterior walls
- Two bedrooms on the first floor for convenience and two bedrooms on the second floor for privacy
- L-shaped kitchen adjacent to dining room accesses the outdoors
- First floor laundry area
- 4 bedrooms, 2 baths
- Crawl space foundation, drawings also include basement and slab foundations

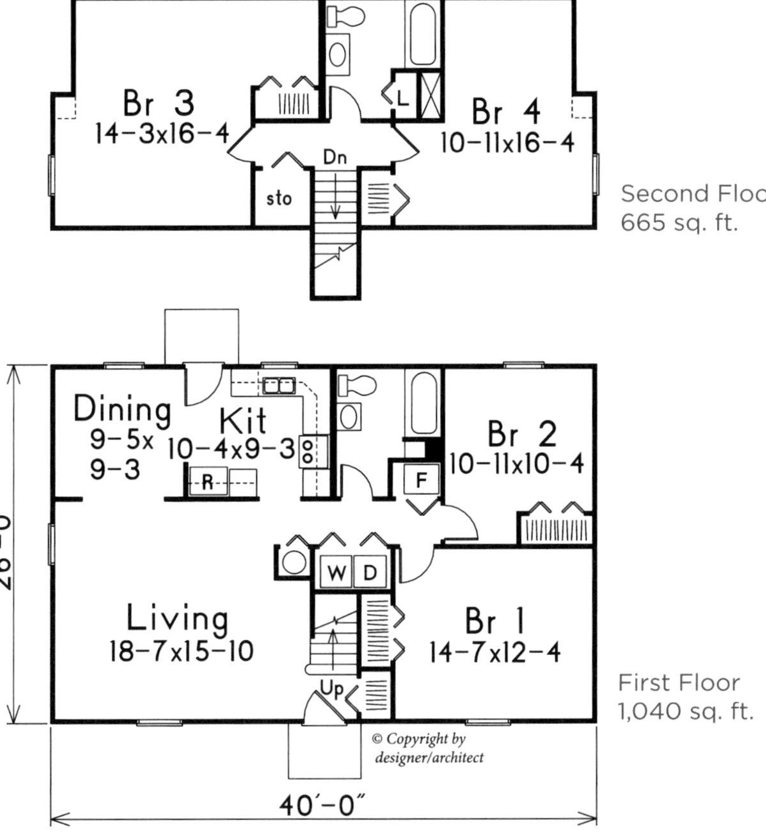

LOWE'S LEGACY SERIES

Plan #541-007D-0134 • Price Code A

Affordable Simplicity

- 1,310 total square feet of living area
- The combination of brick quoins, roof dormers and an elegant porch creates a classic look
- This home's open floor plan has vaulted kitchen, living and dining rooms
- The master bedroom is vaulted and enjoys privacy from other bedrooms
- A spacious laundry room is convenient to the kitchen and master bedroom with access to an oversized garage
- 2" x 6" exterior walls available, please order plan #541-007E-0134
- 3 bedrooms, 2 baths, 2-car garage
- Basement foundation, drawings also include crawl space and slab foundations

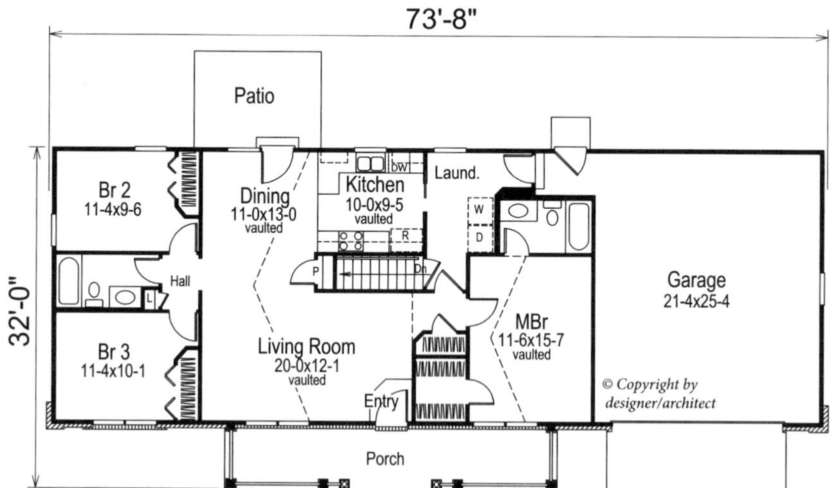

• To Order See Page 288 or Call Toll-Free 1-877-379-3420

Plan #541-057D-0041 • Price Code AA

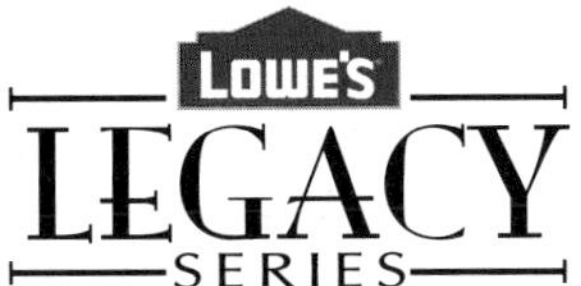

Inviting Ranch Home

- 1,274 total square feet of living area
- Attractive exterior with covered entry porch
- Kitchen is designed for efficiency and includes ample cabinet space
- Dining room opens to the delightful patio area
- 2 bedrooms, 2 baths, 2-car garage
- Basement foundation

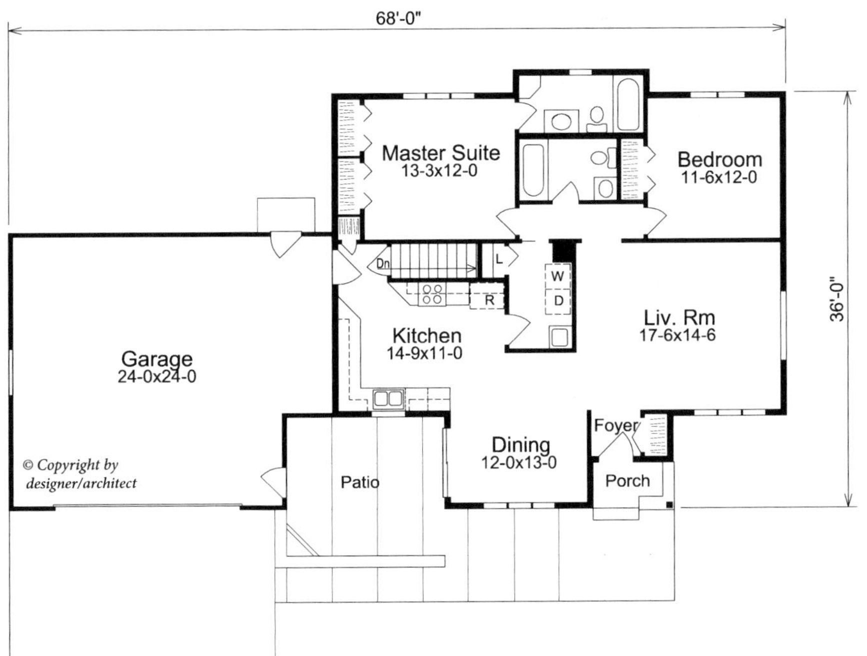

Plan #541-037D-0031 • Price Code C

Inviting And Cozy Covered Arched Entry

- 1,923 total square feet of living area
- The foyer opens into a spacious living room with fireplace that provides a splendid view of the covered porch
- Kitchen has a walk-in pantry adjacent to the laundry area and breakfast room
- All bedrooms feature walk-in closets
- Secluded master bedroom includes unique angled bath with spacious walk-in closet
- 3 bedrooms, 2 baths, 2-car garage
- Slab foundation

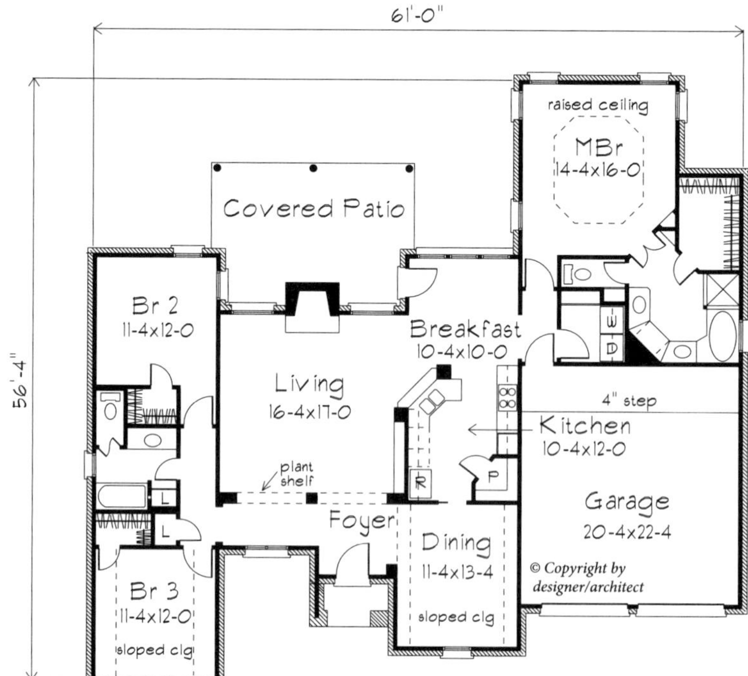

• To Order See Page 288 or Call Toll-Free 1-877-379-3420

Plan #541-058D-0064 • Price Code A

Cheerful Bayed Breakfast Area

- 1,323 total square feet of living area
- The vaulted family room provides an elegant first impression
- The master bedroom enjoys a walk-in closet and private bath
- The kitchen/breakfast area has a spacious feel with a bay window and outdoor access
- 3 bedrooms, 2 baths, 2-car garage
- Basement foundation

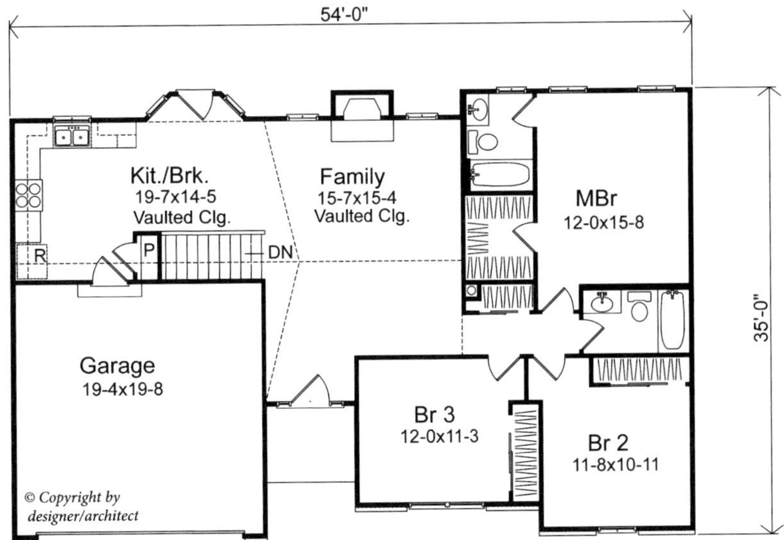

Plan #541-007D-0126 • Price Code A

Simplicity With Livability

- 1,365 total square feet of living area
- Home is easily adaptable for physical accessibility featuring no stairs and extra-wide entrances for the hall bath, laundry room and garage
- Living room has separate entry and opens to a spacious dining room with view of rear patio
- L-shaped kitchen is well equipped and includes a built-in pantry
- All bedrooms are spaciously sized and offer generous closet storage
- 3 bedrooms, 2 baths, 1-car garage
- Slab foundation

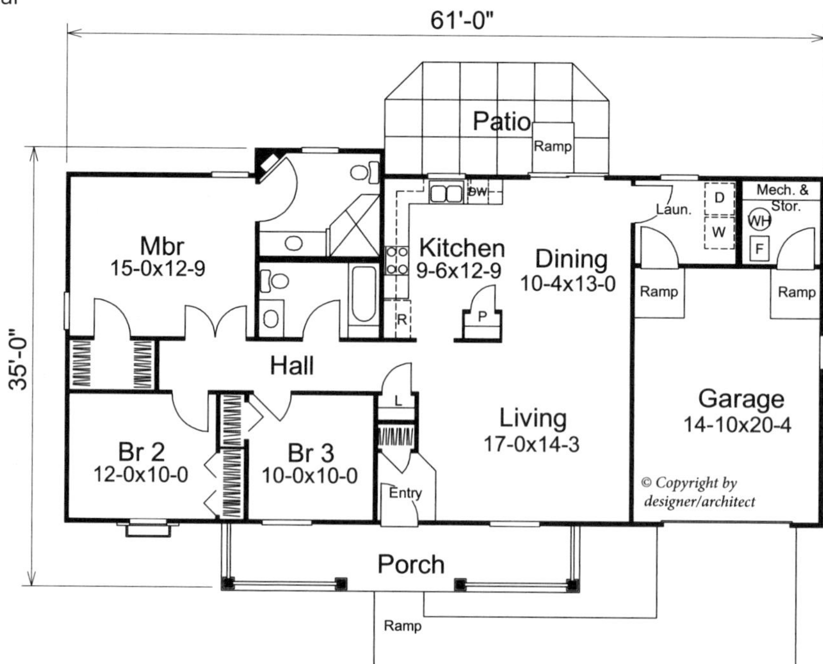

• To Order See Page 288 or Call Toll-Free 1-877-379-3420

Plan #541-037D-0012 • Price Code B

Sheltered Entrance Opens To Stylish Features

- 1,661 total square feet of living area
- Large open foyer with angled wall arrangement and high ceiling adds to spacious living room
- The kitchen and dining area have impressive cathedral ceilings and a French door allowing access to the rear patio
- Utility room is conveniently located near the kitchen
- Secluded master bedroom has a large walk-in closet, unique brick wall arrangement and 10' ceiling
- 3 bedrooms, 2 baths, 2-car garage
- Slab foundation

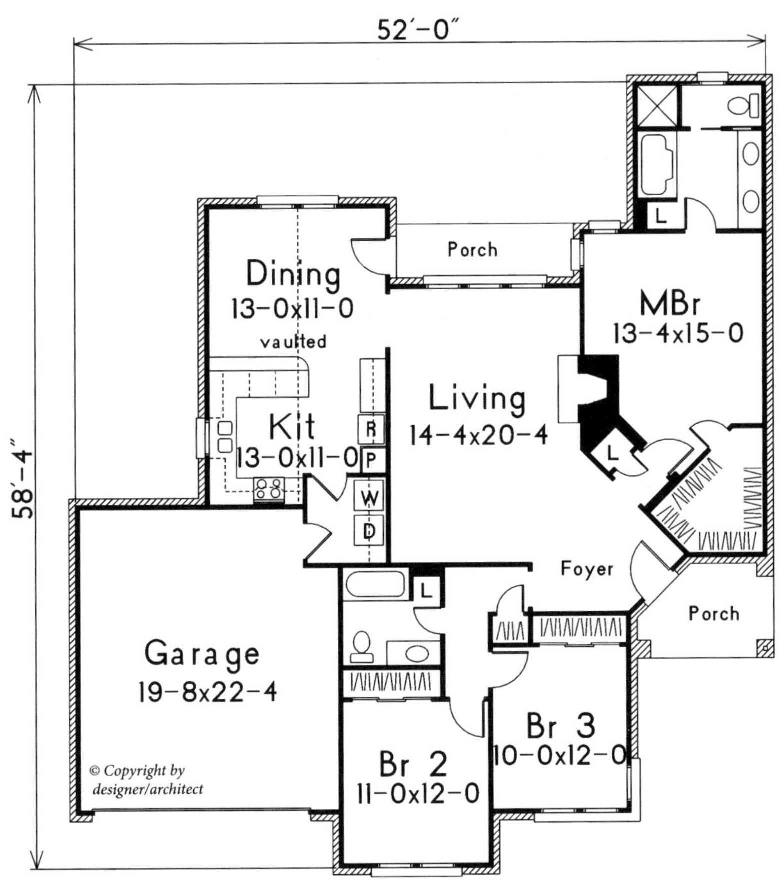

Plan #541-033D-0011 • Price Code D

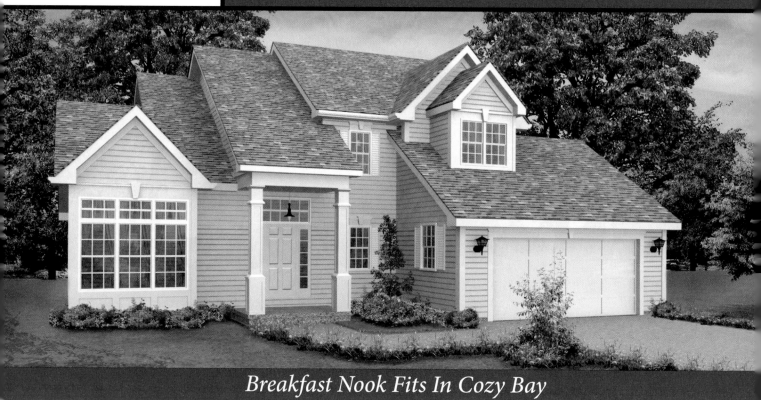

Breakfast Nook Fits In Cozy Bay

- 2,045 total square feet of living area
- Master bedroom includes a walk-in closet and private bath with corner tub and separate shower
- Both the family and breakfast rooms access the outdoors
- Two-story foyer with attractive transom windows opens into the formal living room
- 3 bedrooms, 2 1/2 baths, 2-car garage
- Basement foundation

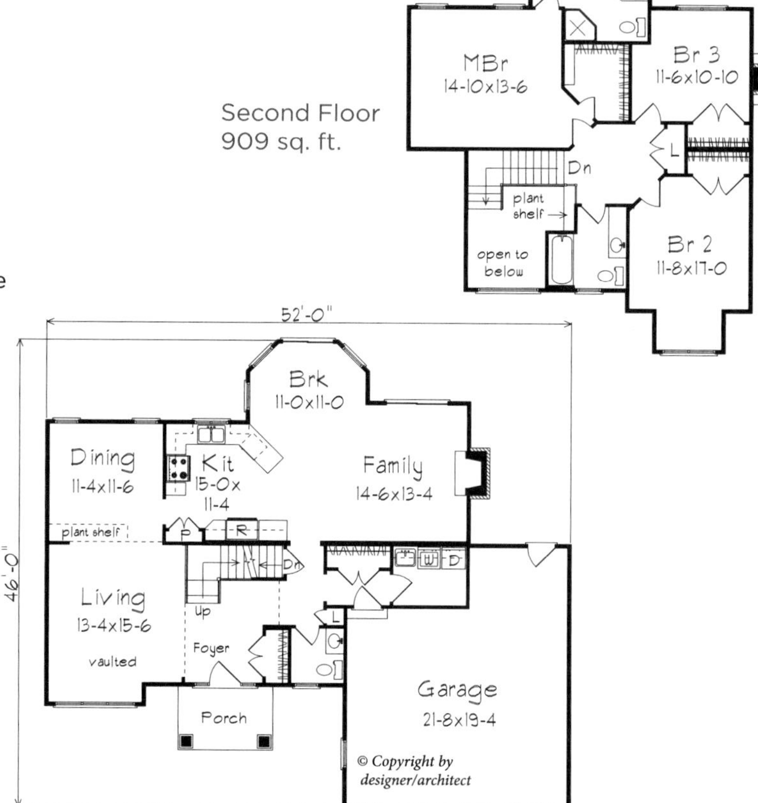

First Floor
1,136 sq. ft.

• To Order See Page 288 or Call Toll-Free 1-877-379-3420

Plan #541-001D-0040 • Price Code AAA

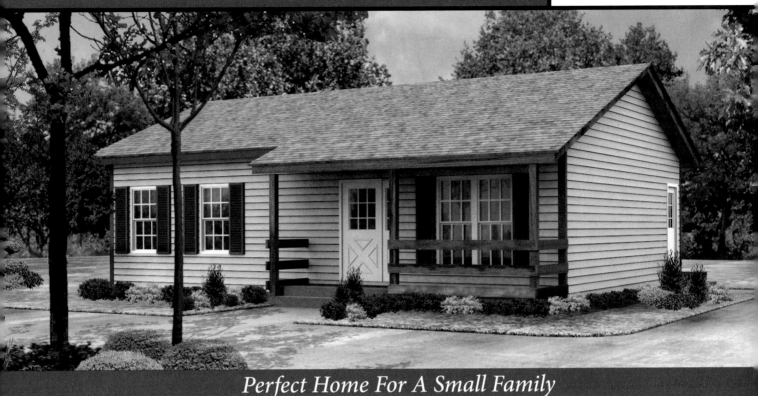

Perfect Home For A Small Family

- 864 total square feet of living area
- An L-shaped kitchen with convenient pantry is adjacent to the dining area
- This home has easy access to the laundry area, linen closet and storage closet
- Both bedrooms include ample closet space
- 2 bedrooms, 1 bath
- Crawl space foundation, drawings also include basement and slab foundations

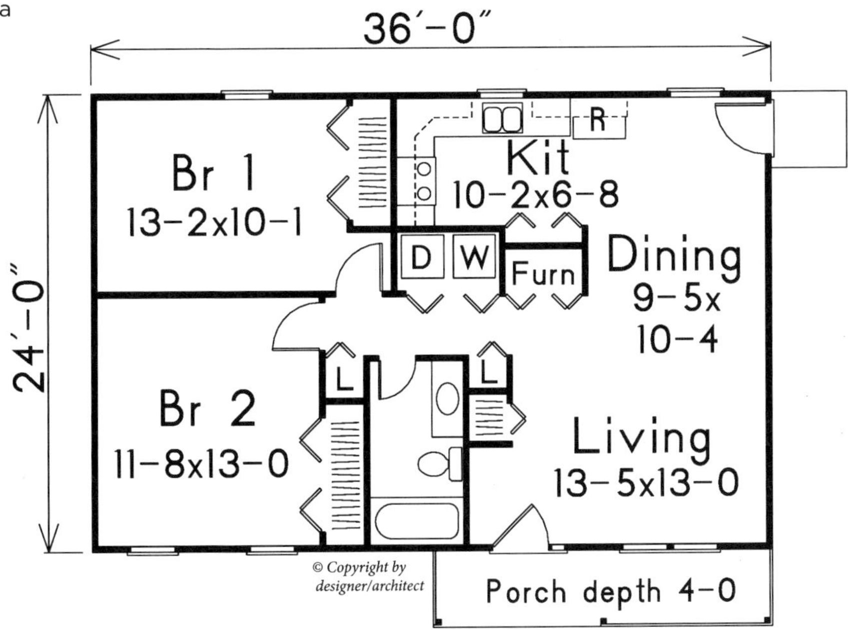

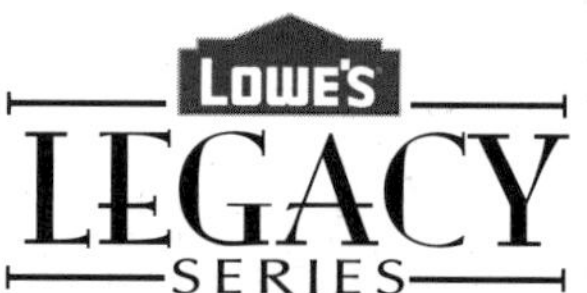

Plan #541-007D-0119 • Price Code B

Sensational Home Designed For Views

- 1,621 total square feet of living area
- The front exterior includes an attractive gable-end arched window and extra-deep porch
- A grand-scale great room enjoys a coffered ceiling, fireplace, access to the wrap-around deck and is brightly lit with numerous French doors and windows
- The master bedroom suite has a sitting area, double walk-in closets and a luxury bath
- 223 square feet of optional finished space on the lower level
- 3 bedrooms, 2 baths, 2-car drive under side entry garage
- Basement foundation

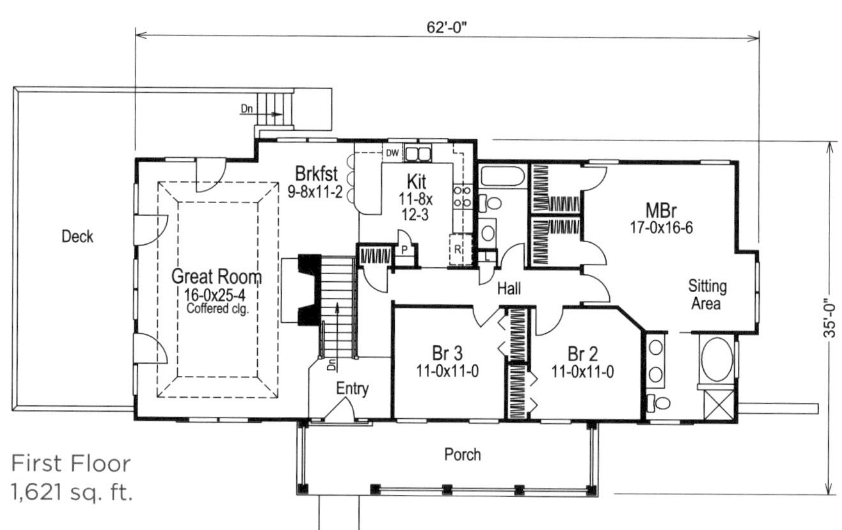

First Floor
1,621 sq. ft.

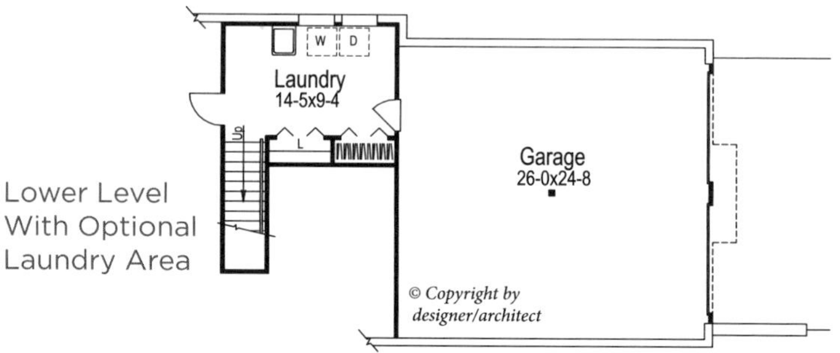

Lower Level
With Optional
Laundry Area

• To Order See Page 288 or Call Toll-Free 1-877-379-3420

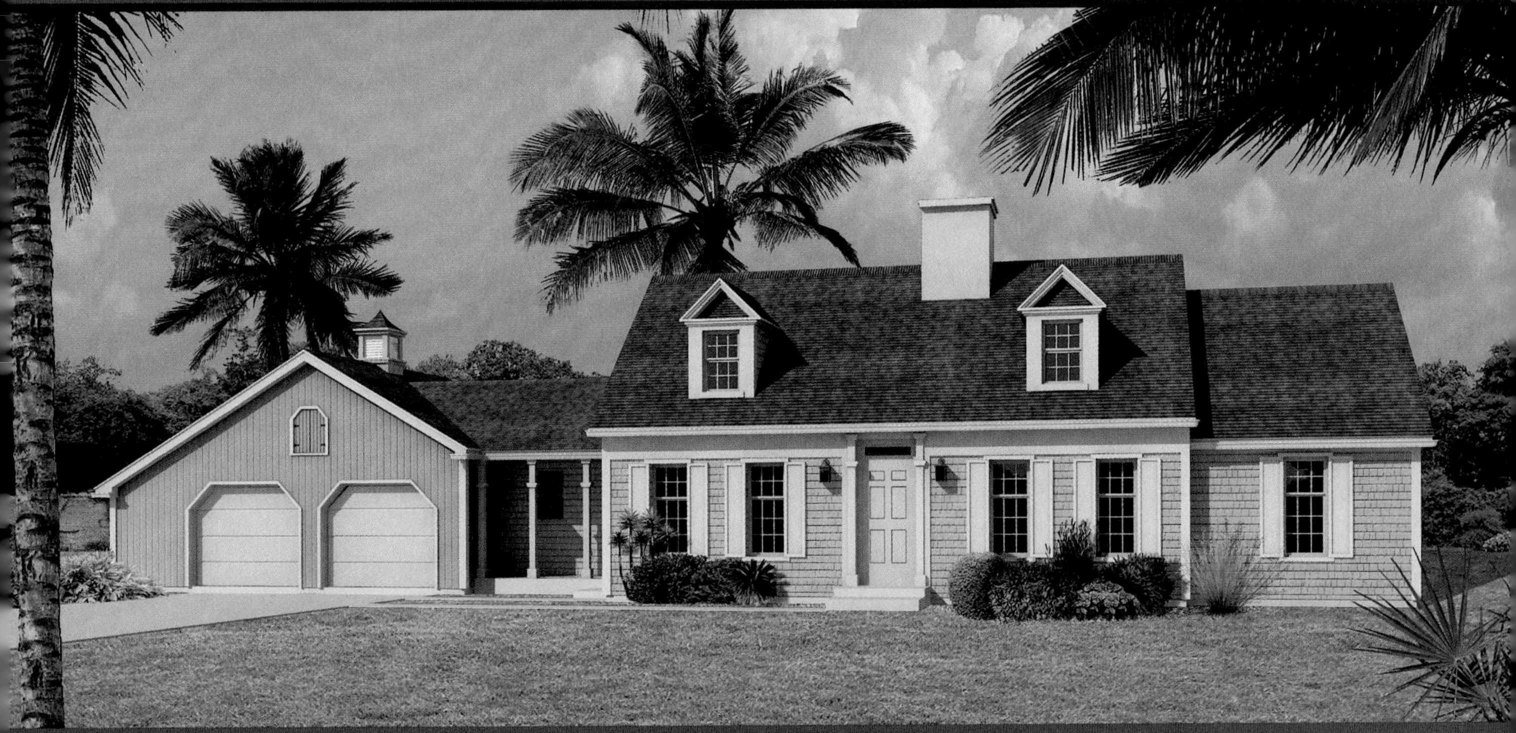

Timeless Design Offers Prestige

- 1,973 total square feet of living area
- This country colonial offers a grand-sized living room with views to the front and rear of the home
- Living room features a cozy fireplace and accesses the master bedroom complete with a walk-in closet and compartmented bath
- Laundry room with half bath and coat closet is convenient to the garage
- Second floor is comprised of two large bedrooms and a full bath
- 3 bedrooms, 2 1/2 baths, 2-car garage
- Partial basement/crawl space foundation

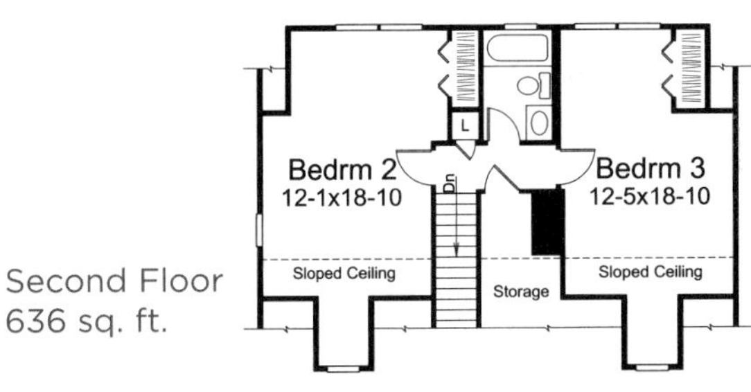

Second Floor
636 sq. ft.

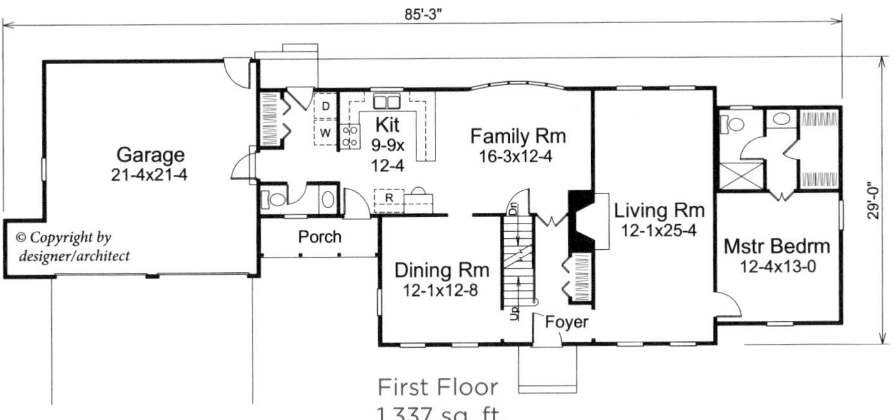

First Floor
1,337 sq. ft.

Plan #541-013L-0022 • Price Code C

Triple Dormers Create Terrific Curb Appeal

- 1,992 total square feet of living area
- Interesting angled walls add drama to many of the living areas including the family room, master bedroom and breakfast area
- Covered porch includes a spa and an outdoor kitchen with sink, refrigerator and cooktop
- Enter the majestic master bath to find a dramatic corner oversized tub
- Bonus room above the garage has an additional 247 square feet of living area
- 4 bedrooms, 3 baths, 2-car side entry garage
- Basement foundation, drawings also include crawl space and slab foundations

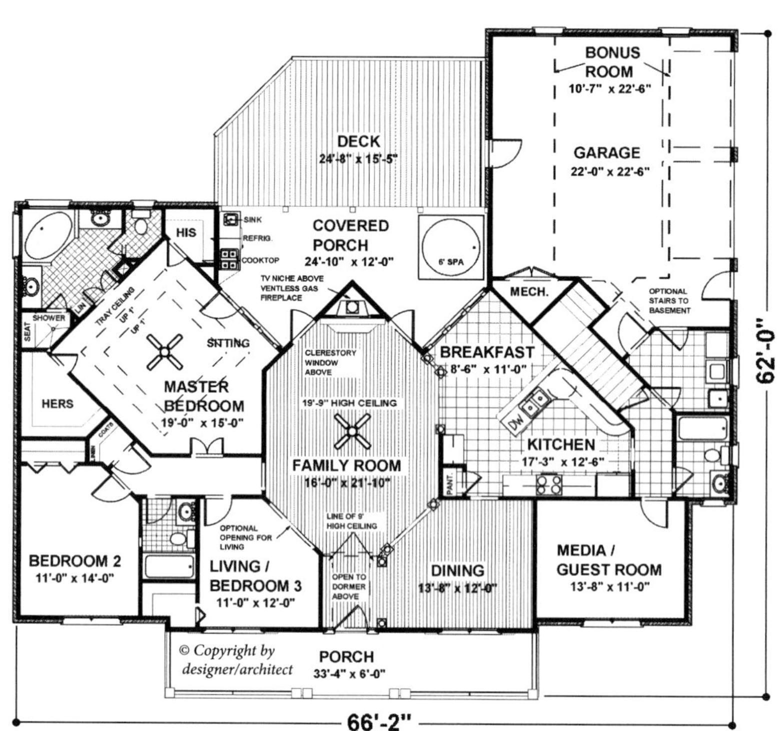

To Order See Page 288 or Call Toll-Free 1-877-379-3420

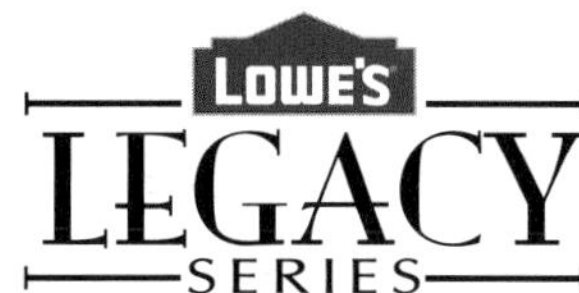

Plan #541-053D-0007 • Price Code A

Two-Story Foyer Adds To Country Charm

- 1,922 total square feet of living area
- Varied front elevation features numerous accents
- Master bedroom suite is well-secluded with a double-door entry and private bath
- Formal living and dining rooms are located off the entry
- 3 bedrooms, 2 1/2 baths, 2-car garage
- Basement foundation

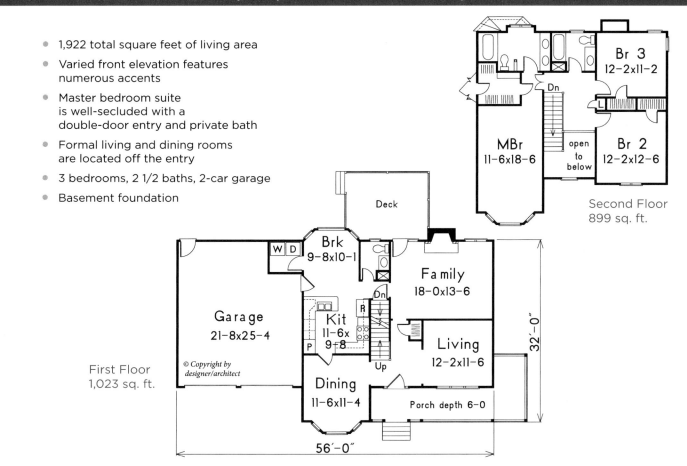

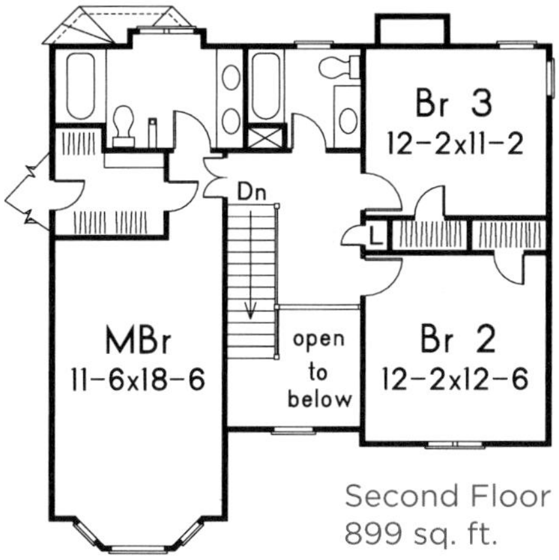

Second Floor
899 sq. ft.

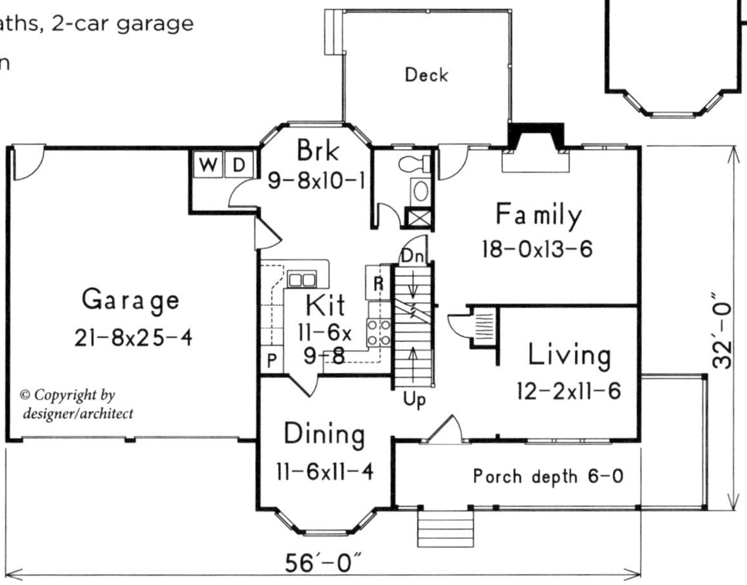

First Floor
1,023 sq. ft.

Plan #541-007D-0105 • Price Code AA

Stylish Retreat For A Narrow Lot

- 1,084 total square feet of living area
- Delightful country porch for quiet evenings
- The living room offers a front feature window which invites the sun and includes a fireplace and dining area with private patio
- The U-shaped kitchen features lots of cabinets and a bayed breakfast room with built-in pantry
- Both bedrooms have walk-in closets and access to their own bath
- 2 bedrooms, 2 baths
- Basement foundation

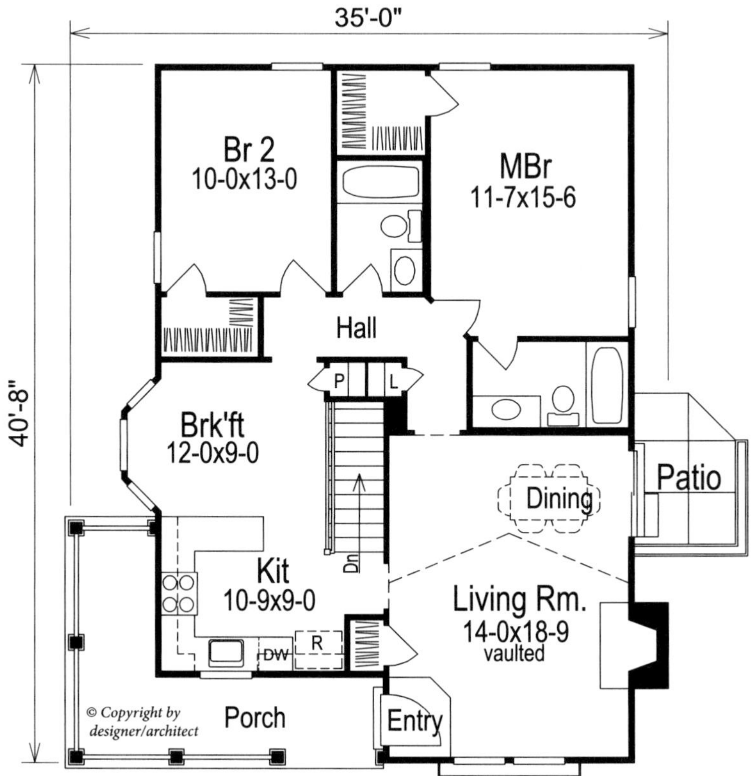

• To Order See Page 288 or Call Toll-Free 1-877-379-3420

Plan #541-007D-0075 • Price Code B

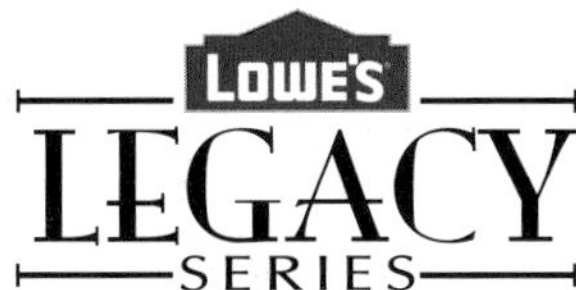

A Special Home For Views

- 2,194 total square feet of living area
- Delightful wrap-around porch is anchored by a full masonry fireplace
- The vaulted great room includes a large bay window, fireplace, dining balcony and atrium window wall
- Double walk-in closets, large luxury bath and sliding doors to an exterior balcony are a few fantastic features of the master bedroom
- Plan also available with energy efficient R-Control® SIPs (Structural Insulated Panels), please call 1-877-379-3420 for more information
- 3 bedrooms, 2 baths, 2-car drive under rear entry garage
- Walk-out basement foundation

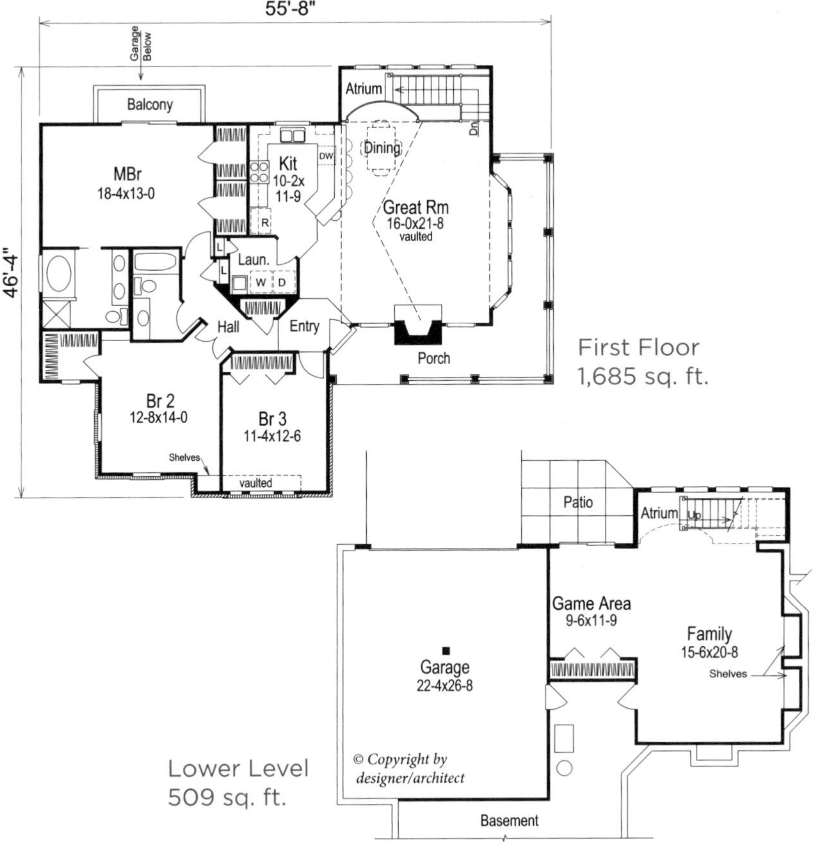

First Floor
1,685 sq. ft.

Lower Level
509 sq. ft.

Plan #541-121D-0012 • Price Code AA

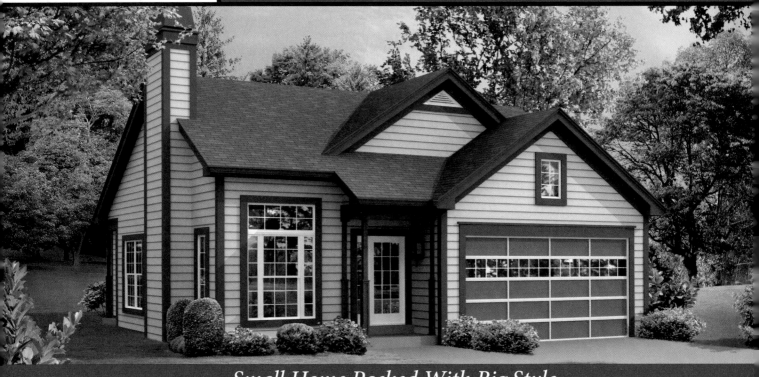

Small Home Packed With Big Style

- 1,281 total square feet of living area
- The well-appointed kitchen enjoys an angled raised counter perfect for casual dining
- The great room has an 11' ceiling, a fireplace for warmth and easy access to the breakfast area
- The vaulted master bedroom enjoys a sizable walk-in closet and its own private bath
- 3 bedrooms, 2 baths, 2-car garage
- Basement foundation

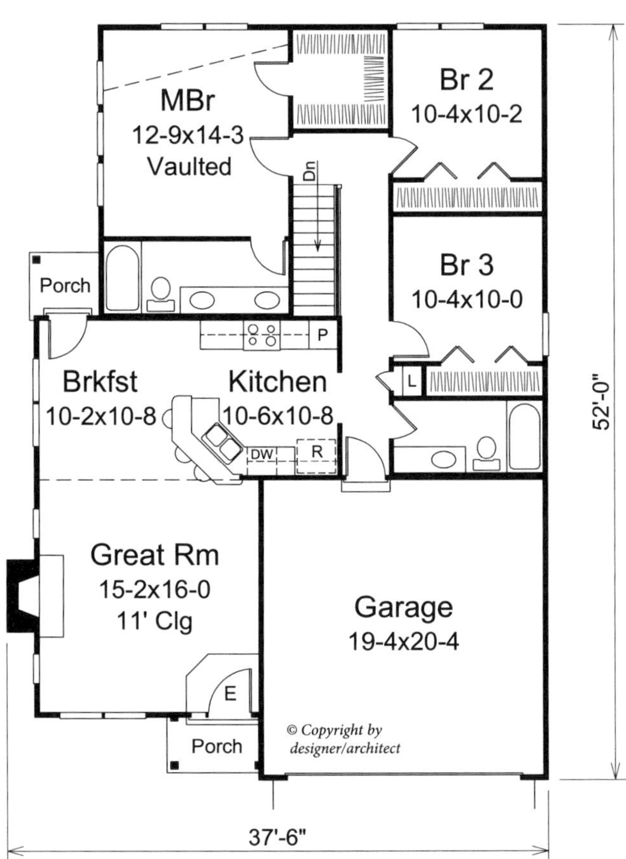

Plan #541-008D-0159 • Price Code AAA

Covered Porch Adds To Perfect Outdoor Getaway

- 733 total square feet of living area
- Bedrooms are separate from the kitchen and living area for privacy
- Lots of closet space throughout this home
- Centrally located bath is easily accessible
- Kitchen features a door accessing the outdoors and a door separating it from the rest of the home
- 2 bedrooms, 1 bath
- Pier foundation

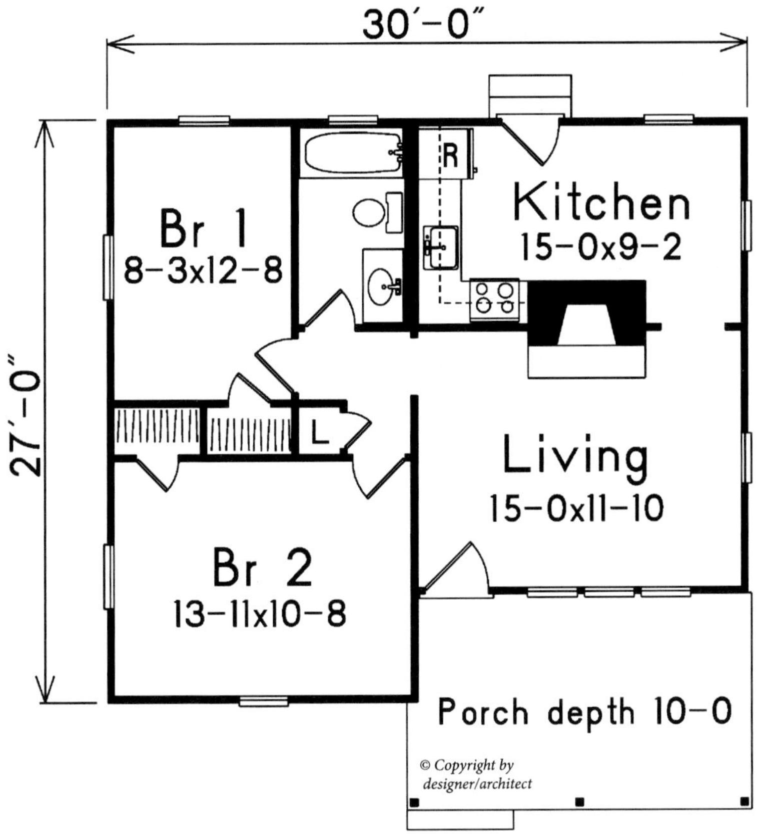

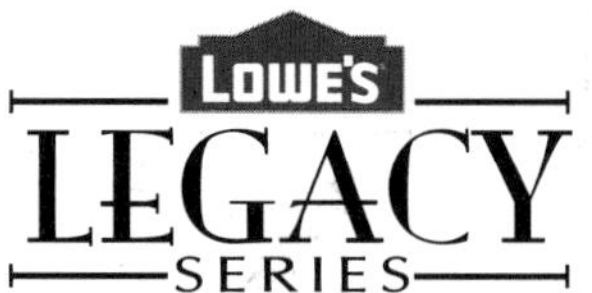

Plan #541-013L-0130 • Price Code E

Exciting One-Level Home

- 1,798 total square feet of living area
- A gourmet kitchen, casual dining room and a rear covered porch overlooking the pool make this home a delight for entertaining
- The generous master suite features a sitting area and large walk-in closet with separate his and her sections
- The front home office can easily become a guest bedroom with its walk-in closet and private bath access
- 3 bedrooms, 2 1/2 baths, 2-car side entry garage
- Slab foundation

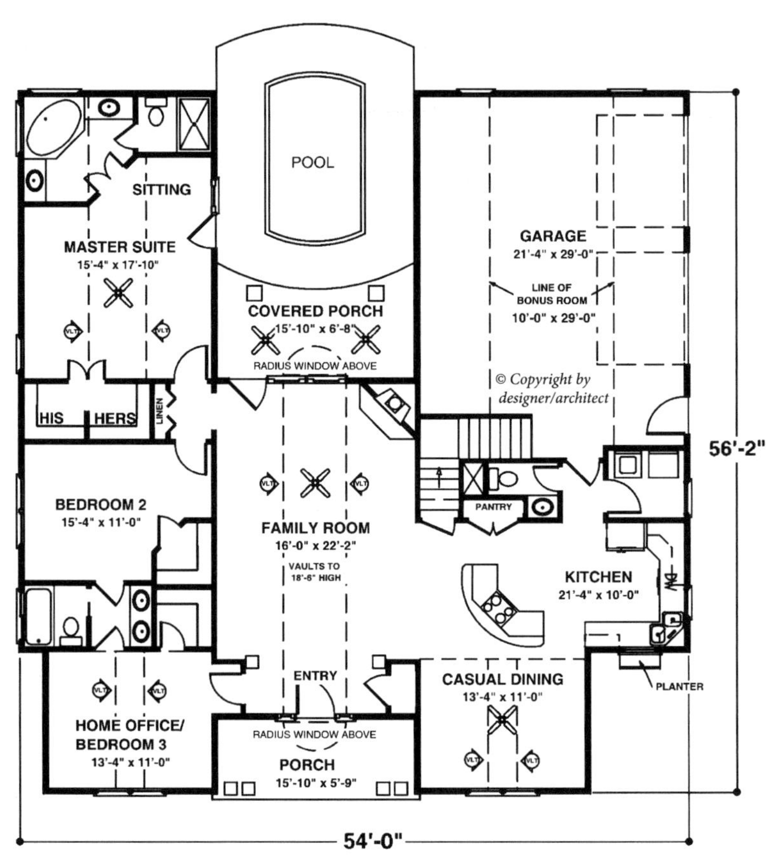

• To Order See Page 288 or Call Toll-Free 1-877-379-3420

Plan #541-058D-0009 • Price Code AAA

Irresistible Retreat

- 448 total square feet of living area
- Bedroom features a large walk-in closet ideal for storage
- Combined dining/sitting area is ideal for relaxing
- Galley-style kitchen is compact and efficient
- Covered porch adds to front facade
- 1 bedroom, 1 bath
- Slab foundation

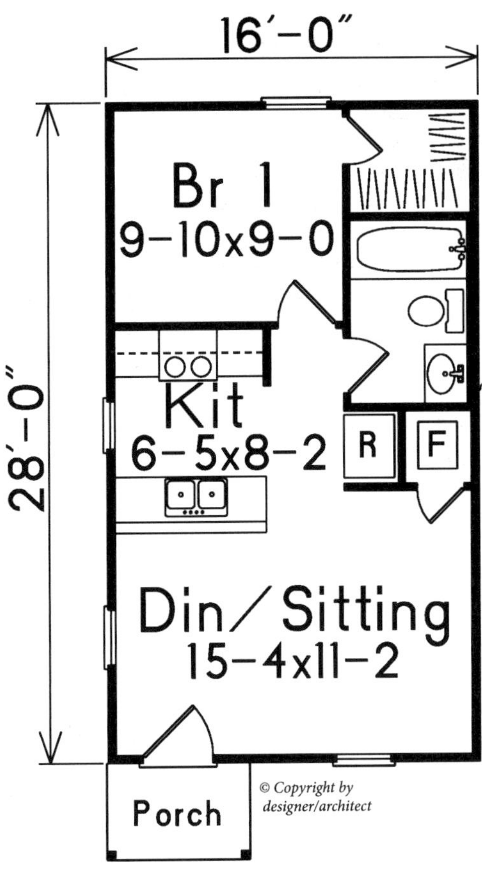

Plan #541-007D-0244 • Price Code C

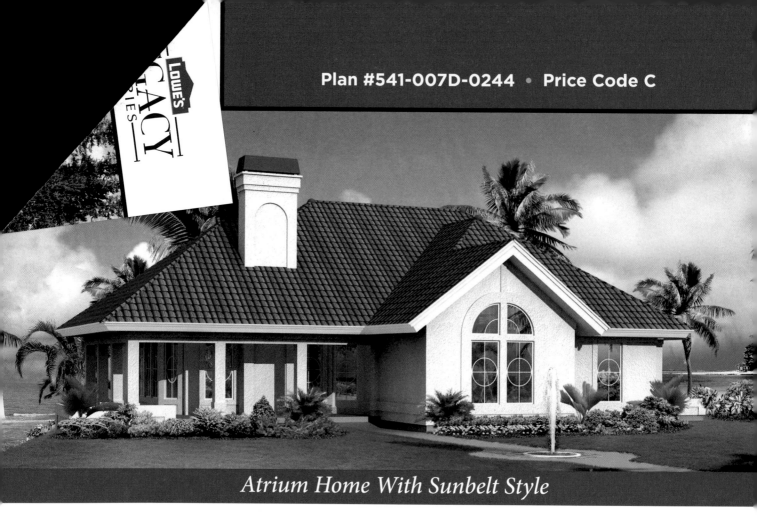

Atrium Home With Sunbelt Style

- 1,605 total square feet of living area
- Stucco exterior, wrap-around columned porch and Palladian windows with custom grilles are a few unique design features making this home very special
- The great room offers a huge bay window, fireplace, access to rear deck, separate entry and a dining balcony with views of the two-story atrium with feature window and stair to lower level
- The U-shaped kitchen has a snack bar and a convenient adjacent laundry room
- Double-entry doors lead you into the master bedroom which enjoys an awesome luxury bath and walk-in closet
- 2 bedrooms, 2 baths, 2-car side entry garage
- Walk-out basement foundation

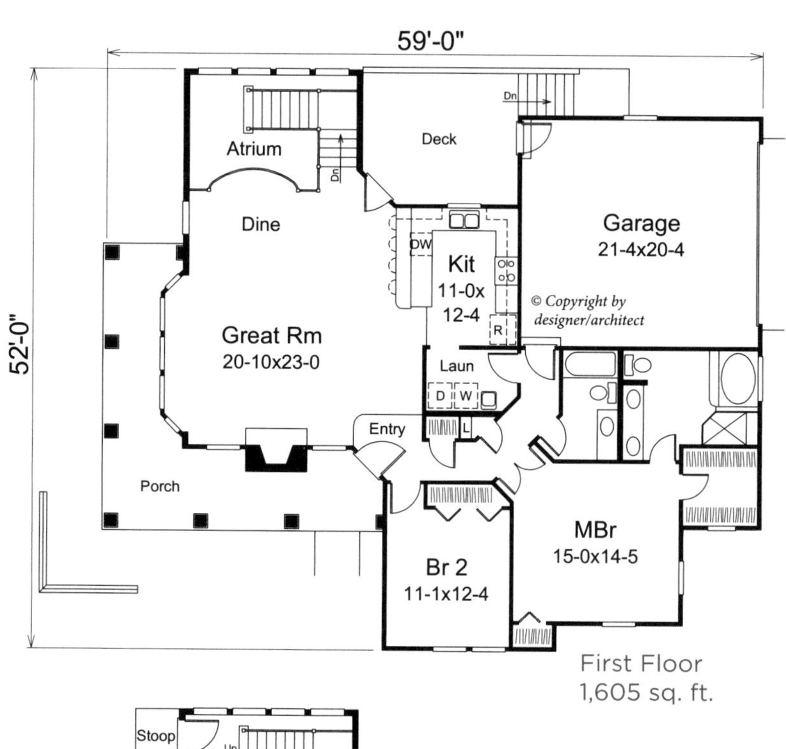

First Floor
1,605 sq. ft.

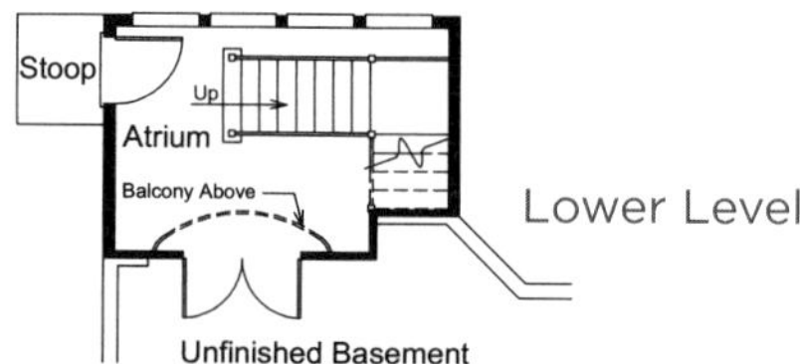

Lower Level

• To Order See Page 288 or Call Toll-Free 1-877-379-3420

Plan #541-058D-0127 • Price Code A

Covered Entryway

- 1,416 total square feet of living area
- Energy efficient home with 2" x 6" exterior walls
- A breakfast nook extends off the kitchen and has a vaulted ceiling for a spacious, open feel
- The large vaulted family room is the perfect place to enjoy the warmth of the fireplace or watch a movie
- A large walk-in pantry organizes the kitchen designed for efficiency
- 2 bedrooms, 2 baths, 1-car garage
- Basement foundation

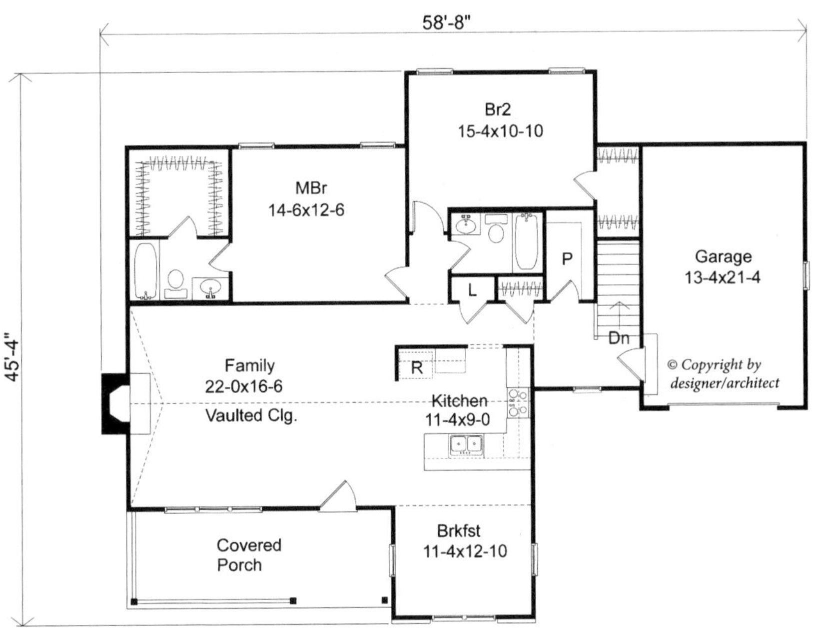

Plan #541-087L-0145 • Price Code G

Enchanting Wrap-Around Porch

- 1,792 total square feet of living area
- A massive family room with fireplace and access onto the porch is the perfect place to relax or entertain
- The spacious kitchen and dining area includes a cooktop island and walk-in pantry
- All the bedrooms are located on the second floor for extra peace and quiet
- 3 bedrooms, 2 1/2 baths
- Slab foundation

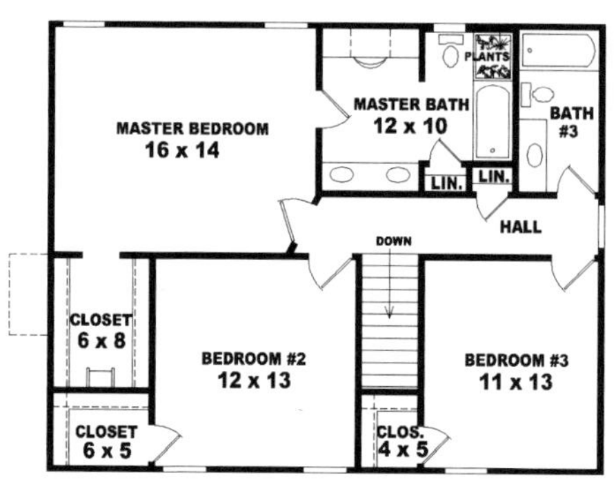

Second Floor
932 sq. ft.

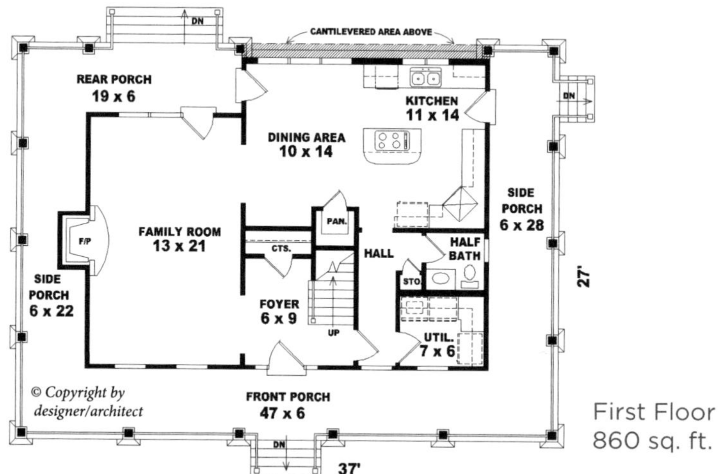

First Floor
860 sq. ft.

• To Order See Page 288 or Call Toll-Free 1-877-379-3420

Plan #541-065L-0061 • Price Code A

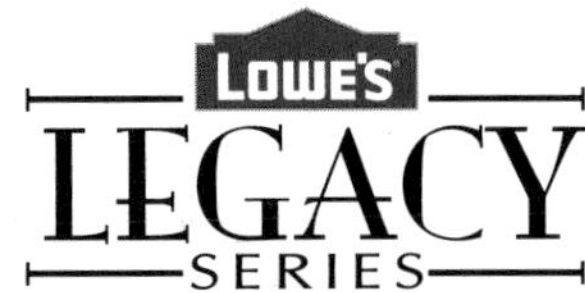

Step-Saving Convenience

- 1,498 total square feet of living area
- The great room with fireplace and sloped ceiling is visible from the foyer, dining room and kitchen creating a large, open gathering area
- The master bedroom enjoys a luxurious bath, large walk-in closet and raised ceiling
- A snack bar, walk-in pantry and nearby laundry room enhance the spacious kitchen
- Two generously sized bedrooms share a full bath with convenient linen closet
- 3 bedrooms, 2 baths, 2-car garage
- Basement foundation, drawings also include crawl space and slab foundations

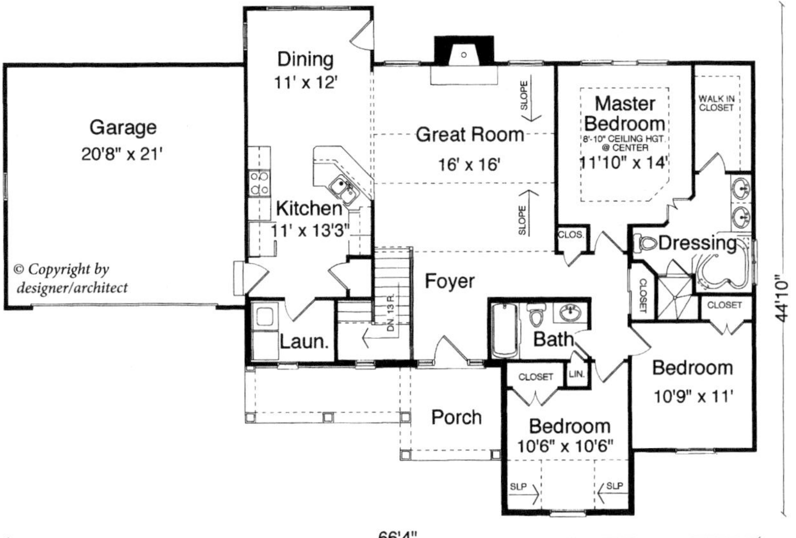

Plan #541-053D-0044 • Price Code A

Open Living Area Adds Drama To Home

- 1,340 total square feet of living area
- Master bedroom has a private bath and walk-in closet
- Recessed entry leads to the vaulted family room that shares a see-through fireplace with the kitchen/dining area
- Garage includes a handy storage area
- Convenient laundry closet is located in the kitchen
- 3 bedrooms, 2 baths, 2-car side entry garage
- Slab foundation, drawings also include crawl space foundation

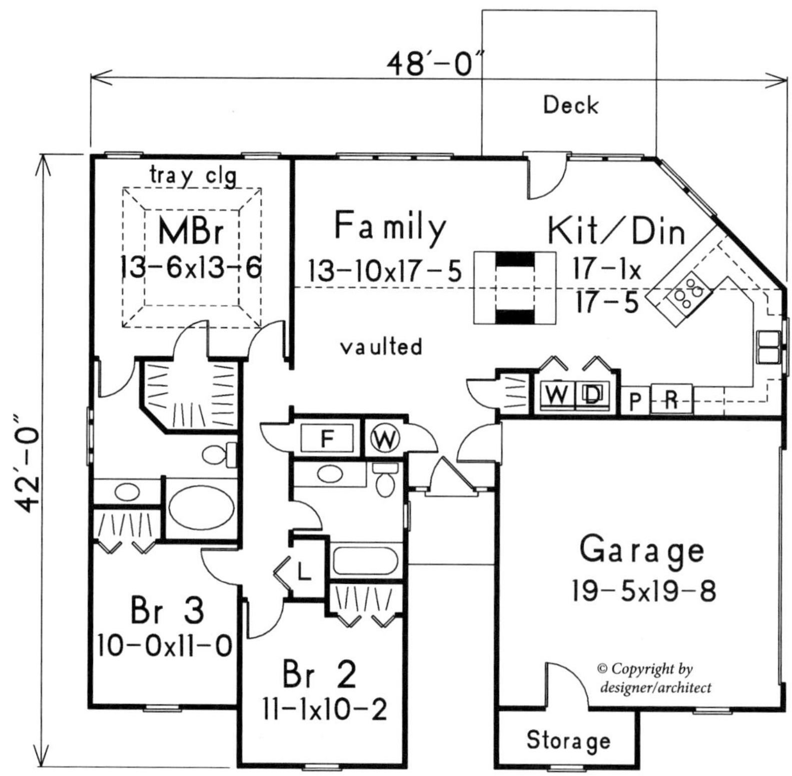

• To Order See Page 288 or Call Toll-Free 1-877-379-3420

FREE Lowe's Gift Card Offer

Lowe's Special Rebate Offer

Purchase any plan package featured in this book PLUS at least $15,000 of your materials from Lowe's and receive a gift card for the purchase price of your plans.

To receive the rebate:

1. Purchase any of the plan packages in this publication PLUS at least $15,000 of the materials to build your home at Lowe's before 12/31/13. Requests must be postmarked by 1/31/14. Claims postmarked after this date will not be honored.
2. Limit one gift card per set of plans.
3. Please allow 3-4 weeks for processing. If you do not receive a gift card after 4 weeks, visit www.lowes.com/rebates, or you may call 1-877-204-1223.
4. Please keep a copy of all materials submitted for your records.
5. Copy the entire sale receipt(s), including store name, location, purchase date, and invoice number, showing blueprint purchase and total amount spent.
6. Mail this complete page with your name, address and other information below, along with a copy of the receipt(s).

Name ________________________________

Street Address ________________________

City ________________________________

State/Zip ____________________________

Daytime phone number (____) - ____________

E-mail address ________________________

Plan number purchased 541- _____________

I purchased a
- ☐ One-Set Plan Package
- ☐ Five-Set Plan Package
- ☐ Eight-Set Plan Package
- ☐ Reproducible Masters
- ☐ Builder's CAD Package

MAIL TO:
Lowe's Free Gift Card Offer
P.O. Box 3029
Young America, MN 55558-3029

Check the status of your rebate at www.lowes.com/rebates

Other terms and conditions. Requests from groups will not be honored. Fraudulent submission of multiple requests could result in federal prosecution under the U.S. Mail Fraud Statutes (18 USC, Section 1341 and 1342). Offer good in the U.S.A. only. Void where prohibited, taxed or restricted by law. If you do not receive your rebate within 3-4 weeks, please call 1-877-204-1223 or visit www.lowes.com/rebates. This page may not be reproduced, traded or sold. Please keep a copy for future reference.

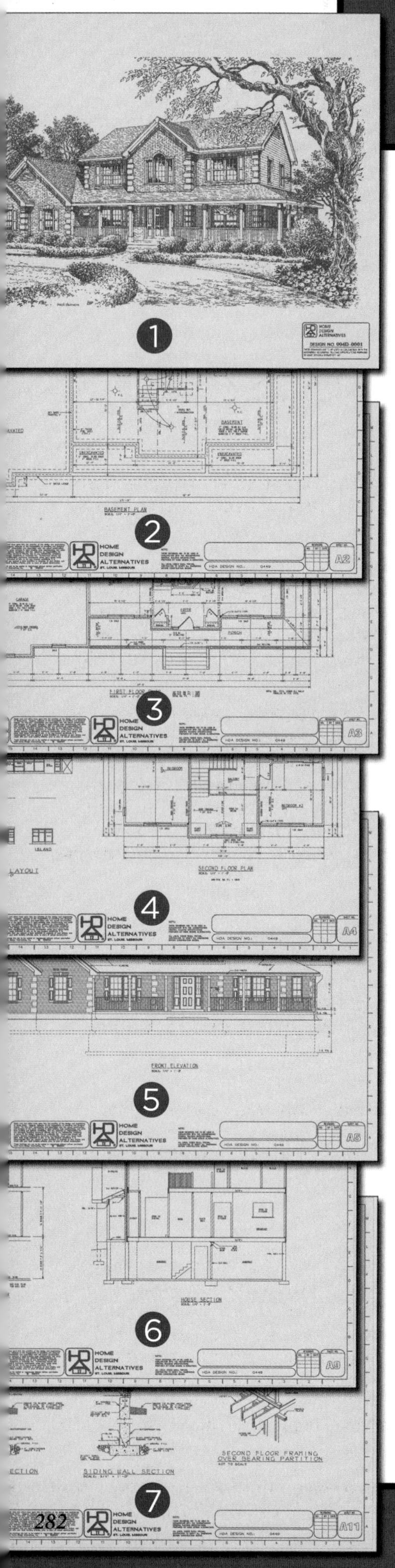

Our Blueprint Packages Offer...

Quality plans for building your future, with extras that provide unsurpassed value, ensure good construction and long-term enjoyment.

A quality home - one that looks good, functions well, and provides years of enjoyment - is a product of many things - design, materials, and craftsmanship.

But it's also the result of outstanding blueprints - the actual plans and specifications that tell the builder exactly how to build your home.

And with our BLUEPRINT PACKAGES you get the absolute best. A complete set of blueprints is available for every design in this book. These "working drawings" are highly detailed, resulting in two key benefits:

- Better understanding by the contractor of how to build your home and...
- More accurate construction estimates.

Below is a sample of plan information included for most of the designs in this book. Specific details may vary with each designer's plan. While this information is typical of most plans, we cannot assure the inclusion of all the following referenced items. Please contact customer service for plan specific information, including which of the following items are included.

1. *Cover Sheet* is the artist's rendering of the exterior of the home and is included with many of the plans. It will give you an idea of how your home will look when completed and landscaped.

2. *Foundation* plan shows the layout of the basement, crawl space, slab or pier foundation. All necessary notations and dimensions are included. See the plan page for the foundation types included. If the home plan you choose does not have your desired foundation type, our Customer Service Representatives can advise you on how to customize your foundation to suit your specific needs or site conditions.

3. *Floor Plans* show the placement of walls, doors, closets, plumbing fixtures, electrical outlets, columns, and beams for each level of the home.

4. *Interior Elevations* provide views of special interior elements such as fireplaces, kitchen cabinets, built-in units and other features of the home.

5. *Exterior Elevations* illustrate the front, rear and both sides of the house, with all details of exterior materials and the required dimensions.

6. *Sections* show detail views of the home or portions of the home as if it were sliced from the roof to the foundation. This sheet shows important areas such as load-bearing walls, stairs, joists, trusses and other structural elements, which are critical for proper construction.

7. *Details* show how to construct certain components of your home, such as the roof system, stairs, deck, etc.

What Kind Of Plan Package Do You Need?

Now that you've found the home you've been looking for, here are some suggestions on how to make your Dream Home a reality. To get started, order the type of plans that fit your particular situation.

Your Choices

- ☐ *The One-Set Study Package* - We offer a One-set plan package so you can study your home in detail. This one set is considered a study set and is marked "not for construction." It is a copyright violation to reproduce blueprints.

- ☐ *The Minimum 5-Set Package* - If you're ready to start the construction process, this 5-set package is the minimum number of blueprint sets you will need. It will require keeping close track of each set so they can be used by multiple subcontractors and tradespeople.

- ☐ *The Standard 8-Set Package* - For best results in terms of cost, schedule and quality of construction, we recommend you order eight (or more) sets of blueprints. Besides one set for yourself, additional sets of blueprints will be required by your mortgage lender, local building department, general contractor and all subcontractors working on foundation, electrical, plumbing, heating/air conditioning, carpentry work, etc.

- ☐ *Reproducible Masters* - If you wish to make some minor design changes, you'll want to order reproducible masters. These drawings contain the same information as the blueprints but are printed on reproducible paper and clearly indicates your right to alter, copy or reproduce. This will allow your builder or a local design professional to make the necessary drawing changes without the major expense of redrawing the plans. This package also allows you to print copies of the modified plans as needed. The right of building only one structure from these plans is licensed exclusively to the buyer. You may not use this design to build a second or multiple dwelling(s) without purchasing another blueprint. Each violation of the Copyright Law is punishable in a fine.

- ☐ *Mirror Reverse Sets* - Plans can be printed in mirror reverse. These plans are useful when the house would fit your site better if all the rooms were on the opposite side than shown. They are simply a mirror image of the original drawings causing the lettering and dimensions to read backwards. Therefore, when ordering mirror reverse drawings, you must purchase at least one set of right-reading plans. Some of our plans are offered mirror reverse right-reading. This means the plan, lettering and dimensions are flipped but read correctly. See the Home Plan Index on page 285-286 for availability.

- ☐ *PDF File Format* - A complete set of construction drawings in an electronic format that allows you to resize and reproduce the plans to fit your needs. Since these are electronic files, we can send them to you within 24 hours (Mon-Fri, 8-5 CST) via email and save you shipping costs. They also offer printing flexibility by allowing you to print the size and number of sets you need.

  Note: These are not CAD files and cannot be altered electronically.

- ☐ *CAD Packages* - A CAD package is a complete set of construction drawings in an electronic file format. They are especially beneficial if you have a significant amount of changes to make to the home plan you have selected or if you need to make the home plan fit your local codes. If you purchase a CAD Package, you have the option to take the plan to a local design professional who uses AutoCAD or DataCAD and they can modify the design much easier and quicker than with a paper-based drawing, which will help save you time and money. Just like our reproducible masters, with a CAD package you will receive a one-time build copyright release that allows you to make changes and the necessary copies needed to build your home. For more information and availability, please call our Customer Service Department at 1-877-379-3420.

More Helpful Building Aids...

Your Blueprint Package will contain the necessary construction information to build your home. We also offer the following products and services to save you time and money in the building process.

Material List

Material lists are available for all of the plans in this book. Each list gives you the quantity, dimensions and description of the building materials necessary to construct your home. You'll get faster and more accurate bids from your contractor while saving money by paying for only the materials you need. See your Commercial Sales Specialist at your local Lowe's Store to receive a free take-off.

Note: The material list is designed with the standard foundation only and does not include alternate or optional foundations.

Express Delivery

Most orders are processed within 24 hours of receipt. Please allow 7-10 business days for delivery. If you need to place a rush order, please call us by 11:00 a.m. Monday through Friday, 8am-5pm CST and ask for express service (allow 1-2 business days).

Technical Assistance

If you have questions, call our technical support line at 1-314-770-2228 Monday through Friday, 8am-5pm CST. Whether it involves design modifications or field assistance, our designers are extremely familiar with all of our designs and will be happy to help you. We want your home to be everything you expect it to be.

Other Great Products...

Below are a few products sure to help the beginner as well as the experienced builder.

Legal Kit

Home building can be a complicated process with many legal regulations being confusing. This Legal Kit was designed to help you avoid many legal pitfalls and build your home with confidence using the forms and contracts featured in this kit. Included are request for proposal documents, various fixed price and cost plus contracts, instructions on how and when to use each form, warranty statements and more. Save time and money before you break ground on your new home or start a remodeling project. Instructions are included on how to use the kit and since the documents are universal, they are designed to be used with all building trades. Since review by an attorney is always advised before signing any contract, this is an ideal way to get organized and started on the process. Plus, all forms are reproducible making it a terrific tool for the contractor and home builder. At a price of $35.00, this kit is ideal.

Detail Plan Packages

Framing, Plumbing and Electrical Plan Packages

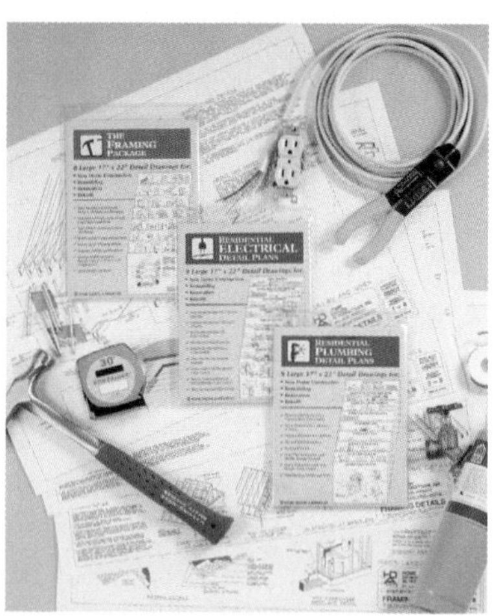

Three separate packages offer home builders details for constructing various foundations; numerous floor, wall and roof framing techniques; simple to complex residential wiring; sump and water softener hookups; plumbing connection methods; installation of septic systems, and more. Packages include 3-dimensional illustrations and a glossary of terms. These drawings do not pertain to a specific home plan making them perfect for your building situation.

Each package is $20 or purchase all three for $40 making it a great bargain.

To order any of the products on this page, please see the Home Plan order form on page 288.

Home Plan Index

Plan Number	Square Feet	Price Code	Page	Right Read.
541-001D-0003	2,286	E	49	
541-001D-0013	1,882	D	60	
541-001D-0018	988	AA	95	
541-001D-0024	1,360	A	100	•
541-001D-0029	1,260	A	232	
541-001D-0031	1,501	B	147	•
541-001D-0036	1,320	A	195	
541-001D-0040	864	AAA	265	
541-001D-0053	1,344	A	223	
541-001D-0064	2,262	D	41	
541-001D-0081	1,160	AA	205	
541-001D-0110	1,705	B	257	
541-001D-0112	2,050	C	152	
541-001D-0121	1,664	B	253	
541-001D-0126	2,080	C	213	
541-003D-0001	2,058	C	74	
541-003D-0002	1,676	B	216	
541-003D-0005	1,708	B	91	
541-004D-0002	1,823	C	120	
541-005D-0001	1,400	B	88	•
541-006D-0003	1,674	B	76	
541-007D-0010	1,845	C	12	•
541-007D-0014	1,985	C	146	
541-007D-0017	1,882	C	90	
541-007D-0031	1,092	AA	127	
541-007D-0037	1,403	A	67	•
541-007D-0038	1,524	B	30	
541-007D-0042	914	AA	153	
541-007D-0049	1,791	C	101	•
541-007D-0053	2,432	D	198	
541-007D-0054	1,575	B	21	
541-007D-0055	2,029	D	75	•
541-007D-0060	1,268	B	11	•
541-007D-0067	1,761	B	218	•
541-007D-0068	1,922	B	244	•
541-007D-0075	2,194	B	271	
541-007D-0077	1,978	C	237	•
541-007D-0085	1,787	B	80	
541-007D-0103	1,547	A	105	
541-007D-0105	1,084	AA	270	
541-007D-0107	1,161	AA	176	
541-007D-0119	1,621	B	266	
541-007D-0120	1,914	C	252	
541-007D-0121	1,559	B	180	
541-007D-0123	1,308	A	229	
541-007D-0124	1,944	C	83	
541-007D-0125	1,302	A	160	
541-007D-0126	1,365	A	262	
541-007D-0128	1,072	AA	235	
541-007D-0134	1,310	A	258	•
541-007D-0135	801	AAA	111	
541-007D-0161	1,480	A	188	•
541-007D-0168	1,814	C	158	
541-007D-0177	1,102	AA	149	•
541-007D-0185	1,977	B	217	•
541-007D-0216	1,510	A	137	
541-007D-0218	1,828	C	86	
541-007D-0219	1,939	B	70	
541-007D-0222	1,522	A	190	
541-007D-0229	2,014	D	249	
541-007D-0230	1,923	D	132	
541-007D-0232	1,915	D	79	
541-007D-0235	2,213	E	141	
541-007D-0236	1,676	B	163	
541-007D-0240	1,663	C	108	
541-007D-0244	1,605	C	276	
541-007D-0249	1,740	C	123	
541-008D-0004	1,643	B	174	
541-008D-0013	1,345	A	209	
541-008D-0068	1,932	C	73	
541-008D-0078	1,971	C	106	
541-008D-0159	733	AAA	273	
541-008D-0178	1,872	C	167	•
541-008D-0179	1,973	C	267	
541-010D-0001	1,516	B	114	
541-010D-0002	1,776	B	124	
541-010D-0005	1,358	A	225	
541-010D-0006	1,170	AA	119	
541-013L-0014	1,728	C	93	
541-013L-0015	1,787	C	15	•
541-013L-0022	1,992	C	268	•
541-013L-0043	1,343	B	121	
541-013L-0044	1,420	B	161	
541-013L-0045	1,695	C	166	
541-013L-0047	1,897	C	156	
541-013L-0050	2,098	D	122	
541-013L-0130	1,798	E	274	
541-013L-0132	2,296	F	145	
541-013L-0149	2,058	D	139	
541-013L-0156	1,800	B	112	•
541-013L-0159	1,992	B	164	
541-013L-0160	1,898	B	169	
541-014D-0001	2,159	C	142	
541-014D-0005	1,314	A	69	
541-014D-0007	1,453	A	118	
541-014D-0009	1,428	A	172	
541-014D-0011	2,106	C	96	
541-014D-0013	2,041	C	134	
541-017D-0001	2,043	D	196	
541-017D-0002	1,805	D	178	
541-017D-0007	1,567	C	256	
541-021D-0004	1,800	D	85	
541-021D-0010	1,444	B	16	
541-021D-0011	1,800	E	51	
541-021D-0015	1,700	C	109	
541-021D-0016	1,600	C	246	
541-021D-0018	2,255	E	28	
541-022D-0002	1,246	A	104	
541-022D-0004	1,359	A	29	
541-022D-0005	1,360	A	240	
541-022D-0008	1,565	B	56	
541-022D-0011	1,630	B	242	
541-022D-0019	1,283	A	23	
541-022D-0024	1,127	AA	241	
541-022D-0026	1,993	D	35	
541-023D-0006	2,357	D	154	
541-023D-0009	2,333	D	9	
541-023D-0012	2,365	D	214	
541-023D-0016	1,609	B	230	
541-027D-0003	2,061	D	17	
541-027D-0006	2,076	C	199	
541-027D-0011	2,164	B	50	
541-029D-0002	1,619	B	81	
541-033D-0002	1,859	D	10	
541-033D-0009	1,711	C	84	
541-033D-0011	2,045	D	264	
541-033D-0012	1,546	C	126	
541-033D-0013	1,813	D	99	
541-037D-0001	1,703	B	197	
541-037D-0003	1,996	D	87	
541-037D-0006	1,772	C	210	
541-037D-0007	2,282	D	239	
541-037D-0010	1,770	B	138	
541-037D-0012	1,661	B	263	
541-037D-0022	1,539	B	175	
541-037D-0031	1,923	C	260	
541-040D-0004	2,128	C	140	
541-040D-0006	1,759	B	186	
541-040D-0007	2,073	D	128	
541-040D-0027	1,597	C	116	
541-040D-0030	1,543	B	227	
541-045D-0009	1,684	B	202	
541-045D-0014	987	AA	191	
541-048D-0001	1,865	D	143	
541-048D-0008	2,089	C	72	
541-048D-0009	2,056	C	136	
541-048D-0011	1,550	B	103	
541-051L-0060	1,591	B	22	
541-051L-0143	2,193	D	43	
541-051L-0238	1,873	D	14	
541-051L-0439	1,735	E	33	
541-053D-0002	1,668	A	177	
541-053D-0003	1,992	A	59	
541-053D-0004	1,740	A	208	
541-053D-0007	1,922	A	269	
541-053D-0010	1,983	A	200	
541-053D-0015	2,214	A	245	
541-053D-0029	1,220	AA	215	
541-053D-0031	1,908	A	221	
541-053D-0032	1,404	A	212	
541-053D-0043	1,732	A	173	
541-053D-0044	1,340	A	280	
541-053D-0049	1,261	AA	248	
541-053D-0053	1,609	B	251	
541-053D-0058	1,818	A	219	
541-055L-0026	1,538	B	77	
541-055L-0158	1,636	C	78	
541-055L-0192	2,096	E	207	
541-055L-0205	1,989	D	135	
541-055L-0289	1,504	C	62	
541-055L-0508	1,894	C	231	
541-055L-0526	2,146	D	113	
541-055L-0530	2,237	D	117	
541-057D-0010	1,242	A	82	
541-057D-0019	1,838	C	97	
541-057D-0028	1,775	A	243	
541-057D-0036	1,042	AAA	107	
541-057D-0037	1,608	A	155	
541-057D-0038	1,229	AA	234	
541-057D-0041	1,274	AA	259	
541-057D-0043	2,024	B	204	
541-057D-0044	1,935	B	150	
541-058D-0006	1,339	A	92	•
541-058D-0008	1,285	A	255	•
541-058D-0009	448	AAA	275	
541-058D-0016	1,558	B	19	•
541-058D-0022	1,578	B	220	
541-058D-0030	990	AA	159	•
541-058D-0033	1,440	A	247	
541-058D-0056	2,150	C	238	•
541-058D-0064	1,323	A	261	
541-058D-0065	1,512	B	165	
541-058D-0067	1,587	B	130	
541-058D-0081	1,477	A	206	
541-058D-0083	2,164	C	189	
541-058D-0094	1,895	B	193	
541-058D-0123	1,144	AA	184	
541-058D-0124	1,897	C	157	
541-058D-0127	1,416	A	277	
541-058D-0129	1,217	A	226	
541-058D-0136	480	AAA	183	•
541-058D-0143	665	AAA	170	
541-058D-0168	1,568	AA	211	
541-058D-0174	1,682	D	250	
541-061D-0001	1,747	B	179	
541-065L-0001	1,768	B	24	
541-065L-0002	2,101	C	54	

Index (cont.)

Before You Order

Exchange Policies

Since blueprints are printed in response to your order, we cannot honor requests for refunds. However, if for some reason you find that the plan you have purchased does not meet your requirements, you may exchange that plan for another plan in our collection within 90 days of purchase. At the time of the exchange, you will be charged a processing fee of 25% of your original plan package price, plus the difference in price between the plan packages (if applicable) and the cost to ship the new plans to you.

Please note: Reproducible drawings can only be exchanged if the package is unopened. PDF and CAD files are not returnable and non-refundable.

Building Codes & Requirements

At the time the construction drawings were prepared, every effort was made to ensure that these plans and specifications meet nationally recognized codes. Our plans conform to most national building codes. Because building codes vary from area to area, some drawing modifications and/or the assistance of a professional designer or architect may be necessary to comply with your local codes or to accommodate specific building site conditions. We advise you to consult with your local building official for information regarding codes governing your area.

Additional Sets†

Additional sets of the plan ordered are available for an additional cost of $45.00 each. Five-set, eight-set, and reproducible packages offer considerable savings.

† Available only within 90 days after purchase of plan package or reproducible masters of the same plan.

Pricing & Shipping Info

Blueprint Price Schedule

Price Code	1-Set	SAVE $80 5-Sets	SAVE $115 8 Sets	PDF File/ Reproducible Masters	CAD
AAA	$310	$410	$510	$610	$1,000
AA	$410	$510	$610	$710	$1,250
A	$470	$570	$670	$770	$1,370
B	$530	$630	$730	$830	$1,490
C	$585	$685	$785	$885	$1,600
D	$635	$735	$835	$935	$1,700
E	$695	$795	$895	$995	$1,820
F	$750	$850	$950	$1,050	$1,930
G	$1,000	$1,100	$1,200	$1,300	$2,130
H	$1,100	$1,200	$1,300	$1,400	$2,320
I	$1,150	$1,250	$1,350	$1,450	$2,420
J	$1,200	$1,300	$1,400	$1,500	$2,650
K	$1,250	$1,350	$1,450	$1,550	$2,900

Plan prices are subject to change without notice.
Please note that plans and material lists are not refundable.

Shipping & Handling Charges

U.S. Shipping - (AK & HI express only)	1-4 Sets	5-7 Sets	8 Sets or Reproducibles
Regular (allow 7-10 business days)	$15.00	$17.50	$25.00
Priority (allow 3-5 business days)	$35.00	$40.00	$45.00
Express* (allow 1-2 business days)	$50.00	$55.00	$60.00
Canada Shipping (to/from)**			
Standard (allow 8-12 business days)	$35.00	$40.00	$45.00
Express* (allow 3-5 business days)	$75.00	$85.00	$95.00

Overseas Shipping/International -
Call, fax, or e-mail (plans@hdainc.com) for shipping costs.
* For express delivery please call us by 11:00 a.m. Monday-Friday CST
** Orders may be subject to custom's fee and/or duties/taxes.

NOTE: Shipping and handling charges do not apply on PDF files.
Orders will be emailed within 24 hours (Mon-Fri., 8-5 CST) of purchase.

Questions? Call Our Customer Service Number

1-877-379-3420

Many of our plans are available in CAD.
For availability, please call our Customer Service Number above.

Order Form

1.) *Call* toll-free 1-877-379-3420 for credit card orders. Mastercard, Visa, Discover and American Express are accepted.
2.) *Fax* your order to 1-314-770-2226.
3.) *Mail* the Order Form to: *HDA, Inc.*
944 Anglum Road
St. Louis, MO 63042
attn: Customer Service Dept.

4.) *Visit* your Commercial Sales Specialist at your local Lowe's store.

For fastest service, Call Toll-Free
1-877-379-3420 day or night

Order Form

Please send me -

PLAN NUMBER 541-________________

PRICE CODE______ *(see pages 285-286)*

Specify Foundation Type *(see plan page for availability)*

☐ Slab ☐ Crawl space ☐ Pier
☐ Basement ☐ Walk-out basement

☐ CAD Package *(call for availability)* $ ______
☐ Reproducible Masters $ ______
☐ PDF File *(call for availability)* $ ______
☐ Eight-Set Plan Package $ ______
☐ Five-Set Plan Package $ ______
☐ One-Set Study Package *(no mirror reverse)* $ ______

Additional Plan Sets† *(see page 286)*

☐ ____ (Qty.) at $45.00 each $ ______

Mirror Reverse† *(see page 283)*

☐ Right-reading $150 one-time charge
(see index on pages 285-286 for availability) $ ______

☐ Print in Mirror Reverse
(where right-reading is not available)
____ (Qty.) at $15.00 each $ ______

☐ Legal Kit (002D-9991, *see page 284)* $ ______

Detail Plan Packages: *(see page 284)*

☐ Framing (002D-9992) ☐ Electrical (002D-9993) ☐ Plumbing (002D-9994) $ ______

SUBTOTAL $ ______

Sales Tax *(MO residents add 7%)* $ ______

☐ Shipping / Handling *(see page 287)* $ ______

TOTAL *(US funds only - sorry no CODs)* $ ______

I hereby authorize HDA, Inc. to charge this purchase to my credit card account (check one):

☐ MasterCard ☐ VISA ☐ DISCOVER ☐ American Express Cards

Plan prices are subject to change without notice.
Please note that plans and material lists are not refundable.

Credit Card number ________________

Expiration date ________________

Signature ________________

Name________________
(Please print or type)

Street Address________________
(Please do not use a PO Box)

____

City ________________

State ________________

Zip ________________

Daytime phone number (_____) - ________

E-mail address ________________

I am a ☐ Builder/Contractor
☐ Homeowner
☐ Renter

I ☐ have ☐ have not selected my general contractor.

Thank you for your order!

†Available only within 90 days after purchase of plan package or reproducible masters of same plan.
Note: Shipping and handling does not apply for PDF files. Orders will be emailed within 24 hours (Mon.-Fri., 8am-5pm CST) of purchase.